F

los de abajo

MARIANO AZUELA

LOS de ABAJO

Novela de la Revolución Mexicana

complete edition

edited with introduction, notes, and vocabulary by

JOHN E. ENGLEKIRK

University of California, Los Angeles

LAWRENCE B. KIDDLE

University of Michigan

Prentice-Hall, Inc., Englewood Cliffs, New Jersey

Printed in the United States of America

ISBN: 0-13-540690-0

Library of Congress Catalog Card Number: 75-133900

10 9 8 7 6 5 4 3 2

PRENTICE-HALL INTERNATIONAL, INC., *London*
PRENTICE-HALL OF AUSTRALIA, PTY. LTD., *Sydney*
PRENTICE-HALL OF CANADA, LTD., *Toronto*
PRENTICE-HALL OF INDIA PRIVATE LIMITED, *New Delhi*
PRENTICE-HALL OF JAPAN, INC., *Tokyo*

TO

THE MEMORY OF

FREDERICK COURTNEY TARR

(1896–1939)

PREFACE

The publication of *Los de abajo* as a class text in 1939 was a pioneering venture. There were then very few works by Spanish-American authors available in textbook form for our English-speaking students of Spanish, and none possessed the literary excellence of Mariano Azuela's masterpiece. We predicted in our text that *Los de abajo* would continue to grow in stature and in importance with the passing of time. Our forecast of over three decades ago has proved to be today's reality. *Los de abajo* is truly a classic of modern Hispanic literature. In this deeply-moving picture of the turmoil of the first great revolution of the twentieth century, the Mexican Revolution of 1910, we see depicted the anarchy and the idealism, the base human passions and the valor and nobility of the simple folk, and, most striking of all, the fascination of revolt—that peculiar love of revolution for revolution's sake that has characterized most of the social upheavals of our century.

In 1939 classroom editions of foreign language texts were customarily cut, not only to reduce the length of the work and the difficulties of vocabulary, but also to avoid the classroom presentation of what were called "overly realistic" episodes. This excessively protective attitude on the part of both editors and publishers amounted to a form of censorship. Such a procedure is highly out of place today. Our present edition of *Las de abajo* is, therefore, the complete text of Azuela's novel. In this edition we have updated the literary introduction and corrected and enlarged the Spanish-English vocabulary. The pattern of collaboration that we followed thirty years ago has been retained: the introduction is largely the work of Mr. Englekirk and the vocabulary is largely the work of Mr. Kiddle.

We cherish the memory of the two men who aided us so much in the preparation of the original edition of the novel, Mariano Azuela, the author, and Frederick Courtney Tarr, the editor of the text series in which *Los de abajo* first appeared.

J.E.E.
L.B.K.

CONTENTS

INTRODUCTION

I. MARIANO AZUELA (1873–1952)

His Life

Mariano Azuela was born in Lagos de Moreno, Jalisco, on January 1, 1873. His childhood days revolved about the family's modest store in town and their small ranch some twelve miles away. Azuela received his early training at the Liceo del Padre Guerra, a lay school which formerly had been the old Capuchín convent of Lagos. In 1887 he went to Guadalajara where he completed his secondary studies at the Liceo de Varones de Estado and pursued the study of medicine from 1892 to 1898. He won his M.D. degree in 1899, and that same year he returned to his native city where he began his life-long practice of medicine. In 1900 he married Carmen Rivera, niece of Agustín Rivera, priest and historian of Lagos. Five sons and five daughters were born of their union. None of the children has followed in his father's footsteps either in medicine or in writing.

Quietly Azuela pursued his practice until the eventful year 1911. Immediately following Madero's surprise victory in the elections of May of that year Azuela was named *jefe político* of Lagos. But two months later he renounced this, his first and only political post, for he foresaw that the appointment of Alberto Robles Gil to the governorship of Jalisco was a significant step toward undermining the work of Madero. He withdrew from all overt participation in politics, but was still a loyal *maderista,* carrying on *sub rosa* his work of propaganda in behalf of the Revolution.

Madero was murdered on February 22, 1913. The reactionaries regained control under Victoriano Huerta. Carranza, Obregón, and Villa rose against him. Huerta resigned in July 1914. Carranza and Villa split. Meanwhile, in Lagos, Azuela had openly espoused the movement against Madero's assassin.

Then, in Irapuato, in late October 1914, Azuela joined the band of

Julián Medina as the only doctor on his staff. Medina, one of Villa's generals, was at the time provisional governor of Jalisco. Within a month he was forced to withdraw to Guadalajara. There he appointed Azuela state Director of Public Education. But Azuela's term was brief. When the *carrancistas* took the city on January 19, 1915, Medina withdrew to Lagos where he established his headquarters until the *carrancistas* again closed in on him during May and forced him to retire to Aguascalientes. From this city a large part of Medina's force moved on Guadalajara, but Azuela remained behind in Tepatitlán to care for the wounded; a short time later, with some hundred of Medina's men in flight from Guadalajara, he returned to Aguascalientes. It was during these early maneuvers in retreat with Medina that Azuela conceived and wrote the preliminary sketches of *Los de abajo.*

From Aguascalientes, Azuela and this small band fled north by train with the wounded to Chihuahua, while Medina and his main force remained behind fighting in Jalisco. In Chihuahua, Azuela practiced medicine for several months until the approaching *carrancistas* drove him north to Ciudad Juárez. In October 1915 he had to take refuge in El Paso, Texas, where *Los de abajo* first appeared in print. Early in 1916 he returned to Guadalajara, and that same year he and his family moved to Mexico City, where they settled in the district of Santiago Tlaltelolco. Here Azuela resumed the practice of medicine and once again he responded easily to the relentless urgings of his pen. But economic security and literary recognition were slow in coming. It was not until late 1924 that good fortune finally came his way with the belated "discovery" of his sharply-etched memoirs recorded some ten years earlier in the pages of *Los de abajo.*

In 1923 Azuela took occupancy of the house in Colonia Santa María la Ribera that four years later was to become the family home. In the rear of this rambling, spacious dwelling he occupied a small room that served both as his office and his library. It was here that he administered to all who came for aid, here that he wrote well over half of his total output, here that he was never too busy or too tired to receive the growing numbers of those who came to chat or to do him honor. Azuela continued his formal practice at home until his seventieth year. However, his door thereafter remained ever open and his services free to the poor nearby in need of care. And it was not until 1949, after twenty-seven years of dedicated service to the poor, that he finally consented to relinquish his cherished public health clinic commitments.

As Azuela gradually earned release from his arduous professional duties, he was able to devote more and more time to writing, even though, as he would jestingly remark, he no longer reacted to the old urge as in days gone by: "Y por eso ahora reparto mi tiempo entre encuadernar libros o criar gallinas, que es lo menos ofensivo que se puede hacer, salvo para los libros y las gallinas" (OC, III, 1192). Modest and unassuming, not a little bewildered and yet naively pleased by the fame he had so deservedly won, Azuela found himself compelled to yield ever more of his precious waning moments to other affairs that to him proved considerably more *"ofensivos"* than "raising chickens and binding books."

Among those other affairs there was, however, an interest that Azuela could once again pursue to his heart's content. From his earliest student days he had nurtured a very special fondness for the theater. But he had never tried his hand at writing a play. Small wonder, then, that while still aglow with the world-wide "discovery" of *Los de abajo,* he should have responded warmly to the exciting possibility of seeing his own creations become flesh-and-blood characters before his very eyes. Adapted by José Luis Ituarte, *Los de abajo* was first performed in the Teatro Hidalgo of Mexico in 1929, and shortly thereafter in Los Angeles, California. Neither presentation met with favor. In passing it should be recalled that a later adaptation of the novel, done by Víctor Moya and staged in the Palacio de Bellas Artes, was received with warm approval from all quarters—winning awards in all categories—except from the "doblemente desencantado" and "estupefacto" author-collaborator himself (OC, III, 1150–1151). Disheartened by the early fiasco of 1929, some years were to pass before Azuela would decide to try his own hand at an adaptation of *Los caciques.* Entitled *Del Llano Hermanos S. en C.,* the play was performed in the Palacio de Bellas Artes on November 20, 1936. It too failed. Undaunted, Azuela also adapted *El desquite,* under the title *El buho en la noche.* The play never reached the footlights. Nevertheless, Azuela did have the satisfaction of seeing all three dramatizations of the novels published together in 1938 in a volume entitled *Teatro,* though the *Los de abajo* version was "rigurosamente inédito."

It was to the motion picture, and particularly to those made in Mexico, that Azuela would turn with excitement and expectancy during these latter years. And yet he did make one final attempt at writing, or rewriting, for the theater. Shortly before his death he adapted *Pedro Moreno, el insurgente* for a special performance in the Teatro del Sindicato de Electricistas on March 28, 1951. The occasion was a gratifying experience for the "inofensivo viejo ... encantado de ver la realización perfecta de lo que ... había proyectado" (OC, III, 1152). But, save for one notable exception, the motion picture proved even less yielding to his hopeful curiosity than had the theater. Both *Los de abajo* and *Mala yerba* were seen on the screen for the first time during 1940. Azuela was genuinely elated over the production of the former: "Es la única ocasión en que he visto los personajes que he imaginado convertidos en hombres y mujeres de carne y hueso" (OC, III, 1163). But *Mala yerba* was a failure, and for a time Azuela lost interest in the motion picture as a promising national art form. However, his curiosity had been whetted, and seven years later he decided to try his hand at writing original scripts. Several attempts, one based on materials taken from his novelized biography of Pedro Moreno, never reached the screen. Unfortunately, *La Marchanta* did. Written "intencionalmente con miras a su filmación," the picture had its first showing on Christmas night of 1947 under the "ignominious title" *La carne manda* (OC, III, 1167–1168). *La Marchanta* ended as a novel, as did other luckless attempts at scenarios, such as *Sendas perdidas* (1949), and the posthumous *Madero, biografía novelada* (published in 1958), both marred by their unhappy birth. Azuela has given us an entertaining and forthright account of his flirtation with both dramatic forms in his article "Mi experiencia en el cine y en el teatro" (OC, III, 1148–1173). His evaluation of that experience is aptly summed up in these terms: "... el teatro y el cine han sido mi calvario, puesto que en tales andanzas he pagado muchas culpas de vanidad por mis novelas" (*ibid.,* 1161).

Honors, and the onerous chores they often bring with them, came to disturb the nurtured solitude and quiet routine that were the hallmarks of the latter years of Mexico's most discussed novelist of the time. In 1941 the Ateneo Nacional de Ciencias y Artes conferred upon

Azuela their 1940 literary award. In 1942 the Seminario de Cultura Mexicana welcomed him to their fold; he was also invited to become a member of the Academia Mexicana de la Lengua, an invitation that Azuela declined. In 1943 the Mexican government named him one of the twenty founding members of the Colegio Nacional, the nation's most prestigious institution of higher studies in the sciences and the arts, and the Hispanic Society of America made him a corresponding member. There were other honors, with their corresponding duties—the invitation from the Mexican Academy to deliver the two series of lectures (1943 and 1947) that were to constitute his book on *Cien años de novela mexicana* (1947), and the invitation from the National University (1951) to deliver still another series, this one on the Revolution. It was in 1951 also that Jalisco honored Azuela, in the company of Enrique González Martínez, as one of the state's most distinguished sons. But the highest of all honors awarded to him was the Premio Nacional de Artes y Ciencias in literature which he received in 1949.

Three years later Azuela's heart began to fail. He died on March 1, 1952, early in his seventy ninth year.

His Works

The Writer. Beginning with his student days in Guadalajara, when he early identified himself with the anti-Díaz movement, Azuela was keenly alert to the passing scene. A born novelist, he has mirrored faithfully in all of his work the human drama of his people. He did not entrust to his memory the multiple impressions he would some day weave into his novels. Through the years he kept a minute and careful record: "En absoluto todos mis asuntos son reales, logrados tras de una labor constante de meditación y de apuntes. Usted no sabe cómo todo lo anoto, hasta el detalle más insignificante. Es una costumbre" (Ortega, "Azuela dijo . . . ," *El universal ilustrado,* 29 January 1925).

Azuela was not a professional writer: "Le juro que no soy literato." He only turned to his pen when strongly moved by injustice and suffering among his fellow men: "Sí, yo escribo cuando un dolor hace reaccionar mi espíritu." We may understand more clearly now the biting satire of his remarks and the reason for his attacks upon the *literatos de profesión*. When asked to give his opinion on the future of the Mexican novel, at the very moment (January 1925) when he was being acclaimed for his recently "discovered" *Los de abajo,* he limited his comments to a statement that he had given to the press some nine years earlier. How can professional writers ever be expected to produce anything really significant? "¿Qué saben ellos de esas enormes palpitaciones del alma nacional que están sacudiendo en estos mismos instantes a nuestra raza?" In these moments of supreme anguish, when the very soul of their people is bathed in tears and still shedding its blood, the great literary lights of the period are writing such books as *Senderos ocultos, La hora del Ticiano,* and *El libro del loco amor* ("Lo que opina un novelista," *El universal ilustrado,* January 22, 1925). Completely detached from and ignorant of the life of the masses, the writers born and reared during the opulent days of the Díaz regime continued to cultivate "el arte por el arte," thoroughly European in outlook and technique. Azuela recalls his acquaintance with many of these intellectuals in the very throes of the Revolution, and his impression of them was anything but flattering: "... los intelectuales que yo conocí dentro de ella; tal parece que no vibraron, que no sintieron" (Ortega, *op cit.*).

Unlike those Gallic admirers of the swan, whose pens rarely dipped deep into the founts of national life, Azuela was moved to write of the common people because of his compassion and sympathy for them. The middle classes inspired him with indifference and the aristocracy with disdain; Azuela was the apostle of the poor, the afflicted, the oppressed. As a young medical student in the provinces, as a juryman in the lower courts, and during his years of practice in the lowly quarters of the capital, he had seen much suffering and he had had ample time to study types and to gather dramatic material for his novels. But he was not content to tell us these things in an objective and disinterested way, intent alone on an artistic portrayal of the tragic fate of Mexico's poor. Indignation and concern were the motive forces of his pen, and he did not write either for pleasure or for fame. The abject poverty and the age-old injustices that stood out so sharply in the Mexican *comédie humaine* moved him deeply and demanded him to explain their causes, incited him to cry out against those responsible for his country's plight. And so throughout his novels, in greater or less degree, he is fighting for a cause. Social conflict is his theme. In his earlier works, he points accusingly to social conditions that bespeak the tyrannical oppression of *los de arriba;* later, when caught up in the ruthless brutality of the Revolution itself, he boldly condemns those guilty of having plunged his people into a class war without any clearly defined program of social reform; and, later still, he paints a somber picture of post-Revolutionary society, more corrupt and degenerate than before, for the Revolution had unleashed new forces of evil hitherto held in check through fear of a powerful centralized control. It is in this sense, then, that Azuela is the one writer best qualified to be called the "novelist of the Revolution," for he is the novelist not only of the more tragic and more sensational movement, the bloody years from 1910 to 1917, but also of the more vital and more significant movement, the social revolution that is still going on and of which the earlier one was but an episode.

Early Writings (1896–1906). Azuela's literary career dates from 1896, when his first article, "impresiones de un estudiante," a series of sketches of the life of a seminary student in the provinces, appeared in *Gil Blas cómico* of Mexico (from March 5 to November 22) under the pseudonym Beleño. In this first product of his pen Azuela revealed interests and traits that would characterize all of his future writing—an interest in types, especially in the poor and unfortunate, and in character study; and a touch of humor and of satire. The germ of his first novel, *María Luisa,* is to be found in the last of these "Impresiones." He continued writing a number of pieces in those early years, usually under one or another pseudonym, for newspapers and literary reviews of Lagos, Guadalajara, and Mexico. In 1903 he received his first public recognition for his literary efforts when he was awarded a diploma at the Juegos Florales of Lagos for his story "De mi tierra" (*El imparcial,* Mexico, June 1903). In this first outburst against social injustice, he calls accursed the land that enslaves the peon and enriches the licentious *hacendado*—and here we have *Mala yerba* in the making. This first outcry was soon followed by another when in an article entitled "Víctimas de la opulencia," published in *Ocios literarios* of Mexico for October 1904, he bitterly attacked "la injusticia eterna, en una de tantas de sus modalidades"—the "monstrous" sacrifice of the wet nurse who must deprive her own starving children of what they most need. Then, finally, to *Ocios* *literarios* for 1905 he contributed an excerpt from what would appear two years later under the title *María Luisa*. Azuela had written his first novel. He was in his thirty-fourth year.

The Pre-Revolutionary Novels (1907–1910). The setting of *María Luisa* (1907) and the tragic fate of the heroine spring directly from Azuela's early experience as a medical student in Guadalajara, where in the hospital in which he was an intern he learned the sad story of a beautiful young girl who had died of tuberculosis after a brief love, subsequent abandonment, and three years of hopeless moral and physical decline. The student life he portrays was his life, and against this background he projects the girl's story in the fated career of María Luisa, fatherless daughter of Cuca, mistress of a *pensión,* abandoned by the young medical student Pancho. In the final chapter the girl's former lover enters the hospital room to pronounce her dead; he fails to recognize her because of the ravages of exposure and disease.

Azuela's penchant for contrasting opposite types is already apparent. Consider his portrayal of "doña Cuca, madre de María, la buena de su prima, el revés de Juana, antigua soldadera," and his confrontation of conservatives and liberals as exemplified in the *seminaristas* and in Pancho, the medical student. He fills in his canvas with many other familiar provincial types—no one completely escapes his caustic scrutiny. He is outspoken in his anticlerical feeling and his criticism of religious education. And in this first novel there is much of the fatalism of *Los de abajo* and the same concern for the future of his people.

Los fracasados (1908) is another of Azuela's early attempts to expose and to denounce the social inequities and injustices of the familiar local scene. His target here is the easy disposition of those of the middle class to sacrifice any ideal for wealth and power. There is the same gallery of authentic provincial types, again in clear-cut confrontation as good or bad, liberal or conservative. A few do emerge, however, as strong, well-knit characters. Azuela's hand is beginning to move now with the assurance of one caught up with a passion for the pen.

The Álamos of the story is the author's own native city of Lagos, and Azuela directs his satire against the ambitious and unscrupulous politicians he knew personally; against the conservative, hypocritical upper class; and against the blighting influence of the church. Pitted against these basic elements of the Díaz regime, the young lawyer Reséndez, fresh from his studies in the capital, meets only with frustration. And Consuelo, loved by the thwarted idealist for her intelligence and for the freshness and joy of her youth, is also reviled and driven out by these same deadening forces.

When questioned by Ortega (*op. cit.*) as to the setting for his following novel, *Mala yerba* (1909), Azuela replied: "*¿Mala yerba,* ambiente de Lagos? No sólo de Lagos, sino de todas las poblaciones de su categoría. Fui médico municipal y este empleo permitióme indagar en los delitos de los hacendados. ¡Quedé espantado del número de causas! Un terrateniente mataba a un peón con el menor pretexto, o sin él. Durante el porfirismo, porque las cosas hoy son distintas, ¡qué de crímenes!" *Mala yerba* is, as the subtitle indicates, a novel of national customs. But it is much more than a *costumbrista* novel; more precisely, it is a portrayal and indictment of the old colonial landholding system as it still prevailed in the days of Porfirio Díaz. Julián, "tierno vástago de una raza de chacales, de ladrones, de bandidos de camino real," is the degenerate proprietor of the vast *hacienda* of San Pedro de las Gallinas. Like the other *hacendados* of his day, he rules supreme and unmolested by the law, in fact, rather protected by it in his dastardly work as oppressor and assassin of the long-suffering peons whose life and honor are of no concern to him. Marcela, the beautiful, sensuous daughter of Pablo Fuentes, dean of the servants of the *hacienda,* becomes the prey of Julián's sexual appetite and finally the victim of his mad jealousy when he plunges into her heart the very dagger with which she hoped to rid herself of him. And in the face of irrefutable evidence, rural justice decrees that killing a mere woman of the people is far less of a crime than that of defaming the character of a wealthy *hacendado!*

Mala yerba is Azuela's first important work and must be classed among the best of his novels. Though melodramatic and none too original in plot, it offers splendid characterization and a vigorous, artistic portrayal of rural customs and types. And for the first time Azuela assigns nature an inescapable and effective role in the setting and in the lives of his protagonists. Although given to overdrawing his principal characters because of the intensity with which he flays the feudal scene, Azuela is especially adept in his delineation of minor types such as Pablo Fuentes, "servidor de los más *apegados a la casa*" but never so beaten or cowed as not to speak out boldly against his masters; and the local judge, who rebukes Petrolino, his secretary, for wishing to make child's play of justice by accusing Julián as the obvious perpetrator of Marcela's death without examining first the circumstantial evidence that will bring him acquittal. A stereotyped conception of the gringo and the current anti-Yankee attitude are here expressed for the first time. This attitude, more pointedly directed years later in his *San Gabriel de Valdivias, comunidad indígena,* reveals Azuela's growing concern for the gradual breakdown of Mexican customs and the Mexican way of life in the face of the cultural invasion from the north. The barbed satire and heavily charged pessimism that prevail throughout are momentarily relieved by Azuela's avowal of faith in Mexican womanhood, an avowal he will voice more artistically and with even greater conviction in *La luciérnaga. Mala yerba* is not without its blemishes, but it is a forceful novel, compelling in its interest.

The Novels of the Revolution (1911–1918). *Andrés Pérez, maderista* (1911) is Azuela's first novel of the Revolution. Artistically it is a decidedly inferior work, overly sententious, poorly and hurriedly written, at times difficult to follow; but ideologically it is one of his most significant novels. Conceived during those very months when Azuela already foresaw the tragic turn the revolt of the idealist Madero was soon to take, when he sensed the impending triumph of the "enjambre de negros y pestilentes moscones" of the Díaz regime, who, as "maderistas de ocasión," were soon to wrest the control of the Revolution from those who had suffered to see it born, it is the work of one who boldly, fearlessly, and prophetically, in defiance of *maderistas* and *porfiristas* alike, decried the Revolution as "una gran mentira, una pobre alucinación de moribundo..."

Andrés Pérez, forced by circumstances to become a "maderista de ocasión," limps confusedly through the initial period of the Revolution, fearful of being identified with a movement that may soon be crushed. Not even the sarcastic smile of Octavio, true "maderista de convicción," who witnesses the tremendous ovation given "Coronel Andrés Pérez," awakens him to the real significance of the movement. Into the hands of opportunists like Andrés Pérez and Colonel Hernández—"ahora es general el coronel, por no poder ser algo más" —fall the fruits of the "Revolución Triunfante." *Andrés Pérez, maderista* is Azuela's first attack against the type that he characterized later as "las moscas" in the novel of that name. Because of their eternal presence, Mexico will continue to suffer from her age-old wounds: a feudal land system, military dictatorship, a spineless, abject press and intellectual class—old grievances exposed by Azuela in the course of his novel. And, completely disillusioned, in his next novel, *Sin amor,* Azuela withdraws from militant, open support of the already fatally undermined Madero revolt.

In *Sin amor* (1912) he caustically remarks, "En México se acabaron las revoluciones," even though he is supposedly speaking of Don Porfirio's patriarchy. There is no interest or concern evinced here in the Madero revolt. In theme and in manner the novel reverts to those of the prerevolutionary period. It is charged, however, with more relentless satire, which is directed especially against those whom the nascent movement had failed to convert to its cause—the bourgeoisie, "la del puro dinero, la burguesía brutal y nada más," whom he characterizes as hypocritical, presumptuous, unprincipled, and immoral. Here again we have the same technique of contrasts. The procedure, unfortunately, is too forced and too marked, and the novel loses in style and in effect. Especially overdrawn is Ana María Romero, of the aristocracy of wealth, who is contrasted with Julia Ponce, of the aristocracy of good birth and breeding; her characterization borders on caricature, and her complete spiritual identity with the class to which she aspired to belong is anything but convincing.

Three years of literary inactivity followed the publication of *Sin amor,* but fruitful years they were, because it was then that Azuela lived and recorded the experiences and impressions of his world-famous novel. *Los de abajo* was conceived in the very heat and horror of the conflagration, at the very moment when the Revolution seemed to have gone completely out of control, when those in whom the *maderistas* had placed their hopes of revenge for their leader's assassination and of carrying out his program of reform had parted ways. Azuela, as army doctor of the forces of the rebel chief Julián Medina of Jalisco, was in the most disheartening part of the strife; he was swept along with Villa's men and witnessed the pitiless struggle among the very leaders who but a short time before had mobilized troops along the Río Grande to fight their way south to the capital to oust the assassin Huerta. Azuela lived and fought and suffered with the *villistas* in their hurried retreat north, hotly pursued by the combined forces of Carranza and Obregón. When he reached Zacatecas, a spring mattress was indeed a rare treat to one "acostumbrado a dormir en las piedras y las malezas." It was shortly before this, when in flight from Guadalajara to Aguascalientes, "en pura sierra," and in the company of assassins and thieves, idealists and cynics, that he began to jot down notes of that historic episode, notes which he carried with him over the border into El Paso sometime in October 1915. Penniless and in dire need of food and clothing, he finished *Los de abajo* in exile and set out at once to find a publisher. He succeeded in selling his manuscript for some twenty dollars to the Mexican newspaper *El Paso del Norte,* in which it appeared during the last three months of that same fateful year. Early in 1916 the novel appeared for the first time in book form in a run-off edition published by the same "El Paso del Norte" press.

Azuela has told how amazed and concerned his friends were upon learning that *El Paso del Norte* had purchased *Los de abajo.* They advised him to flee, for his novel had fallen into the hands of a *carrancista* editor whose newspaper was being subsidized by the Carranza authorities. Later, he was wont to recall with relish the praise with which those *carrancistas* received his work—a good omen, so it seemed, for the success of his novel, however belated that success was to be in coming. Why this fear of persecution from the Carranza faction? As a friend of his warned him at the time: "Van a calificarla de 'reaccionaria.'" But Azuela assured him "que no, porque es la verdad."

Appearing when and where it did, *Los de abajo* failed to attract immediate attention. In the course of the decade following its first printing, two more editions, one in Tampico (1917) and the other in Mexico City (1920), both limited in number, failed likewise to arouse critical comment. It was not until late December 1924 that Mexico hailed its "unknown provincial doctor . . . as a true novelist" and *Los de abajo* as the "only novel of the Revolution." The "discovery" of Azuela and his novel was one of the more felicitous fruits of a now historic literary polemic over the question of whether the nation of that early post-revolutionary period could yet lay claim to "una literatura mexicana viril . . . una literatura mexicana moderna" (see J. E. Englekirk, "The 'Discovery' of *Los de abajo,*" *Hispania,* XVIII, 1935, pp. 53–62). Since that memorable spring of 1925, *Los de abajo* has been published, in the original and in more than twenty-seven editions, from Mexico and Madrid to New York and Buenos Aires; and, in addition, English, French, Russian, German, Japanese, Yugoslav, Portuguese, Czech, Italian, Swedish, and Yiddish translations have made Azuela and his novel famous the world over.

Demetrio Macías, contented, humble Indian of a little mountain village in Zacatecas, incurs the enmity of the *cacique* of Moyahua, who denounces him to the Federals as a *maderista.* Demetrio is forced to abandon his family and home and take to hiding. He knows nothing about the Revolution; what he does know is that, like many others who gather about him in his mountain hideout, he is being hunted by men who are hirelings of the *caciques* and *hacendados,* men who have shot his dog and burned his thatched hut, and that capture means certain death. He is proclaimed chief of a small band and wins his first encounter with the Federals in a deep ravine not far from his own land. Others soon flock to join him, among them the opportunistic, smooth-tongued, pseudointellectual Cervantes, who urges Demetrio to identify his cause with that of the great revolutionary leaders, Villa, Carranza, Natera. Demetrio's rise is rapid; under Natera he becomes a colonel; after his daring action under Villa at Zacatecas, a general. Fighting, pillaging, killing, loving, and drinking, he and his men are swept along in the path of the hurricane that is the Revolution. It is their hour of triumph. But soon Carranza and Villa split. Villa is defeated at Celaya, and from that moment on Macías and his men are in retreat. They take their final stand in the very canyon where two years before they had tasted the blood of their initial triumph. And in this spot, at the foot of a mighty crag as lofty and magnificent as the portico of an old cathedral, Demetrio Macías, his eyes forever fixed, continues sighting along the barrel of his rifle.

But the Revolution was not all horror, lust, and bloodshed, as many would believe; as Azuela says in the words of Solís, the idealist, "How beautiful the Revolution is, even in its very barbarism!" And so, artist that he was, Azuela softened the harsh, brutal realism of his canvas with many a lyric touch; in striking contrast to the sordid primitiveness of most of his characters, the natural background is awe-inspiring in its grandeur and serenity. The language, sometimes racy and virile, sometimes poetic and subdued, is in every instance in perfect accord with the mood and character of the story. Apparently as aimless as the Revolution itself, the novel unfolds easily and naturally. Just as out of the chaos of guerrilla warfare and the clash of human pawns is born the primal, well-defined motif of the movement it has indelibly engraved for all time, so too out of the individual scenes that are here brought together there springs an artistic unity that only one who had experienced them could have achieved. In Waldo Frank's happy phrasing: "It is well joined as a Greek ode."

Los caciques (1917), or "bosses," is Azuela's indictment of those who wielded political as well as economic and social power over the life of Mexico's small towns and villages. The plot is laid in the early years of the Revolution. Juan Viñas, a humble merchant, has laboriously saved a sum sufficient to keep his wife Elena—whose characterization is another tribute to Mexican womanhood—and his children Esperanza and Juanito from economic want during his declining years. When advised by the Llanos, the *gente de bien* whose word is law and whose counsel Juan has never questioned, to invest his modest savings in a business enterprise which, they assure him, will bring in better returns, Juan does so without inquiring into the obviously important matter of how much capital will be needed to build his model tenement house. His money runs out long before the building is completed; the Llanos advance him funds against a mortgage on his little store; the loan is inadequate, but the *caciques* turn a deaf ear to his plea for further support; building stops; Juan cannot meet his payments on the loan, and the Llanos take all. Juan dies of mortification and grief in the miserable shack that is his new home on the outskirts of the town. Esperanza and Juanito find employment in the grocery store, La Carolina, across the street from the magnificent mansion being built by the Llanos out of profits realized from the sale of their father's store and his nearly completed Vecindad Modelo. The *antihuertistas* sweep down upon the town, and in the general looting and pillaging that follows, Juanito and Esperanza seek as their share of the spoils nothing more than a can of oil with which they set fire to the *cacique's* home.

Rodríguez is one of Azuela's finest characters. No longer young and with little to show in any tangible way for his native ability and clear thinking, Rodríguez towers above all, both oppressors and oppressed, because of the thoroughly human virtues of sympathy, tenderness, and understanding that serve to embellish his superior wisdom and courage. He is betrayed and shot when the *antimaderista* faction gains control. But in Esperanza and Juanito he left enkindled something of a righteous hatred for those who were responsible for much of their country's sorrow. He had taught Juanito to cry out: "¡Mueran los caciques!"

Although *Los caciques* was written shortly after definite steps had been taken to rid the country of local bossism, and when land and labor reforms were being written into the Constitution of 1917, the general tone of the novel is one of disillusionment and gloom. However, a gleam of hope flickers upward with the flames of the burning dwelling of the caciques—Azuela's symbolically voiced hope that something good might yet come out of the bloody strife.

Las moscas (1918) is one of Azuela's finest pieces of satire and humor; it is the classic presentation of a type already exposed in *Andrés Perez, maderista.* The novel—or, as the subtitle more accurately describes the work, the "sketches and scenes of the Revolution"—abounds with inimitable characters of the "ista" type: the *gente decente* family of the Reyes Téllez of Culiacán, *soldaderas* (women camp-followers), generals, lawyers, government employees, who yesterday all were *huertistas,* today are *villistas,* and tomorrow, through the simple procedure of tearing the *estrella* from their hats, will be *carrancistas,* for Villa and his *dorados* have just been defeated at Celaya. This heterogeneous band is cleverly brought together through the happy device of using as a setting for the story a military train crowded with soldiers and civilians in common retreat. Choice satiric sketches of new types in Azuela's already large gallery of his compatriots are Sinforoso, director of a public school, and Donaciano Ríos, government employee. The final chapter, "Un ocaso," is exceedingly well done. Villa appears in shirt sleeves on the rear platform of the Pullman car of his special train to survey final preparations for the flight north. Imposing silence is maintained by those who watch his *dorados* enter the cars. His gaze is fixed on his horsemen, who are covering the retreat. It is evening: "Y entre el polvo hay celajes de oro, pinceladas de sangre caliente de un sol que se extingue . . . que se extingue para siempre. En el hálito tibio de la noche llega de allá muy lejos un rumor sordo y misterioso, un rumor solemne como la voz del mar: '¡México se ha salvado!' y en el horizonte, la luna enharinada y bizca ríe . . . ríe . . ."

The first edition of *Las moscas* in 1918 includes two stories, "Domitilo quiere ser diputado" and "De cómo al fin lloró Juan Pablo," that illustrate other facets of the same basic theme. Based on Remy de Gourmont's maxim, "Vivre c'est l'art de se plier à la nécessité," a maxim that also serves as the key to *Las moscas,* "Domitilo quiere ser diputado" is a masterful portrayal of political chicanery and intrigue. Serapio, local political boss notorious for his ability to accommodate the color and tone of village politics to those of each successive wave of *redentores* that gains control, has been guided from his early youth by the French saying Azuela renders as "Vivir es adaptarse al medio." Companion of Serapio is the chameleonic, sententious *carrancista* general who changes his name from "don Lolo" to Xicoténcatl Robespierre Cebollino, intent on proving to the whole world that he is no longer a slave, not even to a name imposed upon him at birth. In the second story, Juan Pablo, who is awaiting execution on a charge of treason, fails to comprehend the political psychology and maneuvering of the "moscas"; he cannot get it through his "mezquite brain" how even after the Revolution has been won, some still continue to be slaves to others. The *civilistas,* or civilian turncoats, have become the new masters; they are now the ones who, in the words of Juan Pablo, "se han sentado a la mesa y a nosotros nos arrojan como al perro, las sobras del banquete."

The year 1918 was a fruitful one for Azuela. He wrote feverishly, as if fearing that time would dim the priceless memories of the Revolution he had known, as if striving to record for future generations the human side of that historic period and to preserve in pen sketches the myriad types morally uprooted and distorted by the seething chaos of those years. *Las tribulaciones de una familia decente* (1918) is just such a record. It is Azuela's first-hand account of the tragic struggle of the Vázquez Prado family of Zacatecas to begin life anew in the capital, whither they had fled to escape the approaching hordes of the *"ladrones,"* Carranza and Villa. The family itself, symbolic of the Revolution and of the nation, is torn between conflicting ideologies. Procopio, the father, and his daughter Lulú courageously face the future with unwavering faith in the age-old virtues of honesty, dignity, and loyalty—for Azuela does not condemn all the *gente decente.* Agustinita, the mother, and the sons created in her image, César and Francisco José, would not blaspheme the sacred memory of their "amados muertecitos" by stooping to become mere breadwinners.

Berta, another daughter, deceived at first by Pascual's magnanimous manner, finally comprehends her husband's true character when he would stake her virtue to aid him in his rise to power.

The first part of the novel, entitled "El libro de las horas amargas," is narrated by César, "hijo de su mamá." Characterized to the point of caricature, César provides genuine entertainment in many a scene of clever satire; César is anything but a "Caesar"; cowardly, weak, effeminate, spineless, he is the pitiful offspring of a too long pampered, degenerate social class. César's death prepares the way for the second part of the novel, "El triunfo de Procopio." The ensuing shift in emphasis and narrative technique lends added meaning to Procopio's moral stature and exemplary conduct.

The novel abounds in penetrating, prophetic observations on the nature and course of the Revolution; it is also a remarkable document of the manners and types of middle class Mexican society of the period. Unquestionably, the novel is one of Azuela's most effective pieces of satire, and of those works dealing with the years 1910–1917, it stands second only to *Los de abajo.*

The Hermetic and Historical Novels (1919–1935). With the writing of *Las tribulaciones de una familia decente* Azuela brought to a close the series of novels inspired by what is popularly thought of as the Revolution, the war years from Madero to the presidency of Carranza. The social revolution, however, had just begun, and Azuela was to follow it with the same keen concern and perspicacity with which he had observed and documented the chaotic years that had cradled the move for an ever-expanding reform of the entire social structure. Five years were to pass, however, before the release of Azuela's first picture of postwar Mexico. Furthermore, they were years of disillusionment and frustration, unproductive years that yielded but several prose fragments. Azuela had tried to tell his story of the national upheaval, share his misgivings over what had come to pass. He was willing to try again if only someone would evince genuine interest in his effort; he was deeply disheartened, "cansado del anonimato." Realism and Revolution had little appeal, obviously, for the writers and critics of the day. Azuela could not and would not cast aside his convictions and his commitments as a social critic and commentator. But what about his manner of writing? Why not place a bid for response by applying the new literary techniques then in vogue to the themes and situations and human conditions that would ever arouse his compassionate concern and challenge his sharp clinical eye?

La Malhora (1923) was Azuela's first attempt to cultivate the new manner—"...ese truco tan sobado ahora de martirizar las palabras, para dárselas de inteligente, ingenioso y agudo" (OC, III, 118). And the theme was there for the trial run. Azuela's services as a juryman during most of 1921 had given him ample opportunity to study at first hand the many unfortunates whose miserable pleading fell on unsympathetic ears. And shortly after, during 1922, as a member of the staff of the Consultorio No. III, the public clinic of the Tepito quarter of the city, he came again into intimate contact with the tragic lot of the poor, misunderstood and maligned by those who were best able to help them—the courts and the medical profession. In *La Malhora* Azuela repudiates the inhuman professionalism of the former and the crass commercialism of the latter and satirizes the smug morality of those who have never experienced economic want.

Malhora, a girl of fifteen, is abandoned by Marcelo and falls an easy prey to vice and sin. Her father is killed by her former lover, who is now enamored of Tapatía. Marcelo and Tapatía attempt to rid themselves of Malhora, lest she denounce them, and of Epigmenio, a former suitor of Tapatía. Epigmenio is killed, but Malhora, although gravely wounded, is saved by a "santo médico" and is physically and spiritually healed in the service of three pious women of Irapuato. She is now known as Altagracia. But hereditary forces surge again within her, and she reverts to her former life of sin. Unconsciously she knows what is troubling her, but others do not, and she is reviled by them. Her vision clears at last, at the very moment she is intent on killing her old enemies, Marcelo and Tapatía; Altagracia sees them now in their true state, helpless and aging, and she turns away to leave them to their meaningless and miserable destiny.

In style the novelette represents a radical departure from Azuela's earlier work. Azuela readily admitted that he wrote *La Malhora* "según los últimos procedimientos," explaining thereby why it may seem somewhat "obscure." It is by no means easy reading; many lines and some passages must be read again and again before their complete meaning and symbolic strength can be fully appreciated. Azuela abides by no accepted standards of sentence structure or style: substantives and adjectives are endowed with verbal power; adjectives are given unexpected and amazingly suggestive meanings; recondite images, often one upon another, dazzle one into incomprehension; there is occasionally an excessive grouping of adjectives, not always to the best effect. The obvious narrative thread is repeatedly interrupted and definitely subordinated to a more profound and more suggestive one which knits together the many soliloquies that illumine the intricate psychological pattern of subconscious forces motivating the surface action. This baffling but provocative style places *La Malhora* among the best of the earliest attempts to elaborate new novelistic techniques in the America of that day.

El desquite (1925) follows the stylistic and structural pattern of *La Malhora,* but is far less artistically done. Azuela's striving for inordinate effects has definitely marred the work. Psychological bits of retrospect, too frequently interspersed, nearly obliterate the main narrative and impede and distort character portrayal; the imagery is challenging but too often obscure. The novel suffers from hasty composition and from a blurred conception at the outset of just how the rather involved theme—especially complex because of structure and style—was to be carried to a logical end.

The picture Azuela paints for us here is a somber one indeed, distinctly Zolaesque in the sordidness and the physical and mental degeneracy it portrays. It is the tragedy of a woman who married beneath her in spiritual and moral dignity, for, as Azuela says, "en los matrimonios desiguales es ella, a menudo, quien desciende." Lupe, upon her mother's insistence, rejects Martín, a young law student, and marries Blas, a wealthy opportunist given to excessive drinking and overindulgence in sex. Two years pass and there are still no children; but Ricardito, offspring of "la Huilota" of ill fame and of the older Blas, is reared by his half brother and Lupe as their own. He grows up in the image of Blas, covets his wealth, and plots to have Lupe put out of the way so that he may become the sole heir. He accuses Lupe of illicit relations with other men and urges Blas to ask for a divorce. When confronted by Blas, Lupe melodramatically hands him a pistol, indignantly commanding him to shoot her if he believes her guilty. Blas begs for forgiveness. They continue living together, but now Lupe cunningly plans to rid herself of him by becoming his drinking companion, thus encouraging him in his vice and hastening his death as a victim of cerebral congestion. Martín, her former love, defends her successfully at the trial, and shortly after they are married. Lupe soon realizes that Martín has married her for her money; already physically undermined by drink, she succumbs completely to her vice and breaks mentally under the strain, obsessed by thoughts of "el otro."

La luciérnaga (1932) testifies to Azuela's liberation from forced and unfortunate stylistic techniques that marred *El desquite* and that made the reading of *La Malhora* a marked intellectual challenge. Azuela was never a slave to any literary movement; he might have been attracted for a time by the mood and manner of the day, but he was too vigorous a writer not to emerge soon with a style decidedly his own. For example, Azuela became an avid reader of Proust during the years immediately preceding the publication of *La luciérnaga,* and he who will can find occasional echoes of the French writer in Azuela's novel. But there is no servility, either here or in any of his writing.

In passing it will be recalled that Azuela openly admitted his debt to others. He confessed that Balzac, Zola, Flaubert, Daudet, and the Goncourts had been the dominant influences in the writing of his first four novels and that French contemporary novelists continued to guide his steps until he turned his pen toward the Revolution: "In my composition of these last, I do not think I was affected by any additional literary influences." He does add, however, that Conrad and Proust became his favorite authors in later years, but he would reject the suggestion that he had been influenced in any way by Proust, since, he explains, "I have always read him with the inalterable idea that he is unique and inimitable" ("My Debt to Books," *Books Abroad,* XII, Winter 1938, p. 26).

La luciérnaga is a psychological study of two brothers, a study again in contrasts: Dionisio, who left the provinces with his family and with his share of the inheritance to conquer the capital, and José María, who remains behind with his money—not all rightfully his—and with his remorse to argue himself into believing, in a convincing display of casuistry, that his soul will be saved. Dionisio, naive, spineless, credulous, vacillating, is soon stripped of his inheritance—and of his family—by the avaricious horde of opportunists, politicians, government employees, doctors, lawyers, who swoop down upon him and drive him to the brink of death. He is saved by the infinite courage and understanding of his wife, Conchita, who returns to help him face life anew. José María, miserly, superstitious, mistrusting, immersed in casuistry and in longed-for pain in an effort to gain peace of mind and eternal salvation, finds an early resting place for his "carnes magulladas y sus huesos rotos."

The opening chapter is a brilliant piece of concise exposition and psychological portrayal. Through his masterful depiction of the thought processes of the *pulque*-soaked, drug-befuddled brain of Dionisio and his studied treatment of the sophistry of José María, Azuela introduces naturally and artistically those elements of the narrative that, had they been presented in any other way, would have impeded and distorted the development of the story. In style *La luciérnaga* ranks with *La Malhora* as the best of Azuela's experimental work.

Azuela's flirtation with modern novelistic techniques was brash but brief. He had taken the plunge with *La Malhora* in 1923 and some three years later he was already completing the first draft of what was to be his third and final attempt in the new manner, *La luciérnaga,* which, although not published until 1932, had gone to press in chapter form as early as midyear 1927 ("El grifo," *Ulises,* I, June 1927, pp. 10–13). The sudden and unexpected fame which came to him with the "discovery" of *Los de abajo* in early 1925 must have contributed, in part at least, to his decision to once again "decir las cosas con claridad" and, repentant, he confessed: "Hice un serio y detenido examen de conciencia y me sentí pecador" (OC, III, 1118).

Azuela returned to his old style and even to his traditional role as a scathing critic of the sociopolitical scene. By 1928 he had completed the writing of *El camarada Pantoja* (1937), the first product of his renewed attack; but because of the tense political situation of the day he decided to withhold publication until a more propitious hour. Momentarily thwarted and perplexed, he hopefully sought a way out of his dilemma by turning to his country's turbulent past for a fresh vantage point from which to view the troubled present.

Scanning the century and more of his country's existence as an independent nation, Azuela discovered that the socioeconomic struggle of his day was essentially the same as the one that ended in freedom from Spain, the same, too, as the long civil war that came to a close with the passage of the reform laws and the execution of Maximilian.

He soon spotted human material to his liking and a silence of several years was broken at last by the appearance of *Pedro Moreno, el insurgente* in 1933 and *Precursores* in 1935. These two historical novels, or "biografías noveladas" as Azuela preferred to call them, served to bridge the years and satisfy the author's keen interest in his country's past.

Based on the work of the Lagos historian Agustín Rivera, *Pedro Moreno, el insurgente* is a dynamic account of the unselfish and little-known labors and supreme sacrifice of the discreet and modest insurgent Pedro Moreno, who fought to free his country from foreign domination. Here, too, as in *Los de abajo,* through his choice of a minor hero who was of the people, Azuela has dramatized the hardships and suffering of the "underdogs." And in *Precursores* also he prefers to tell the story of three famous bandits of the Bajío, "El Amito," Manuel Lozada (the Tiger of Alica), and Antonio Rojas—bandits beloved of the people, bandits who found living beyond the law in the fifties and sixties of the last century a very costly business because officialdom demanded a high price for certain dispensations, bandits whose story had been distorted by official history, the "ramera cobarde (que) entrapuja siempre la verdad."

The Protest Novels of Populist Social Reform (1936–1941). For almost twenty years Azuela had withheld open, specific criticism of the Revolution. He had not, however, remained indifferent to the emerging social reform program of the period. To the contrary, he had, in fact, reacted immediately and impassionedly to the glaring hypocrisy of distorted revolutionary policies, and his reactions surfaced in the pages of *El camarada Pantoja* (1937), the first draft of which he had completed by 1928. The result was not a happy one. The story treats of Pantoja, member of CROM (Confederación Regional de Obreros Mexicanos) and warm devotee of the opportunists of the Revolution. Pantoja is lifted from his station as a humble, ignorant man of the masses into a responsible government position because of his virtue of blind obedience to the dictates of the political boss. Although simple in plot, the novel becomes unnecessarily involved and confusing because of Azuela's passionate bent for lashing out long and vehemently against the Carranza-Calles-Obregón group. The picture of the twenties that he paints for us is, if anything, more somber and more revolting than those of the war years. As Azuela puts it, "Porque entonces yo no conocía a sus émulos, los civilizados

Carranza, Obregón, Calles y Cía. Francisco Villa, fuerza de la revolución estuvo siempre en su sitio. Mató mucho y aun con sus propias manos. Pero nunca fue el cobarde pálido criminal que dice: 'mato en nombre de las Instituciones, mato en defensa de mi credo filosófico'."

The novel is weak in structure and characterization; its message is heavy with the angry hand of the moralist; its style, in sharp contrast to that of his experimental novels, is loose and elliptic and suffers from the clipped intensity with which Azuela satirizes the tyranny of that tragic decade. Chapter VIII, "¡Héroe, dame un abrazo!," is the only outstanding bit of writing in the novel. It is an excellent satire of both factions, the Constitutionalists and the reactionaries, and is to be commended for its concision and rapidity of style and for its delightful ironic humor.

San Gabriel de Valdivias, comunidad indígena (1938) is in style, character delineation, and thematic structure far superior to *El camarada Pantoja*. It is especially reminiscent of *Mala yerba*. Azuela is at his best in the depiction of provincial life and types. His style is clear and concise, his language is racy, his types smell of the soil, and his tone is chiaroscuro—in pleasant relief to the heavy, somber note especially characteristic of his urban novels. For its folkloric qualities and for the happy interjection of a humorous, less mordantly satiric vein (even though it, too, ends on the typical Azuela note of resigned pessimism), this novel on the agrarian policy of the Revolution is much better reading than its urban counterpart.

Ramoncito, the always inebriated rural school teacher, never wearies of repeating the motif of the novel: "Hermano campesino, acabaste con el hacendado; ahora te falta acabar con el líder!" San Gabriel de Valdivias, formerly the *hacienda* of Carlos and his son Arturo, reactionary, landholding *caciques,* is now a modern agrarian colony, product of the Revolution. But it is so in name only, for conditions are as bad as or worse than before; it is now known as Comunidad Quintana and the *hacendados* no longer enrich themselves on peon land and toil, but Quintana is the name of a new kind of tyrant, the revolutionary *líder,* under whom the old *hacendado* system flourishes as never before. Dámaso was the only one courageous enough to growl his eternal discontent: " 'La misma jeringa con otro palo' y peor tantito, porque si el amo don Carlos es un caballero aquí y en tierra de mecos, el tal Saturnino Quintana ni cara de gente tiene."

In *Regina Landa* (1939) Azuela once again attacks those responsible for the miscarriage of revolutionary ideals and exposes the resultant conditions. Regina Landa, orphaned daughter of a most unusual individual, a revolutionary general who did not reward himself for his services to the cause, is forced to make her own living. She obtains a position in a government office, but she soon abandons it because she refuses to lose her independence and her individuality in the service "del Estado que prostituye a sus servidores." Regina Landa is yet another symbol of Azuela's faith in the sincerity and resolve of Mexican womanhood. During her brief contact with the bureaucratic world, the heroine comes to know and despise "los pillos que se llaman los 'redentores del proletariado'," who have misled the masses by urging them to set themselves up as the ruling class instead of exhorting them merely to "sostener derechos que ahora nadie les niega." In addition to criticizing certain aspects of the Mexican proletarian movement, Azuela sharply satirizes the hypocritical appreciation of art so ludicrously displayed by the bourgeois class with whom Regina associates while in the employ of the state.

This urban novel loses by comparison with the splendid depiction of rural Mexico in *San Gabriel de Valdivias;* it has none of the fine humor, sprightly satire, and earthy charm of the earlier work. *Regina Landa* lacks color and drive. It is poorly structured; one leaves it with the impression that Azuela interpolated much of his material without forethought or plan. This is especially marked in the chapter entitled "Irma, la Modelito." And yet, despite these defects, the novel can still be read with interest by those intent on recording Azuela's relentless repudiation of many aspects and phases of the social revolution.

Avanzada (1940) represents another step forward in Azuela's dogged determination to expose those elements of human power that had emerged as the modern tyrants of his people under the revolutionary social program of Cárdenas. Azuela's sword is now double-edged. In the first part of the novel he strikes yet another blow at those who had betrayed the high purposes of agrarian reform—"el nuevo feudalismo de una Revolución descarriada"; and in the second part he lays bare the tragic plight of the proletariat caught up in the violence and hatred of a macabre class struggle between the workers and leaders of embattled labor unions.

The first part of the novel takes place in Jalisco, where the small landholder Miguel is sacrificed on the altar of an agrarian movement that miscarries under a "liderismo babeante de estupidez." And even though trained and spurred on by five years of study in advanced agricultural techniques in the United States and Canada, Miguel's son Adolfo is also forced finally to give up the unequal fight. Adolfo goes to Veracruz to work in a sugar mill and to give his life for the cause of the growing army of the landless proletariat, just as his father before him had given his life for the cause of his fellow *campesinos,* "lo mejor de nuestro México."

In structure, character portrayal, and descriptive power *Avanzada* is a better novel than either *El camarada Pantoja* or *Regina Landa;* and even though the work was written out of a fierce but confused conviction that the social revolution had backfired against the Mexican masses, Azuela did succeed in recovering a measure of the balance between art and social criticism that is characteristic of his best efforts. Clearly, however, *Avanzada* signals the closing of a cycle that is rapidly losing fire and force for want of new source materials and for want, too, of a firm liberal stance.

Nueva burguesía (1941) is a final stab at the revolutionary program under Cárdenas, which Azuela saw degenerate into a dangerously divisive force that threatened to split the country into two irreconcilable camps—the "revolucionarios," now more readily decried as the "comunistas," and the "conservadores," now more effectively denounced as the "reaccionarios." The novel is set in 1939 in the latter days of the Cárdenas era, and much of the action is loosely hung on the flimsy framework of two political rallies engineered in support of the presidential candidates Ávila Camacho and Almazán. But the rallies are merely pretexts for the introduction of the gallery of characters—"álbum de almas burguesas" (Leal, p. 70)—who live or come together in a tenement house in the Nonoalco district of the capital. They are the urban poor, a bizarre lot of the emerging lower middle class, the ill-starred offspring of the Revolution. Azuela knew them all too well—they were his neighbors, and he had been witness to the proliferation of their misery and misfortune in the same humble surroundings to which he had come to begin a new life, as had countless thousands of others who abandoned the provinces for the promises of the teeming metropolis. Azuela was acutely aware of the hypocrisy, the meaningless slogans and shibboleths, the tragic amorality so sharply etched by the endlessly reiterated phrases: "me limpiaron," "me estafaron."

And so once again Azuela's treatment is dark and cynical, revealing his deep-seated pessimism about the hope that this post-Revolution urban mass might yet recover the pristine virtues of the nation's rural folk from whom most of them had come. Azuela now seems inclined to doubt that any of the worn whipping boys, either individually or collectively, was fundamentally to blame for the miscarriage of the Revolution, or even for the country's age-old ills. He would appear to sense that there was something endemic in his people that must be diagnosed and corrected before the nation could aspire to a higher purpose and potential for its multiplying millions.

Miscellaneous and Posthumous Writings (1942–1952). *Nueva burguesía,* then, was Azuela's final plea for a return to the old faith and the old ways that had always sustained his people in the turbulent passage through time. The most recent "storm" had passed and once again the moment had come for all Mexicans to return to their appointed tasks, just as in the novel Bartolo gratefully and gladly returned to his cobbler's bench, determined to work quietly, and with Christian faith, for a better life. Azuela had dedicated his life and his pen to his task as chronicler of the stormy years of his country's dramatic bid for a social Revolution worthy of his people and worthy, too, of a permanent place in the annals of man's struggle for justice and equality. In his closing years Azuela came to realize that others of a younger generation had picked up the challenge that he had only partially met in his attempt to document and appraise the years of national strife that were his years and his cause. The time had come for a more searching and a more profound analysis of his country's past and present, for an analysis that would assure a more certain base from which to scan the future and forestall the violence that must inevitably follow when men fail to appreciate their common dependence and their common cause.

After 1942 Azuela's novels and miscellaneous writings reflect the changing times as well as the changed pace of the author's waning years. With World War II, an aging and ailing era drew quickly to a close. Profound changes were taking place everywhere, in every walk of public and private life. And new ways of recording those changes soon gave rise to a manner of writing that would suddenly overshadow the literary efforts of the generation that spoke for the post–World War I years. Mexico would respond to those new impulses. And so too, in a measure, would Azuela.

Six novels were no mean harvest to glean from those ten busy final years. Three of the novels were published before Azuela's death in 1952: *La Marchanta,* in 1944; *La mujer domada,* in 1946; and *Sendas perdidas,* in 1949. The remainder appeared posthumously: *La maldición,* in 1955; *Esa sangre,* in 1956; and *Madero: Biografía novelada,* in 1958. Certain features are common to all of them. Gone, for example, is the old urge to speak out sharply against sociopolitical ills and injustices, and no longer is there any pronounced, purposeful indictment of the on-going social revolution or of the political party in power. Rather, the emphasis now shifts to individual man, and the action is less explicitly grounded in the Mexican scene. This is especially marked in the city novels in which modern attitudes and manners have cast off the colorful garb of the older provincial way of life. In keeping with this emphasis, the settings incline heavily toward the urban. However, there is also a tendency to shift scenes frequently, and disconcertingly, from city to country and back again, often to the detriment of sound plot development. Azuela's loyalties to realism are at play here; he had observed teeming urban living at close hand for well over a quarter century, yet happily nurtured memories of his earlier years continued to well up as vividly as they had in a rapidly receding past. And as a result there is also in these latter novels a reiteration of his belief in the superior moral fiber of provincial Mexico and a reaffirmation of his preference for the rural scene and the rural way of life.

In *La Marchanta* (1944), then, Azuela has no specific social theme to present, unless it be that for most of his country's poor and forgotten, time moves inexorably on with little or no change in their ill-starred destiny. Two passing references to political happenings of the day serve merely to place the novel in the capital during the 1940s, but there is no implication here that given social conditions are a product of misguided political philosophies. Azuela's sole purpose seems to be the dramatization of the fate of Mexico's urban masses in the somber story of the female small stall vendor, the Marchanta of the novel, who passes on her heavy heritage to her daughter, fulfilling thus her humble role before fading back again into obscurity where "se adivina apenas la silueta de una mujer con su niño a cuestas, desvaneciéndose en la masa densa como cualquier otra excrecencia del jardín, hoja, tallo, flor, insecto" (OC, II, 228).

In *La mujer domada* (1946) Azuela once again sidesteps direct criticism of the immediate political scene. His intent, rather, is clearly didactic and wholly in keeping with his deep feeling for rural life: provincial daydreams of the young, unless solidly based and backed, are quickly shattered in the cold, calculating, inhuman urban setting. Unhappily motivated by vain ambition, Serafina aspires to win a place for herself in the intellectual and cultural circles of the metropolis. After three years of suffering and frustration she returns to her native Morelia as "la mujer domada," overwhelmed by the hostile environment of the big city and resigned to accept a role more in keeping with her limited ability and her own true self.

Sendas perdidas (1949), the last novel published in Azuela's lifetime and the end product of a recasting of an original scenario, carries over an excess of the shallow and sensational trappings of a script that was essentially a more melodramatic interpretation of the "carne manda" theme of the film version of *La Marchanta.* Peopled with characters already familiar to us, naturalistic in tone, of rapid dialogue and sparse description, this easy story of Gregorio's futile attempt to convert a beautiful cabaret entertainer reads, curiously, like a throwback of Azuela's earlier period.

There remain the three posthumous novels. Of *Madero: Biografía novelada* (1958) little more need be added to what has already been suggested in reference to its unhappy conception (see p. xiv). It seems clear that this "novelized biography" was the last of several unsuccessful attempts to recast an original film script that had failed to reach the screen. As it now stands it is a faulty work, melodramatic, shallow in characterization, and decidedly inferior to *Pedro Moreno, el insurgente,* Azuela's earlier (1933) effort in the same form.

La maldición (1955) also suffers from serious structural defects, defects that one can easily believe may have deterred Azuela from releasing it for publication before his death. In this novel Azuela again refers to political events of the time and, even more, openly condemns official corruption under Alemán. But these momentary asides do not deter him from advancing yet again his oft-reiterated warning that the city will destroy the provincial who would dare defy the "curse" that was believed to befall him should he seek happiness in the iniquities of urban living. Even so clever a fellow as Rodulfo could not escape a physical and moral decline that would wreak a similar fate on all with whom he associated; not even his own sister Magdalena would be safe from his mad impulse to survive at any cost. Azuela's plea for a return to simple honest living recalls Bartolo's determination to go back to his cobbler's bench in *Nueva burguesía.* This recall would give the reader to understand that the "curse" may be proverbial, but not necessarily infallible—regeneration and hope for a better life are within the reach of all, of provincial rustic and city dweller alike.

Perhaps the best of the novels of his closing years, and also one of the better works of his entire output, is precisely the one in which Azuela, with not a little nostalgia that the reader must perforce share with him, goes back in memory to the incomparable setting of man on his beloved native soil in the company of other small town folk, to give us the sequel to his first important novel, *Mala yerba.* Azuela had completed *Mala yerba* before the Revolution erupted to shake the old Mexican way of life to its very roots, and over the years he had thought many times about writing a second part to the novel, but it was not until some time around 1947 that the manuscript of *Esa sangre* (1956) began to take final form. Julián Andrade, the degenerate proprietor of the extensive holdings of San Pedro de las Gallinas and the murderer of Marcela, the beautiful sensuous heroine of *Mala yerba,* returns after more than two decades of exile in other parts of Latin America to claim his lands that, in keeping with the Revolution, had fallen into the hands of those who for generations had sustained the family mansion and all that it surveyed. Azuela's objective is clear from the outset, and it is later confirmed in his comments under "El novelista y su ambiente" (OC, III, 1109–1111). Although now a decrepit drunkard, Julián is still obsessed with thoughts of his former wealth and power, still driven madly on by the "bad blood" that had been the curse of his family and his kind for generations on end. Times had changed, and the Revolution had righted many wrongs. Agrarian reform had assured Julián's former peons of a measure of justice and of hope. But there were still many on either side of the question who would deny the landless and the underdog the legitimate fruits of the national holocaust. Julián and El Fruncido, the federal representative of the Comisión Nacional Agraria, represent, respectively, the old landholding class and the unscrupulous exploiters of revolutionary programs and ideals. Both of these destructive forces must yield to a higher order of justice. There is no longer any room in Mexico for elements motivated by "esa sangre" that still impede progressive reform espoused by all men of good will. But before Julián and El Fruncido come to the inevitable confrontation, more good blood must yet be shed. The novel ends in a fatal encounter from which Julián's loyal sister Refugio, exemplary of courageous Mexican womanhood and of countless hardworking souls needlessly sacrificed to the cause, is carried off on a stretcher with the two responsible, along with their kind, for having nurtured so much "bad blood" among the nation's people. The thick-lipped Indian Gertrudis, local political leader and nephew and namesake of Julián's early rival and victim, murmurs the inescapable comment, as if in grateful prayer, "Se acabó la mala yerba."

Azuela achieves exceptionally fine character portrayal, especially in his depiction of Julián in his losing battle to control the inherited impulses of his decadent line; and in these and in other pages he reverts to the naturalistic tendency of his early writings, a tendency also manifest in his *Sendas perdidas* (1949). A good array of rural types and regional sketches and a tempo and tone redolent of his country's earthy charm testify once again to the abiding skill and evocative power with which Azuela, until the very last, could recall and recreate immemorable scenes and impressions of an earlier day. One of the best moments in the novel occurs when Julián finds his way back to the old family home abandoned deep in ruins and in the loneliness and silence of a setting in which even the elements of nature share in the strange and wild upsurging of emotions and memories. The experience is vivid and dramatic under the compulsive recall of that long-ago Marcela who comes to life again in the tempting presence of a younger creature, "el vivo retrato de . . . la difunta Marcela."

Esa sangre is a refreshing work. As always in the case of others of its kind, it stands out in sharp contrast to the city novels. Azuela does not intrude, and yet his position is clear: given time for the "old blood" to spend itself in vain resurgence, there is hope that a better day will dawn for those who have the courage and the patience to ride out the aftermath of the storm. Azuela did not live to chronicle that new day, but he did see about him a younger generation who, in a new key and on a more sophisticated level of artistic expression, could and would record the more deliberate and also the more transcendental phase of a Revolution that still had meaning for a people determined to hold the gains so bitterly won.

II. THE MEXICAN REVOLUTION OF 1910

The Historical Setting

In 1519, after having beached his dismantled ships behind him on the shores of Veracruz, Cortés led the first band of Spaniards up from the coast to the amazing Aztec capital, center of authority and power of the Montezumas over their tax-burdened subjects. Bloodshed, cunning statesmanship, and incredible daring characterized the two years that passed before Tenochtitlán finally became Mexico City and New Spain embarked on her colorful colonial career down a path three centuries long as one of the *madrepatria's* wealthiest and most fruitful overseas dominions.

The colonial era was one of slow attrition and of relative peace, during which the blood and culture of conquering Spain, imposed on the native Indian masses, fused and faded into an ethnic and cultural pattern that after three hundred years emerged definitely Mexican in stamp and spirit. The relative peace of colonial times was due largely to the unity enforced by the medieval Spanish system that centralized all political, spiritual, and economic control under church and state, a centralized control administered from distant Spain, which, however, wisely permitted much of the old Indian way of life to survive. With the centuries a caste system evolved that accentuated the fundamental differences within the Mexican population and crystallized the political and economic cleavage of her people. At the bottom of this caste system was the Indian; immediately above him was the *mestizo,* the racial product of the two bloods; and near the top was the *criollo,* the colonial of pure Spanish blood born in Mexico, who, despite the fairness of his skin and his Spanish way of life, was subject to the political and economic tyranny of the *gachupín,* the peninsular Spaniard appointed by the Crown to rule the other three social groups for the greater glory of Spain and, often, for his own greedy gain.

Padre Hidalgo made the first outcry against this rule from abroad in the village of Dolores in the state of Guanajuato, early on the morning of September 16, 1810, a date now commemorated each year as Independence Day. After eleven years the Mexicans—Indian, *mestizo,* and *criollo*—won their freedom from the *gachupín.* Spanish rule was at an end, but the colonial way of life moved on unaltered. The *criollo* and upper class *mestizo* were now on top, but they were novices in the business of government. So Mexico began her national existence with the old colonial weaknesses and defects as pronounced as ever; in addition, however, she was handicapped by intense rivalries within the social groups, which, during the colonial period, had been united spiritually, at least, against their common enemy, the Spaniard from abroad.

For over half a century Mexico battled within herself, and against enemies from without, over conservative and liberal principles of government. The most serious issue centered on the struggle between church and state. The leaders of the church had supported the *gachupín* during the wars for independence and naturally, after separation from Spain, the clergy were looked upon with suspicion. Furthermore, the church had amassed great wealth and extensive landholdings which gave it a stranglehold on the national economy. The church refused to accept the state's dictum that the colonial relationship of the two be continued, the church subservient to and upholding the state. The landed aristocracy, the monarchists, and conservative groups in general identified their cause with that of the church.

Iturbide, self-appointed emperor, ruled highhandedly until 1823. Then one president succeeded another, each heralded by a new *cuartelazo,* or barracks revolt, until the most spectacular of them all—the one-legged, unscrupulous, ever-recurring "Napoleon of the West," the notorious Santa Ana, who had championed the conservative cause and had lost for his country the great American Southwest as a result of the war of 1846–1848—was finally routed forever by the triumph of the liberal cause under Juárez in the late fifties.

Benito Juárez, the father of his country, enacted the liberal reform laws that culminated in the famous Constitution of 1857 and that dealt the temporal ambitions of the church a blow from which it recovered only momentarily to some degree during the closing years of the Díaz regime. In an effort to reestablish the Mexican economy Juárez declared a moratorium on foreign debts, which Napoleon III immediately seized upon as a pretext to bring Mexico under French domination (1863), setting up his hapless pawns, Maximilian and Carlota, as emperor and empress of the Mexican nation. This colorful period came to a close with the execution of Maximilian at Querétaro in 1867, in which year the liberals once more gained control and Juárez became president until his death in 1872.

Porfirio Díaz, who had made his debut with Juárez during the War of Reform (1858–1861), now occupied the center of the Mexican stage until his resignation from the presidency in 1911. Mexico enjoyed a period of peace and prosperity unequaled by any other era in her long history; but it was a peace based on the absolute suppression of the democratic political aspirations of a theoretically free people; a colonial-revival period in which Mexico forgot all she had learned of self-government in the strife-torn years since independence; a prosperity that is best symbolized in the sumptuous Teatro Nacional, a prosperity that set the foreign world agog but that never seeped down to the masses or spread out from the capital, a prosperity achieved by granting to foreign capital excessive and shameful concessions of Mexico's natural resources, a prosperity, in short, that made Mexico the "mother of foreigners and the step-mother of Mexicans." But rumblings of discontent became increasingly more significant as the reelection year of 1910 drew near. In 1908 Francisco I. Madero published his book *La sucesión presidencial en 1910*. In 1909 revolutionary bands were abroad in the northern states of Coahuila and Chihuahua. The Revolution of 1910 was imminent.

The Revolution

The Revolution of 1910 began as a purely political revolt against the unconstitutional Díaz regime. Madero, leader of the so-called lyric phase of the Revolution, naively believed that Mexico's great need was the enforcement of the liberal political program of the Constitution of 1857. And so the real Revolution—the Revolution that Mexicans spell with a capital R, the only true revolution Mexico has ever had, was born without any preconceived program for social reform.

The Díaz government crumbled away before the first stirrings in the north. Díaz resigned on May 25, 1911. A little over a month later Madero entered Mexico City in triumph and on October 1 was elected constitutional president. And thus would have ended the Revolution, had not Zapata and his hordes early set up the first sharply-defined issue, the return of the land to the people, on which the movement was later to take a firm stand, and had not the old reactionary Díaz government actually retained most of its former power. Madero, the idealist, was caught between the two factions, and sooner or later one or the other was destined to put him out of the way. That deed fell to the lot of the *porfiristas;* on February 23, 1913, Madero was murdered, and the reactionary General Victoriano Huerta assumed the presidency. Almost immediately the revolutionary forces united to drive out Huerta, and the bloody years of the Revolution had begun.

Zapata, lone wolf of the Revolution, came up from the south, gathering about him all who were stirred by the magic cry "tierra." Carranza, Obregón, and Villa swept down from the north. Huerta resigned on July 15, 1914. Mexico City was filled with the forces and staffs of victorious generals. Carranza called them to a convention to set up a constitutional government. Villa, who had long been pulling away from Carranza and Obregón, marched on the city and called for the convention to meet at Aguascalientes, where he could dominate it. This was on November 10, 1914, and from then until April 15, 1915, when he was defeated at Celaya, Villa dominated the scene.

It was during this period of strife among the revolutionary leaders themselves that the ideals for which the Revolution stands gradually took form and crystallized into the several important articles of the world-famous Constitution of 1917. Mexico at last had definitely broken with the past. It was as if a new people and a new nation had been born. The century-old struggle, climaxed by the seven years of unbridled passions and bloody strife of the 1910–1917 period, a struggle "to formulate a program for the destruction of the feudal structure of Mexico," had come to a close. The social revolution had begun.

The Revolution from now on was to be a struggle to carry out the major principles of the Constitution of 1917: agrarian reform—the breaking down of the great *haciendas,* return of communal lands to the villages, more equitable distribution of Mexican soil; political reform—abolition of local bossism, effective suffrage, guarantee of constitutional rights; religious reform—more rigid enforcement of the *leyes de reforma* of the Constitution of 1857; and social and economic legislation—revision of marriage laws, laws improving the conditions of the working classes, an attempt to undo Díaz's sell-out of Mexico's natural resources.

Carranza was elected president in 1917. He made no serious effort to launch the social program of the Revolution. His administration became notoriously corrupt and incompetent. The attitude of the Carranza revolutionists toward the agrarian demands of the *zapatistas* is indelibly recorded in the cruel conspiracy to which Zapata fell victim on April 12, 1919. The break came when Carranza attempted to name his successor; Obregón and his Sonora group launched the "revindicating revolution." Carranza was killed on May 23, 1920, and Obregón became president on December 1 of the same year.

Under Obregón the passions and hatreds of the preceding decade began to cool off; there was a steady return to normalcy; reconstruction got under way, and revolutionary principles were slowly being applied. Progress was halted momentarily, however, in December of 1923, when a revolt broke out under Adolfo de la Huerta. Earlier in the same year, on July 20, Pancho Villa was assassinated in Durango in what was assumed to have been a political move to avert the impending revolt.

Calles became president in 1924. The revolutionary program was pushed harder then than it had ever been before. Land and labor provisions received more general application. But when, in 1926, Calles pressed the enforcement of the anticlerical provisions of the constitution and enacted land and petroleum legislation, his administration almost crashed before the ensuing Catholic rebellion (the so-called *Cristero* revolt), strained foreign relations, and economic depression.

Obregón was assassinated on June 17, 1928 during a new electioneering campaign. Emilio Portes Gil, Pascual Ortiz Rubio, and Abelardo Rodríguez occupied the presidency from 1928 until the inauguration of Lázaro Cárdenas on November 30, 1934. Under Cárdenas the Revolution continued its cycle of evolution at a higher speed and in a more radical direction under what was known as the six-year plan, a plan that included the whole of the social program variously adopted and promoted by preceding administrations. In particular, the revolutionary slogans of "Mexico for the Mexicans" reached an apogee under a greatly accelerated program of land distribution and under the expropriation of foreign-owned enterprises, symbolized most dramatically by the nationalization of the oil industry in 1938. For many, the Cárdenas era represents the "high water mark" of the Revolution.

Manuel Ávila Camacho (1940–1946) sought, effectively, to moderate the heady pace the Revolution had attained under Cárdenas. Mexico's determined participation in World War II, from which she emerged materially stronger, assured her a prominent role in contemporary American and world affairs; and under successive leaders —Miguel Alemán Valdés (1946–1952), Adolfo Ruiz Cortines (1952–1958), Adolfo López Mateos (1958–1964), Gustavo Díaz Ordaz (1964–)—the nation has continued to grow in political maturity and peace, in social justice, and in economic prosperity.

Tannenbaum has likened the Revolution to a cyclone, unheralded and unguided, that has "shaken every part of the Mexican social structure to its roots." And, in the beginning, it was out of the fire and embers of the years of passion, bloodshed, and groping after justice and a new social order, that Azuela and his younger contemporaries had harvested the first fruits of a vigorous and variegated "literature of the Revolution." But with the approach of a half-century of revolutionary change, the reborn nation sensed the need for a serious and sustained effort toward recapitulation and reappraisal. Thinking men responded, in all possible ways, to the urge to define and to assess the national character, to distill the essence of what it means to be a Mexican. In the final analysis that is what the Revolution had unwittingly set out to do—to achieve a new identity on the ashes of the old. And a younger generation of writers came forward to record this most recent and most necessary phase of a movement that an overwhelming majority of Mexicans still continue to hail, with confidence and with pride, as "our" Revolution.

III. LITERATURE OF THE REVOLUTION

The Revolution in Popular Poetry, Song, and Theater

The Revolution of 1910 had its first artistic expression in popular poetry and song and in a quickening interest in the native arts and crafts. In contrast to the written literature and the music of Mexico's upper classes, which in those years were still heavily oriented toward

Europe, this literary and musical expression of the masses was definitely Mexican, a fact which further reaffirms the contention that the Revolution was eminently a national movement.

The stirring events of the conflict, the personal exploits of the heroes, the humor, the pathos, and the irony of those years were the raw material from which the *juglares* spun entire cycles of *corridos* —the ballad of contemporary happenings—which embody in crude, racy poetry and song the popular history of the Revolution. Who were the real heroes of the Revolution? What, for them, were the memorable battles of those ten years? What were they fighting for? What was their attitude toward the revolutionary movement in general? What their attitude toward intervention? The answers may be found in the *corrido,* which was then, as it always has been, a fairly reliable index of the popular mind.

Zapata and Villa were the greatest heroes of them all, if the number of *corridos* about them may in any sense be a fair measure of their fame. Their names and exploits are current all over Mexico. Beyond the regions from which they sprang, they are seen in better perspective. They are still men, men of fiery passions, Attilas of the north and south; but in their respective homelands, legend and myth have immortalized them as the great saviors of their race. There are *corridos* that extol Zapata as the father of the "Plan de Ayala," that tell of his extraordinary exploits, as in the Tepoztlán ballad "Bola de San Juan Chinameca," and that have made of him a myth, a King Arthur, as the one first sung by a troubadour of Morelos in the summer of 1926, which assures us that Zapata was not killed at Chinameca and that some day he will return (see Redfield, pp. 200–204). *Corridos* about Villa are legion. The following (translated by Gruening, p. 648) is of particular interest to readers of *Los de abajo* because it records an episode in the taking of Zacatecas by Villa and Natera, under whom Demetrio Macías had served. The *corrido* was written in 1916 by Juan Ortega (for the complete ballad in Spanish, see Atl, II, 142–145):

Hah! You drunkard Victoriano,
Your bad heart will slip a beat,
When you hear of Zacatecas
Where your troops have met defeat.

On the twenty-third of June—

I address those who are here,
"Pancho" Villa stormed the city,
Taking it by front and rear.

All the streets of Zacatecas
Were piled high with federal dead,
And the few that were not slaughtered,
Early in the day had fled.

For some federals were so frightened,
That they hid in women's skirts,
Pulling them up over trousers,
And mantillas over shirts.

After Zapata and Villa, the popular heroes of the Revolution are many; and the *juglar* sings not alone of their bravery and daring but of their drunkenness, of their love affairs, and of their love of plunder and of power as well. The *juglar* is frank and outspoken; he describes them as he knew them, for with all their failings and vices, they were the idols of the moment. But for Madero, who failed to give them land, for Huerta and for Carranza and others of the federal clan, he has not a kind word, and many are the ballads in which he puts them to ridicule and scorn.

These *corridos,* improvised and sung by modern troubadours, have passed on into popular tradition. But they have also been printed as broadsides and over the years have been available for a pittance almost anywhere in Mexico. In the last decades students have begun to collect them and to study them, for they realize now their importance as one of the earliest artistic expressions of the Revolution by the folk.

The popular song, likewise peculiarly Mexican, has also been collected and studied. With the possible exception of mural painting and the native arts and crafts, no other manifestation of the Mexican spirit is so well known and appreciated beyond the nation's borders. Popular music and song are products of the Revolution only insofar as they, too, are a part of the national awakening. There is, with few notable exceptions, little that is revolutionary about them either in theme or in spirit. And yet many such compositions caught the appeal of the revolutionary bands and became the marching songs of the day. The *soldadera* Adela Maldonado of Durango, pride of Villa's men, who met her death on the battlefield like a true *dorado,* inspired an anonymous troubadour to compose the most famous battle song of them all, "La Adelita," sung by Villa's and Zapata's troops the nation over. "La cucaracha" was another made popular by the *villistas,* while the strains of "La Valentina" announced the coming of Carranza's men.

This new flowering of the national temperament and genius also became visible in the popular arts and crafts, subsequent appreciation of which is too obvious to merit attention here. The first official recognition of the importance of the native arts was given on September 19, 1921, when the Exhibición de Artes Nacionales was formally inaugurated in conjunction with the celebration of the completion of one hundred years of independence. Dr. Atl, in his two-volume work, *Las artes populares en México,* published in 1922, was one of the first to produce evidence of the incredible national fecundity in the popular arts.

The artistic renaissance of the 1920s found its most authentic expression in the murals and canvases of such world-famous painters as Rivera, Orozco, and Siqueiros. In strokes and colors that are undeniably Mexican these great muralists developed a highly inflammatory and anecdotal type of painting that, in the words of Orozco, responded to the new revolutionary belief in art as "essentially an offensive weapon in the Conflict of Classes." Nationalism, social content, realism, and nativism—these became the key concepts of the sensational muralist movement that cried out for all to see the madness and murder, the sham and sordidness, and the hard-won gains of the Revolution of 1910. The muralist revolt soon spent itself, however, in reiterative propaganda. And even before its demise it became clear that all subsequent art in Mexico would have to be viewed as, in effect, a continuing repudiation of what José Luis Cuevas has called "the cactus curtain" of the muralist school (for a brief nontechnical account, with good illustrations, including color plates, see Alma M. Reed, *The Mexican Muralists,* New York, Crown, 1960, 191 p.).

The popular Mexican theater, too, was born of the Revolution. From the very outbreak of the Madero revolt, coarse comedy and musical revues ridiculed and satirized the guerrilla warfare and the political skirmishing of the day, mocking the municipal authorities who attempted to curb their biting jibes. "However crude, improvised and disreputable," here was a theater "vibrantly alive," here was "entertainment aimed at the common people, speaking their language and reflecting their own peculiar brand of humor." And yet, out of this mire of bad theater, the *carpas*—tent shows that mushroomed everywhere overnight—and the popular musical comedy have stood forth "as the only permanent contribution towards a Mexican theater" (Covarrubias, pp. 587–596). It was out of these prolific popular seedbeds of dramatic expression that Mexican speech and gesture, song and dance, art and artifice emerged, in a unique *mélange* of comedy and satire, to bespeak the unfettered reactions of the illiterate masses to a confused and chaotic present. It was these same seedbeds that gave birth to the famed comedians of a later day, to Roberto Soto and to Mario Moreno (Cantinflas). It was in these very seedbeds—in the ubiquitous *carpas* and at the gay and gaudy "Follies," "Lírico," "Politeama," and other houses that carried on, ineffectually censored or controlled, into the mid-1950s—that the Revolution itself actually mounted the stage; that Zapata and Villa stalked tragicomically across the boards in pieces alluringly labelled *¡Maldita sea la guerra!* (1913) and *La Revolución Mexicana* (1914); that the musical revue, *El país de la metralla,* night after night during May and successive months of 1913, vividly recalled to a madly-demonstrative public the absurdly incredible "Decena Trágica" of February 9–19 just past; and that the rousing marching songs of the time resounded from wing to wing in endless variants and parodies that served further to lighten the burden of a people's perplexity. One of these versions of "La Adelita" gives us the following quatrain, irreverently and refreshingly Mexican:

> Si Carranza se casa con Zapata,
> Pancho Villa con Álvaro Obregón,
> Adelita se casa conmigo
> y termina la Revolución.

Tremendously popular, this theater of "slapstick and venom" exerted considerable influence on the mass mind. Its productions never met with the glacial indifference that confronted the more formal presentation of serious drama inspired by the Revolution or the efforts of the later experimental groups like the Teatro de Ulises (1928) and the Teatro de Orientación (1931). The irreligious play, *The Celestial Rebellion,* opened with riots between the jeering hotheads and the armed claques of the Knights of Columbus; and it is generally acknowledged that Roberto Soto's systematic exposé of the nation's most influential labor leader had much to do with the discredit and downfall of Morones in 1929 (see Covarrubias, *op. cit.*).

The Revolution did not, however, produce a single dramatist of note or a single play that is at all comparable to any of the better narrative writings. Most of the dramas of the so-called "teatro revolucionario" never reached the stage; they remain buried in a wide range of ephemeral journals where they made their first and only appearance. Many of them may be found in such reviews as *Antena* (1924), *La antorcha* (1924–1925), and *Horizonte* (1926–1927) and in the special editions of the Liga de Escritores Revolucionarios of the twenties. Of the small number that won a public hearing, very few were received with more than lukewarm favor. Salvador Quevedo y Zubieta was among the first to dramatize the Revolution in his plays *Huerta* (1916) and *Doña Pía o el contrachoque* (1919), and Ricardo Flores Magón will be remembered, among other things, for his *Verdugos y víctimas* (1924) and *Tierra y libertad* (1924). But the only significant thrust of the Revolution on the stage came after 1925 when the theater either espoused the cause of the proletariat and the peasant, under heavily Marxist direction, or sought, somewhat later still, a deeper understanding of the Revolution in historical perspective and as a vital evolving force. Mauricio Magdaleno and Juan Bustillo Oro best epitomize the left-wing trend in plays that dramatized explosive socio-economic problems like agrarian reform (*Emiliano Zapata*), oil (*Pánuco 137*), and foreign exploitation (*Trópico*), plays that were all performed for the first time during 1932 in the playwrights' own politically-oriented *Teatro de Ahora*. The second and more enduring trend is less obviously discernible in the theater of Rodolfo Usigli and other younger dramatists intermittently but intensely concerned with the problem of identifying and analyzing the national psyche. Taken as a whole, however, the revolutionary theater failed to win popular support. As we have already noted above, Azuela's efforts to dramatize a number of his novels, whether for the stage or screen, were likewise unsuccessful.

The Novel of the Revolution

Azuela was wholly justified in his condemnation of his contemporaries during the war years of the Revolution for failing to be moved by the tragic lot of their country and for continuing to write poetry and prose patterned after European themes and techniques. He is the one outstanding novelist of the Revolution whose works date back to the very beginnings of the struggle. Those who later distinguished themselves as successful writers of the genre did not turn to the theme of the Revolution until the late 1920s. And only two novelists who began writing in the days of Díaz may in any sense be termed precursors of the novel of the Revolution—Heriberto Frías (1870–1925), whose *¡Tomóchic!* (1892) deals with the rebellion against the federal government, in October 1892, of the town by that name in the Sierra Madre of Chihuahua, and whose treatment is similar to that of Azuela; and Salvador Quevedo y Zubieta (1859–1935), definitely inferior to Frías as an artist, who in *La camada* (1912) and in *México marimacho* (1933) exposes the vices and decadence of upper class Mexican society immediately before the outbreak of the Revolution. Azuela alone wrote of the conflict as it swept the country, but his novels passed unnoticed, and he remained unknown. When law and order were gradually restored under Obregón, a few writers, today all but forgotten, tried their hand at writing novels about the decade just past. But their older colleagues and critics shied from this "ungrammatical," crudely Mexican form of novel and withheld all criticism of it until the literary feud of 1925 focused public attention on the Revolution as a theme eminently worthy of fuller literary treatment (see Englekirk, *op cit.*). That feud, and the subsequent recognition and acclaim given *Los de abajo* by Ortega, Monterde, Munguía, and others, was perhaps the one single factor most responsible for the flood of literature on the Revolution that began to appear about 1928. It is the decade immediately following 1928 to which critics generally refer as the "period of flowering" of the novel of the Revolution.

The genre encompasses much more than would strictly come within the classification "novel." Anecdotes, memoirs, short stories, episodes, all nudge easily under the label. Reporters who were with the armed forces and who knew Zapata, Villa, and others of that day began to record their experiences regularly in the Mexican press; many of these accounts were republished soon after in book form. Generals and others in command published their memoirs. Those who were eyewitnesses to the "bola" as it swept past them in the provinces or in the capital gave written form to their impressions. Others conjured up childhood memories of the Revolution. These writings constitute the human record of the years 1910–1917, and are of inestimable value to the historian. They are realistic accounts of the day-by-day events of the period, and they afford excellent close-ups of the leaders. There is no need of fancy or fiction here—unless one would welcome it to soften somewhat the crude, truculent realism of most practitioners of the form.

It is this type of literature that characterizes the early phase in the development of the "novel of the Revolution." Hastily written, with many of the defects common to most journalistic writing, but also with a rapidity and concision of style befitting the stark realism of the subject matter, these "novels" represent a definite break with all past standards of Mexican prose. The urge for native expression of the national theme and temperament gave birth to a body of literature that, whatever posterity may ultimately say of its intrinsic worth and enduring qualities, will be significant as yet another manifestation of the nation's will to free itself of all foreign bondage.

The blood-and-horror theme, however, soon ran its course. Writers became increasingly aware of the broader and more transcendental possibilities of the Revolution as material for their pens. They were aroused by the selfish lust for power and gain that vitiated the movement; they condemned the political turn given to it by those who were as traitors to the cause. The reasons for class conflict and the new problems arising out of it invited a more studied and more conscientious treatment of theme; and as a consequence of a number of the pioneer cultivators of the genre developed a style that improved with each new work. The high point in production was reached about 1935. Since then there has been a marked decline in the output of the loosely conceived narrative that focused on the Revolution as a harbinger of civil strife and social reform. One by one the outstanding creators of the genre began turning their talents to other interests and themes. Of that earlier generation Azuela alone, and he only in rare instances, continued to write of the Revolution.

Martín Luis Guzmán (1887–   ) was to become the most prominent figure of the generation that followed Azuela in the late 1920s. Three significant titles crown his fundamental contribution as activist, exile, and chronicler of the Revolution: *El águila y la serpiente* (1928), *La sombra del caudillo* (1929), and the four-volume *Memo-*

rias de Pancho Villa (1938–1940). In *El águila y la serpiente* Guzmán tells of his experiences as a volunteer journalist with the forces of the north. Possibly one of the most valuable aspects of the novel is the author's frank and penetrating characterization of the leaders: he describes them physically and boldly and candidly states his own estimate of them as men and as revolutionaries. Carranza, Villa, Obregón, Felipe Ángeles, Adolfo de la Huerta, Villarreal, and many others become more familiar and more real under Guzmán's facile pen. Informative, replete with interesting and invaluable data, the book affords a splendid picture of how the "bola" grew; it is, furthermore, a reliable testimonial to the growing pessimism of the small group of idealists who had been forced to relinquish "a los más egoístas y más criminales un movimiento generoso y purificador por esencia." *El águila y la serpiente* has been rightfully acclaimed as one of the most authentic and most artistic chronicles of the Revolution. *La sombra del caudillo* is a *roman à clef,* in which Guzmán exposes the political intrigue and corruption of the twenties. It is easy to pierce the thin veil of fiction and recognize characters and events of the Mexican scene of that period. Fortified with documents from Villa's own files and moved by still vivid memories of the man of action he once had known, Guzmán turned finally to the difficult task of having the "bandit" hero tell his own story in the simple, straightforward language and style of *Las memorias de Pancho Villa.* The four volumes of the *Memorias* are, essentially, a uniquely popular history of the Revolution.

Entering the field along with Guzmán, Rafael F. Muñoz (1899–) soon became the leading storyteller of the Revolution. Born and raised in Chihuahua, it was there, at the age of sixteen, that Muñoz began his life-long career as a journalist. It was then too that he first came to know Villa, with whom he lived and travelled and whose personality and exploits served as timely and sensational material for the cub reporter and the budding raconteur. Several collections of tales and two novels constitute his essential contribution to the literature of the Revolution. His first stories, dating as far back as his early apprenticeship as a journalist in his home state, were finally brought together in 1928 under the title *El feroz cabecilla.* In these "Cuentos de la Revolución en el Norte" Muñoz relates what he himself saw of the social upheaval: episodes of horror and of gruesome detail; tales in which he shows how little the successive waves of pillage and death, which masqueraded under the name of Revolution, really meant to the humble, ignorant folk of rural Mexico; stories of tribute to the ever-present, suffering, silent, loyal *soldaderas;* satiric accounts of the grotesque distortion of revolutionary events by both the national and the foreign press; and, occasionally, a tale of human kindness in the midst of death, of Christian charity bestowed on a group of prisoners on Christmas Eve by the *villista* "bad man." Of a similar nature are the stories that appeared in 1934 under a title, *Si me han de matar mañana*..., inspired by a line from the popular marching song "La Valentina."

¡Vámonos con Pancho Villa! (1931), the first attempt by Muñoz at the extended narrative form, is a classic of the period and undoubtedly the most popular of many works that have been written about Chihuahua's notorious chieftain. Muñoz had often been witness to the hypnotic power Villa exerted over his men. Tiburcio Maya of the novel is the supreme embodiment of the blind, unfaltering faith in their leader that led to the creation of the Villa myth. And, lastly, some ten years later, the unsuccessful revolt of Orozco against Madero in 1913 inspired a second novel, *Se llevaron el cañón para Bachimba* (1941), which critics generally acclaim as the most artistic and the most enjoyable work Muñoz has yet given us on the Revolution. Unlike Guzmán and most of his contemporaries, Muñoz is content to tell a good story; there is no preaching, no condemning, no offering of panaceas.

Born in the Huasteca region of Veracruz, Gregorio López y Fuentes (1897–1966) did not turn to the Revolution as a source of inspiration until after the appearance of two volumes of verse—one in the Modernist manner entitled *La siringa de cristal* (1914)—and two short novels published in the early twenties. Journalism was to be his chosen field, and as a journalist López y Fuentes enjoyed a ready market for his early stories and signal distinction in his later years as the director of two of Mexico's leading newspapers, *El gráfico* and *El universal.* His experiences as a schoolteacher among the Indians of his native state and his active collaboration with the Carranza forces against Villa also served to prime his pen for his special role as an interpreter of the Revolution. Four novels published between 1931 and 1935, *Campamento* (1931), *Tierra* (1932), *¡Mi General!* (1934), and *El* *indio* (1935), were to place him immediately after Azuela as the most promising novelist of those years. And recognition of his increasingly more artistic and more penetrating analysis of his country's basic problems would follow immediately with the bestowal of the national prize in literature for the last of the four novels, *El indio,* in 1935.

Campamento is a series of vivid, authentic pictures of fifteen hours of life in a military camp. The novel is revolutionary in technique and in thrust. There is no hero; the only real protagonist is the anonymous mass. And López y Fuentes depicts his view of the inhuman brutality of an armed conflict in which the nameless Indian plays his timeless role "as the victim of *all* the warring factions." *Tierra* is the conventional version of the agrarian problem, a sober and saddening account of the Indian's pathetic struggle under Zapata to regain ownership of his stolen land. *¡Mi General!* is the story of the life cycle of the most dramatic and most colorful of all the human types of the Revolution; it is the story of Pancho Villa, of Julián Medina, of any one of the countless "generals" born of the "bola," who rose in meteoric flight from the obscure haven of their *ranchos* to the will-o'-the-wisp of military and political glory, only to sink back immediately and inevitably into the oblivion of the soil. And, finally, in the prize-winning allegorical narrative *El indio* the history of the persecution of the Indian village in the story is the history of the suffering the Mexican Indian has endured since the days of the Conquest.

After 1935 López y Fuentes eschewed the war years of the Revolution to essay a variety of techniques and of topics that range from the evocative narrative of folk sayings and tales of the ubiquitous muleteers, *Arrieros* (1937), who in another day had spun their homely philosophy along the uncharted ways of the interior, to the blatantly journalistic account of oil exploitation and expropriation under Cárdenas as reported in *Huasteca* (1939). In *Acomodaticio* (1943) and in *Entresuelo* (1948) he expresses his concern over the threat to the social structure and the moral fiber of urban life when menaced by opportunistic politicians and by problems that attend the city when invaded by rural masses in search of a better living. It is in *Los peregrinos inmóviles* (1944), however, that López y Fuentes places himself among the earliest and the foremost of Mexico's novelists who in more recent years have sought, through increasingly more complex allegorical schemes, to identify universal concepts and truths that will assist them in achieving a more meaningful interpretation of their evolution as a people from the primitive folkways of an Indian past to the ultrasophisticated patterns of modern international living.

José Rubén Romero (1890–1952), poet, journalist, diplomat, and member of the Mexican Academy (1934), took part in the Madero revolt in the state of Michoacán where he was born. He had written much—eight volumes of verse and two collections of stories and sketches—before he discovered his unusual talents as a humorist and chronicler of the "bola" and of the political and social turmoil that emerged from the open warfare in the days of his youth. Four novels, redolent of personal reminiscences, constitute his racy sentimental record of provincial life only momentarily perturbed by the ominous winds of the distant storm. In *Apuntes de un lugareño* (1932), *Desbandada* (1934), *El pueblo inocente* (1934), and *Mi caballo, mi perro y mi rifle* (1936), Romero bespeaks his early disillusionment with the Revolution: "... pillaje y saqueo no son revolución... Hoy, más que ayer, me siento revolucionario porque de un golpe volví a ser pobre" (*Desbandada*), a protest that cries out in ironic despair in the symbolic *Mi caballo, mi perro y mi rifle:* "¡Mi carne, mi pueblo, que la revolución ha hecho pedazos para que los caciques sigan mandando!" It was from among the earthy types of these essentially autobiographical pieces, types who gradually develop character under the Rabelaisian humor and mordant wit of Romero's empathy for all the untarnished and innately responsive poor, that one of the most colorful and caustic prototypes of modern antiheroes stepped into the pages of the masterful picaresque tale *La vida inútil de Pito Pérez* (1938). The peripatetic Pito Pérez, a poet whom society mistook for a shiftless madman, was to bequeath a legacy of bitterness and resentment to a world that failed to accept the unorthodox ways of his unswerving search for goodness and beauty: "Lego a la Humanidad todo el caudal de mi amargura."

Of his three remaining novels, *Anticipación a la muerte* (1939) and *Una vez fui rico* (1942) add little to Romero's essential literary stature. Introspectively humorous and quite obviously contrived, they afford the author an unusual vantage point from which to ridicule the empty vanity of the pompous rich and to ponder the pettiness and the promise of mortal being. *Rosenda* (1946), however, is a poetic novel of tender love and an affirmation of faith in his native land and people, in Mexican womanhood, and in the eternal verities and the dignity of all life. It is unmistakably of his best work and, together with *La vida inútil de Pito Pérez,* it serves to reaffirm Romero's reputation as one of America's uniquely human and humorous writers of our time.

These, then, are the leading novelists of the Revolution. However, a number of other writers deserve mention for having contributed at least one or more important works that serve to broaden our vision and deepen our understanding of Mexico in revolution. There are, for example, the generals. The recollections of those in command provided an inexhaustible mine of persons and events, of anecdote, episode, and story, that came to the surface with the passing years in writings that range from the "isolated visions of the Revolution" as General Francisco L. Urquizo (1891–) recorded them in his *Recuerdo que . . .* (1934) to his engaging tale of a young soldier in *Tropa vieja* (1943), rated as one of the best historical novels of the Revolution.

There is yet another group of writers of memoirs, a group less directly involved in the armed strife, who have either recalled moments of their participation largely as innocent bystanders or who have reconstructed the entire era by virtue of their deep involvement in the total conflict of the time. Nellie Campobello (1909–), historian and interpreter of the dance, is one of the former; and in her remarkable little book *Cartucho* (1931) she relates memories of her childhood spent among revolutionaries in the north. Colossus among the latter is the prodigiously productive and polemical José Vasconcelos (1881–1959), whose *Ulises criollo* (five volumes, 1936–1959) is a personal account and interpretation both of the happenings as well as the spirited and ideological conflict of a people as told in one of the best autobiographies yet to come out of Latin America.

And, finally, there is the impressive number of those who have been ardently committed to the political, economic, and social implications of the Revolution. Some of them have chosen the war years as a backdrop for their narrative. Many have done so for purely political reasons, others from a broadly human and philosophical point of view. Some have been the outspoken apologists of socialist and communist ideas and ideals. Not a few have written an occasional novel of exceptional artistic merit. Any choice of authors and titles must be highly arbitrary, and any listing should be cautiously brief. Such a listing would probably include some of the following, given in order of birth: Teodoro Torres (1891–1944), *La patria perdida* (1935); Xavier Icaza (1892–), *Panchito Chapopote* (1928); José Mancisidor (1894–1956), *La asonada* (1931) and *La ciudad roja* (1932); Jorge Ferretis (1902–), *Tierra caliente* (1935); Mauricio Magdaleno (1906–), *El resplandor* (1937); José Revueltas (1914–), *El luto humano* (1943). Among these, lastly, one should include a mixed assembly of contemporaries who created a whole body of fiction around the tragic armed conflict that erupted later, in the days of Calles, out of the Catholic rebellion, popularly known as the *Cristero* revolt. Two writers contributed significantly to the literature on this latter-day "Guerra Santa." They are José Guadalupe de Anda (1880–1950), with *Los cristeros* (1937), and Jesús Goytortúa (1910–), with *Pensativa* (1945).

Few of the so-called novels of the Revolution will stand the acid test of time merely as outstanding examples of exemplary and relevant form. The vast majority of those that do survive the years will do so because of the unusual insights and perspectives each affords of the sweeping panorama of the Revolution. As one rechecks the roster of those authors who gave of their best, at least in terms of vivid emotional impact and recall, it is easy to concede that one obvious reason for the gross unevenness of their art must lie in the fact that first and foremost they were anything and everything (generals, journalists, doctors, engineers, educators, philosophers, artists, politicians) but writers—to say nothing of being primarily of the genus "novelist"—with a conscious mission of their art. It would only come to pass in the relative peace and prosperity of post–World War II years that the nation could begin to support men and women who would dedicate their special talents wholly and successfully to writing as an art and as a profession. This younger generation, too, could view, with even greater philosophical calm and more enlightened commitment, the passage of their country through time from an Indian past to a computerized present. Furthermore, their search for national identity was to coincide with the emergence of the exciting revolutionary narrative of multiple techniques and self-propelling diction that would give Mexico her full share of outstanding novelists in the new manner. And many of these experimental writers of the so-called *ciclo revolucionario* have sought to discover meaningful answers to problems of identity in the years of violence and of social change that national concern and national pride would still dignify with the magic epithet of Revolution. Doubly revolutionary in technique and in thrust, these artists have added needed and welcome dimensions to the novel of the Revolution.

Two names must suffice. Agustín Yáñez (1904–) has contributed the masterful prelude to the Revolution in his universally-acclaimed *Al filo del agua* (1947), a classic portrayal of the tragically repressed feelings of the inhabitants of a small town in Jalisco on the eve of the storm. And Carlos Fuentes (1928–), in baffling allegory and a bewildering maze of vanguard techniques, has boldly sought to fathom the imponderable paradox of attitudes and values of a generation that would appear to have betrayed the great promise of the Revolution. *La muerte de Artemio Cruz* (1962) and *Cambio de piel* (1967), the latest and most controversial of his novels, hold out even greater promise of yet another novel to line up soon with *Al filo del agua* as a worthy counterpart of *Los de abajo.*

The 1960s, decade of the half-century mark of Mexico in revolution, finds the Mexican public in a receptive mood for a continuing assessment of the national character and the national conscience. The *Revolución* has become the best seller of an identity-starved people. Silva Herzog's *Breve historia de la Revolución Mexicana* sold 4000 copies during two weeks only of its publication year 1960. The *Breve historia* was a new title by a provocative interpreter of the contemporary scene. And yet there was an older work that rose to meet the challenge posited by the Herzog *History,* one that had survived a half-century of public whim and fancy, from utter neglect to international renown. The popular 1960 Fondo de Cultura Económica edition of *Los de abajo* checked out 6310 sales in 173 days! Azuela's "cuadros y escenas de la revolución mexicana" could still rest assured of top priority in any listing of superior works of fact or fiction that have given distinction and durability to the literature of the Revolution.

IV. NOTES ON THE LANGUAGE OF *LOS DE ABAJO*

In the speech of the majority of the characters in *Los de abajo,* Mariano Azuela has recorded many colloquial forms to be found not only in the Spanish of the untutored Mexican but also in the popular Spanish of similar classes throughout the entire Spanish-speaking world. The student of the development of the Spanish language from Vulgar Latin will note in this summary the results of physiological, psychological, and historical tendencies that are as old as or even older than the Spanish language itself. By means of examples from the text we shall illustrate in outline form the principal variations from standard Spanish found in *Los de abajo.*

I. Accent. In popular speech diphthongs are formed from concurrent vowels; the more open vowel receives the accent.
   a-é (or **á-e**) becomes **ai** (and finally **e**): **cai** (**ca-e**), **trair** and **trer** (**tra-er**)
   a-í becomes **ai**: **ai** (**a-hí**), **trai-ba** (**tra-í-a**)
   e-í becomes **ei**: **crei-ba** (**cre-í-a**)

II. Vowels
   A. Stressed
      1. Frequently the common diphthongs **ie** and **ue** are replaced in popular speech by **e**.
         aprebe (**apruebe**), **cualquer** (**cualquier**), **quen** (**quien**), **quero** (**quiero**)
      2. Two like vowels form one vowel sound when they are brought together either by the loss of a consonant or by an intervening **h.**
         pitayo (**pitahayo**), **pué** (**puede**)
   B. Unstressed. Vowels which are unaccented tend to change their nature. This change is frequently aided by the surrounding consonants.
      e becomes **i**: **fuchi** (**fuche**), **icirte** (**decirte**), **insiñar** (**enseñar**), **peliar** (**pelear**), **pior** (**peor**), **sigún** (**según**)

III. Consonants
   A. Throughout the Spanish-speaking world very large numbers of people pronounce **c** (before **e** and **i**) and **z** as **s.** Only twice does Azuela reflect this pronunciation, which is characteristic of Mexican Spanish: **quesque** (**que dice que**) and **pinción** (**pinsión**).
   B. Final **d** and intervocalic **d** disappear entirely. This characteristic of popular Spanish is very common among educated people. **parvedá** (**parvedad**), **usté** (**usted**); **echao** (**echado**), **moo** (**modo**), **naa** (**nada**), **pué** (**puede**), **quería icirte** (**quería decirte**), **viejo e porra** (**viejo de porra**)
   C. Initial **f** and **h** are frequently aspirated (written as **j**).
      jaiga (**haya**), **jallo** (**hallo**), **jue** (**fue**), **juera** (**fuera**)

D. Initial **b, h,** or **v** followed by **ue** becomes **g.**
güeno (**bueno**), **güevo** (**huevo**), **güelvan** (**vuelvan**)

E. Difficult grouped consonants are simplified.
dotor (**doctor**)

IV. Certain words are influenced by other words of a similar type, and their form is changed by this influence (*analogy*).

A. **creiba** and **traiba** (**creía, traía**) show the influence of the imperfect indicative forms of first conjugation verbs as well as those of the verb **ir.**

B. **haiga** and **jaiga** (**haya**) show the influence of the present subjunctive forms of **caer, traer,** *et al.*

C. **naiden** (**nadie**) by its final **n** shows the influence of **alguien** or **quien.**

V. Within a word sounds often change places (*metathesis*).
naiden (**nadie**), **ñervo** (**nervio**), **probe** (**pobre**)

VI. Additional syllables may be added at the beginning of a word (*prosthesis*). These prefixed syllables may or may not change the word's meaning.
afigurarse (**figurarse**), **asigún** (**según**), **emprestar** (**prestar**), **rebién, retemalo**

VII. Syllables may be dropped from the beginning of a word (*apheresis*).
aistá (**ahí está**), **hora** (**ahora**), **horcar** (**ahorcar**), **l'otro** (**el otro**), **mano** (**hermano**), **morragias** (**hemorragias**), **ña** (**señá, señora**), **pal** (**para el**)

VIII. Syllables may be dropped from the end of a word (*apocope*).
compa (**compadre**), **mi** (**mira**), **pa** (**para**), **pal** (**para el**)

IX. Colloquial speech often retains forms that have been rejected in educated speech. The following archaisms are found in our text:
ansina (**así**), **dende** (**desde**), **mesmo** (**mismo**), **muncho** (**mucho**), **pos** (**pues**), **priesa** (**prisa**), **semos** (**somos**)

X. Suffixes. Colloquial Spanish presents a much wider and more colorful use of suffixes than literary Spanish. In Mexico this is especially true of the diminutive suffix **-ito**, examples of which are frequent in *Los de abajo.* For these and for examples of augmentative and pejorative suffixes see the vocabulary.

XI. Dialectal forms. *Los de abajo* naturally has many words that are peculiarly Spanish American or Mexican and, therefore, not common in Spain. As examples we call attention to **cuaco, deque, mero, otate, petaquilla, pozole,** and **puro** (adjective). These dialectal forms are given in the vocabulary and are marked Americanisms or Mexicanisms as the case may be.

BIBLIOGRAPHIES

I. WORKS OF MARIANO AZUELA

For the more recent editions of all works of Azuela cited in the Introduction, as well as for the large body of his other writings—short stories, sketches, essays, lectures, notes and miscellaneous bits, see the *Obras completas,* 3 vols., México, Fondo de Cultura Económica, 1958–1960; Prólogo by Francisco Monterde, Bibliografía by Alí Chumacero. All references are to this edition, which is designated as OC.

Only the first and the more accessible of the separate editions of each work (novels, novelettes, biography, plays) are given below. Each entry will be followed, in parentheses, by (1) the total number of editions of the work, including newspaper printings, and (2) the languages into which the work has been translated. English translations, in book editions only, are given immediately after the original entry.

We do not include a bibliography of works by other writers of the Revolution. The more outstanding ones have already been cited, with dates of publication, in the Introduction in the section "The Novel of the Revolution." For further information concerning them and for data on other important works of fiction inspired by the Revolution, see Alegría, Castro Leal, Gamboa de Camino, González, Leal, Moore, Morton, under II below.

María Luisa. Lagos de Moreno, López Arce, 1907, 136 pp. *María Luisa y otros cuentos.* México, Botas, 1938, 237 pp. (3)

Los fracasados. México, Müller Hnos., 1908, 252 pp.; México, Botas, 1939, 249 pp. (5)

Mala yerba. Guadalajara, "La gaceta de Guadalajara," 1909, 164 pp.; México, Botas, 1945, 262 pp. (5) (English, French)

Marcela. A Mexican Love Story. New York, Farrar and Rinehart, 1932, xi + 244 pp. Translation by Anita Brenner, foreword by Waldo Frank.

Andrés Pérez, maderista. México, Blanco y Botas, 1911, 122 pp. With "Domitilo quiere ser diputado" and "De cómo al fin lloró Juan Pablo": México, Botas, 1945, 202 pp. (3)

Sin amor, México, Müller Hnos., 1912, 228 pp.; México, Botas, 1945, 212 pp. (3)

Los de abajo. In *El Paso del Norte* (El Paso, Texas), October-December, 1915; México, Fondo de Cultura Económica, 1960, 140 pp. (27) (Russian, French, English, German, Japanese, Yugoslav, Portuguese, Czech, Italian, Swedish, Yiddish)

The Underdogs. New York, Brentano's, 1929, xvii + 224 pp. Translation by Enrique Munguía, Jr., preface by Carleton Beals, illustrations by José Clemente Orozco; also 2nd ed., London, Jonathan Cape, 1930, 222 pp.; New York, New American Library, 1963, 151 pp. Foreword by Harriet de Onís.

The Underdogs (preceded by *The Trials of a Respectable Family*). San Antonio, Texas, Principia Press of Trinity University, 1963, pp. 161–261. Translation, preface and introduction by Frances Kellam Hendricks and Beatrice Berler, prologue by Salvador Azuela, biographical note by Luis Leal.

Los caciques. México, Eds. de *El universal,* 1917, 67 pp.; Preceded by *Las moscas:* México, Eds. de "La razón," 1931, pp. 89–177. (5) (English)

Two Novels of Mexico: The Flies, The Bosses. Berkeley and Los Angeles, University of California Press, 1957, xiii + 194 pp. Translation by Lesley Byrd Simpson.

Las moscas (with "Domitilo quiere ser diputado" and "De cómo al fin lloró Juan Pablo"). México, A. Carranza e Hijos, 1918, 196 pp.; Followed by *Los caciques:* México, Eds. de "La razón," 1931, pp. 5–88. (4) (English)

The Flies. See above under *Los caciques.*

Las tribulaciones de una familia decente. In *El mundo* (Tampico), 1918; México, Botas, 1947, 290 pp.; New York, Macmillan, 1966, vii + 192 pp. Edited by Frances Kellam Hendricks and Beatrice Berler, "Introduction" by F.K.H., pp. 1–30. Abridged edition. (7) (English)

The Trials of a Respectable Family. See above under *Los de abajo,* pp. 1–159.

La Malhora. México, Rosendo Terrazas, 1923, 72 pp.; *3 novelas de Mariano Azuela: La Malhora, El desquite, La luciérnaga.* México, Fondo de Cultura Económica, 1968, 177 pp. "Tres novelas de Mariano Azuela" by Raymundo Ramos, pp. 7–18. (5)

El desquite. In *La novela semanal* (de *El universal ilustrado*), México, I, 3, 20 junio 1925, 29 pp.; See *3 novelas de Mariano Azuela* under *La Malhora* above. (4)

La luciérnaga. Madrid, Espasa-Calpe, 1932, 206 pp.; See *3 novelas de Mariano Azuela* under *La Malhora* above. (4)

Pedro Moreno, el insurgente. In *El nacional* (México), December 4, 1933–March 4, 1934; México, Botas, 1949, 261 pp. (5)

Precursores. Santiago (Chile), Ercilla, 1935, 125 pp. (2)

El camarada Pantoja. México, Botas, 1937, 236 pp.; also 2nd ed., 1951. (3)

San Gabriel de Valdivias, comunidad indígena. Santiago, Ercilla, 1938, 141 pp. (2)

Teatro: Los de abajo. El buho en la noche. Del Llano Hermanos, S. en C. México, Botas, 1938, 323 pp. (2)

Regina Landa. México, Botas, 1939, 244 pp. (2)

Avanzada. México, Botas, 1940, 282 pp. (2)

Nueva burguesía. Buenos Aires, Club del Libro A.L.A., 1941, 189 pp. (2)

El padre don Agustín Rivera. México, Botas, 1942, 197 pp. (2)

La Marchanta. México, Secretaría de Educación Pública, 1944, 155 pp.; México, Botas, 1951, 207 pp. (3)

La mujer domada. México, El Colegio Nacional, 1946, 197 pp. (2)

Sendas perdidas. México, Botas, 1949, 250 pp. (2)

La maldición. México, Fondo de Cultura Económica, 1955, 277 pp. (2)

Esa sangre. México, Fondo de Cultura Económica, 1956, 196 pp. (2)

Madero. Biografía novelada. In OC, III, 512–566. (1)

II. SELECTED CRITICAL STUDIES

The following bibliography contains biographical and critical studies on Azuela and his contemporaries, and on other literary and artistic manifestations of the Revolution, selected for their soundness and availability. Many have been included in order to afford the student a broad, provocative approach to *Los de abajo.* Foremost among these is Azuela's own commentary on the novel and his *Epistolario y archivo,* edited by Beatrice Berler. A number of outstanding works on Mexico, and on the Revolution as a movement of dynamic social change, have also been included for the guidance of the student. For the most recent and best bibliography on Azuela, see Leal below. For a good bibliography of the early "novel of the Revolution," see Ernest Moore, *Bibliografía de novelistas de la Revolución mexicana,* México, n.p., 1941. For a good general bibliography on Mexico up to date of publication (1928), see Gruening below. For the most comprehensive, most exhaustive, and most recent bibliography on modern Mexico, see

Luis González (ed.), *Fuentes de la historia contemporánea de México,* 3 vols., México, El Colegio de México, 1961–1962.

Studies on Azuela

Azuela, Mariano. "Azares de mi novela *Los de abajo,*" *Universidad de México,* I (Nov. 1946), 1–4.

Azuela, Mariano. *Epistolario y archivo,* México UNAM, 1969, 324 pp. Recopilación, notas y apéndices de Beatrice Berler. Photograph.

Blom, Franz. (*The Underdogs*), *Saturday Review of Literature,* September 28, 1929.

Brenner, Anita. "Blood and Struggle of Mexico Incarnate in 'Underdogs,'" *New York Evening Post,* August 31, 1929.

Colín, Eduardo. "*Los de abajo* por Mariano Azuela," *Rasgos,* México, Manuel León Sánchez, 1934, pp. 81–86.

Dulsey, Bernard M. "The Mexican Revolution as Mirrored in the Novels of Mariano Azuela," *Modern Language Journal,* XXXV (1951), 382–386.

Englekirk, John E. "The 'Discovery' of *Los de abajo,*" *Hispania,* XVIII (1935), 53–62; reproduced, in Spanish translation, in the author's *De lo nuestro y lo ajeno,* México, Edit. Cultura, 1966, pp. 53–63.

Frank, Waldo. (*The Underdogs*), *The New Republic,* LX (October 23, 1929), 275–276; "Foreword," *Marcela* (see *Mala yerba*), pp. vii–xi.

Freitas, Newton. "*Los de abajo* (de Mariano Azuela)," *Ensayos americanos,* Buenos Aires, Schapire, n.d. (1942), pp. 197–202.

Gannett, Lewis. (*The Underdogs*), *New York Herald Tribune Book Review,* August 25, 1929.

Goldberg, Isaac. (*The Underdogs*), *The New World Monthly,* I (Jan. 1930), 66–68.

González de Mendoza, José María. "Preliminar," *Mala yerba* (Botas 1937), pp. 7–16.

Gruening, Ernest. (*The Underdogs*), *The Nation,* CXXIX (December 4, 1929), 689–690.

Icaza, Xavier. (*Los de abajo*), *El libro y el pueblo* (México), X (Oct. 1932), 24–30.

James, E. K. (*Los de abajo*), *New York Times Book Review,* October 28, 1928.

Larbaud, Valéry. "Preface," *Ceux d'en bas,* Paris, J. O. Fourcade, 1930, pp. i–xviii; see Spanish translation by Bernardo Ortiz de Montellano in *Contemporáneos,* VII (Feb. 1930), 127–143.

Latorre, Mariano. "*Tirano Banderas* y *Los de abajo,* dos novelas sobre la Revolución Mexicana," *Atenea,* V (July 1928), 448–452.

Leal, Luis. *Mariano Azuela, vida y obra,* México, Eds. de Andrea, 1961, 182 pp.

Luckey, Robert E. "Mariano Azuela: 1873–1952," *Books Abroad,* XXVII (1953), 368–370.

Menton, Seymour. "La estructura épica de *Los de abajo* y un prólogo especulativo," *Hispania,* L (1967), 1001–1011.

Montenegro, Ernesto. (*Los de abajo*), *New York Herald Tribune Book Review,* October 14, 1928.

Monterde, Francisco. "Prólogo," *Obras completas de Mariano Azuela,* México, Fondo de Cultura Económica, 1958. I, pp. vii–xxi.

Owen, Arthur. (*Los de abajo*), *Books Abroad,* V (1931), 264–265.

Rodríguez Alcalá, Hugo. "Mariano Azuela y las antítesis de *Los de abajo*," *Ensayos de Norte a Sur,* Seattle and México, University of Washington Press, Eds. de Andrea, 1960, pp. 81–91.

Spell, Jefferson Rea. *Contemporary Spanish American Fiction,* Chapel Hill, University of North Carolina, 1944. For Azuela, see pp. 64–101.

Torres-Ríoseco, Arturo. *Grandes novelistas de la América Hispana,* 2nd ed., 2 vols., Berkeley, University of California Press, 1949. For Azuela, see I, 3–40.

Studies on the Literature of the Revolution

Alegría, Fernando. *Historia de la novela hispanoamericana,* 3rd ed., México, Eds. de Andrea, 1966. For Azuela and others, see chapter on "La novela de la Revolución Mexicana," pp. 141–169.

Beals, Carleton. "The Noisemakers: Los estridentistas," *Mexican Maze,* Philadelphia, Lippincott, 1931, pp. 259–283.

Brushwood, John S. *Mexico in its Novel. A Nation's Search for Identity,* Austin and London, University of Texas Press, 1966, xii + 292 pp.

Brushwood, John S. and Rojas Garcidueñas, José. *Breve historia de la novela mexicana,* México, Eds. de Andrea, 1959. For Azuela and others, see chapter on "Novela de problemas sociales," pp. 91–129.

Castro Leal, Antonio (ed.). *La novela de la Revolución Mexicana,* 2 vols., México, Aguilar, 1958–1960.

Contents: Azuela, *Los de abajo* and *Las moscas.* Guzmán, *El águila y la serpiente* and *La sombra del caudillo.* Vasconcelos, *Ulises criollo.* A. Vera, *La revancha.* Campobello, *Cartucho* and *Las manos de mamá.* Romero, *Apuntes de un lugareño* and *Desbandada.* López y Fuentes, *Campamento, Tierra,* and *¡Mi General!* Urquizo, *Tropa vieja.* Mancisidor, *En la rosa de los vientos* and *Frontera junto al mar.* Muñoz, *¡Vámonos con Pancho Villa!* and *Se llevaron el cañón para Bachimba.* Magdaleno, *El resplandor.* M. Lira, *La escondida.*

Covarrubias, Miguel. "Slapstick and Venom," *Theatre Arts Monthly,* XXII (Aug. 1938), 587–596. The entire number (8), edited by Covarrubias, was dedicated to the "Theatre in Mexico."

Dr. Atl (see Gerardo Murillo below).

Fernández-Arias Campoamor, J. *Novelistas de Méjico,* Madrid, Eds. Cultura Hispánica, 1952. For Azuela and others, see pp. 101–135.

Gamboa de Camino, Berta. "The Novel of the Mexican Revolution," *Renascent Mexico,* New York, Covici-Friedi, 1935, pp. 258–274.

González, Manuel Pedro. *Trayectoria de la novela en México,* México, Botas, 1951. For Azuela and others, see pp. 81–413.

Henry, Elizabeth M. "Revolution as Mexican Novelists See It," *Hispania,* XV (1932), 423–436.

María y Campos, Armando de. *El teatro de género chico en la Revolución Mexicana,* México, Biblioteca del Instituto Nacional de Estudios Históricos de la Revolución Mexicana, 1956, 439 pp.

María y Campos, Armando de. *El teatro de género dramático en la Revolución Mexicana,* México, Biblioteca del Instituto Nacional de Estudios Históricos de la Revolución Mexicana, 1957, 438 pp.

Morton, F. Rand. *Los novelistas de la Revolución Mexicana,* México, Edit. Cultura, 1949. For Azuela, see pp. 29–70.

Mendoza, Vicente T. *El corrido de la Revolución Mexicana,* México. Biblioteca del Instituto Nacional de Estudios Históricos de la Revolución Mexicana, 1956, 151 pp.

Murillo, Gerardo (Dr. Atl). *Las artes populares en México,* 2 vols., México, Edit. Cultura, 1922, Illus.

Ortiz de Montellano, Bernardo. "Literatura de la Revolución y literatura revolucionaria," *Contemporáneos,* VII (April 1930), 77–81.

Pleasants, Edwin Hemingway. *The Caudillo,* Monmouth, Ill., Commercial Art Press, 1959. For Azuela and others, see pp. 1–143.

Simmons, Merle E. *The Mexican Corrido as a Source for Interpretive Study of Modern Mexico (1870–1950),* Bloomington, Indiana University Press, 1957, xviii + 619 pp.

Uribe-Echevarría, Juan. "La novela de la revolución mexicana y la novela hispanoamericana actual," *Anales de la Universidad de Chile,* XCIII (20, 1935), 5–95.

Valadés, Edmundo, and Leal, Luis. *La Revolución y las letras,* México, Instituto Nacional de Bellas Artes, 1960, 132 pp.

Wilgus, A. Curtis (ed.). *The Caribbean: Mexico Today,* Gainesville, University of Florida Press, 1964. See for: John J. Johnson, "Mexico's Nationalist Revolution: An Interpretation" (pp. 10–18); Frank Tannenbaum, "The Measure of a Revolution" (pp. 43–51); John E. Englekirk,

"Mexican Literature Today: 1950–1963" (pp. 152–168); and Gilbert Chase, "Art in Mexico Today" (pp. 169–175).

General Works on Mexico and on the Revolution

Anon. *México: Cincuenta años de Revolución,* 4 vols., Fondo de Cultura Económica, 1960–1962. A collection of essays by specialists on economic (vol. I), social (vol. II), political (vol. III), and cultural (vol. IV) developments during a half-century of Mexico in revolution.

Brenner, Anita. *Idols Behind Altars,* New York, Harcourt, Brace, 1929, 359 pp. Illus. A fascinating study of the pagan spirit that motivates Christian religious practices in Mexico, and of the native art that is a product of this spirit and of the Revolution, through a review of the decisive factors in the historical evolution of Mexico from prehistoric times to the present.

Brenner, Anita. *The Wind That Swept Mexico,* New York, Harper, 1943, 302 pp. Illus. The text, which is subtitled "The History of the Mexican Revolution, 1910–1942," was written by A. Brenner; the 184 well-chosen historical photographs were assembled by George R. Leighton. An illuminating and entertaining view of the Revolution.

Casasola, Gustavo. *Historia gráfica de la Revolución Mexicana: 1900–1960,* 4 vols., México, Trillas, 1960. The latest and best edition of this exhaustive pictorial history of Mexico, brought up to date with a good record of events of recent years.

Cline, Howard F. *Mexico, Revolution to Evolution, 1940–1960,* London, Oxford University Press, 1962, xiv + 375 pp. Illus. In this richly documented and updated description of "a changed Mexico and a changed Mexican Revolution," the author reaffirms an earlier belief (1961) that "beneficial social and economic change *can* be brought about in so-called 'underdeveloped areas' while preserving and increasing political and economic democracy as defined in the New World."

Gruening, Ernest H. *Mexico and Its Heritage,* New York, Appleton-Century-Crofts, 1928, 728 pp. Illus. A scholarly, authoritative, and comprehensive history that provides for a deeper and more enlightened understanding of modern-day Mexico; the classic study of the Revolution as "the culmination of an entire past."

Redfield, Robert. *Tepoztlán, a Mexican Village: A Study of Folk Life* (1930), Chicago, The University of Chicago Press, 1964, xi + 247 pp. The classic study of the Spanish-Indian way of life of a typical Mexican village. For a reappraisal of Redfield's findings and an evaluation of developments in the same community during the 1950s, see Oscar Lewis,

Life in a Mexican Village: Tepoztlán Restudied (Urbana, 1951) and *Tepoztlán, Village in Mexico* (New York, 1960).

Ross, Stanley R. (ed.). *Is the Mexican Revolution Dead?* New York, Knopf, 1966, ix + 255 pp. Twenty-two articles on the great debate by Mexican and other authorities. A sound, critical assessment of the achievements and shortcomings of the Revolution.

Silva Herzog, Jesús. *Breve historia de la Revolución Mexicana,* 2 vols., México, Fondo de Cultura Económica, 1960. Illus. Vol. I, "Los antecedentes y la etapa maderista." Vol. II, "La etapa constitucionalista y la lucha de facciones." A best-seller by one of Mexico's most provocative essayists and interpreters of the national scene.

Simpson, Lesley Byrd. *Many Mexicos* (1941), 4th ed., Berkeley and Los Angeles, University of California Press, 1966, xiii + 389 pp. A popular and "rewarding journey into Mexico's past" for answers to certain insistent questions about the contemporary human landscape. These "notes" from the sharp-witted and personalized pen of a "friendly observer" afford welcome respite from the serious pose of writers of more "scholarly detachment."

Tannenbaum, Frank. *Mexico: The Struggle for Peace and Bread,* New York, Knopf, 1950, xiv + 293 + xi pp. An "excellent summary of the course of the Revolution against which the author endeavors to judge more recent developments." A worthy companion to the earlier *Peace by Revolution* (New York, 1933) in which he interprets the Mexican social revolution "as an attempt to liquidate finally the consequence of the Spanish Conquest."

los de abajo

PRIMERA PARTE

I

—Te digo que no es un animal... Oye cómo ladra el *Palomo* ... Debe ser algún cristiano.

La mujer fijaba sus pupilas en la oscuridad de la sierra.

—¿Y que fueran siendo federales?°—repuso un hombre que, en cuclillas, yantaba en un rincón, una cazuela en la diestra y tres tortillas en taco en la otra mano. 5

La mujer no le contestó; sus sentidos estaban puestos fuera de la casuca.

Se oyó un ruido de pezuñas en el pedregal cercano, y el *Palomo* ladró con más rabia. 10

—Sería bueno que por sí o por no te escondieras,° Demetrio.

El hombre, sin alterarse, acabó de comer; se acercó un cántaro y, levantándolo a dos manos, bebió agua a borbotones. Luego se puso en pie.

—Tu rifle está debajo del petate.—pronunció ella en voz muy baja. 15

El cuartito se alumbraba por una mecha de sebo. En un rincón descansaban un yugo, un arado, un otate y otros aperos de labranza. Del techo pendían cuerdas sosteniendo un viejo molde de adobes, que servía de cama, y sobre mantas y desteñidas hilachas dormía un niño. 20

Demetrio ciñó la cartuchera a su cintura y levantó el fusil. Alto, robusto, de faz bermeja, sin pelo de barba, vestía camisa y calzón de manta, ancho sombrero de soyate y guaraches.

¿Y . . . federales? What if they turned out to be government soldiers?
Sería . . . escondieras It would be a good idea for you to hide anyway

Salió paso a paso, desapareciendo en la oscuridad impenetrable de la noche.

El *Palomo,* enfurecido, había saltado la cerca del corral.

De pronto se oyó un disparo, el perro lanzó un gemido sordo
5 y no ladró más.

Unos hombres a caballo llegaron vociferando y maldiciendo. Dos se apearon y otro quedó cuidando las bestias.

—¡Mujeres..., algo de cenar!... Blanquillos, leche, frijoles, lo que tengan, que venimos muertos de hambre.

10 —¡Maldita sierra! ¡Sólo el diablo no se perdería!

—Se perdería, mi sargento, si viniera de borracho como tú...

Uno llevaba galones en los hombros, el otro cintas rojas en las mangas.

—¿En dónde estamos, vieja?... ¡Pero, con una!... ¿Esta casa
15 está sola?

—¿Y entonces, esa luz?... ¿Y ese chamaco?... ¡Vieja, queremos cenar, y que sea pronto! ¿Sales o te hacemos salir?

—¡Hombres malvados, me han matado mi perro!... ¿Qué les debía ni qué les comía mi pobrecito *Palomo?*°

20 La mujer entró llevando a rastras el perro, muy blanco y muy gordo, con los ojos claros ya y el cuerpo suelto.

—¡Mira no más qué chapetes,° sargento!... Mi alma, no te enojes, yo te juro volverte tu casa un palomar; pero, ¡por Dios!...

No me mires airada...
25 *No más enojos...*
Mírame cariñosa,
luz de mis ojos—,

acabó cantando el oficial con voz aguardentosa.

—Señora, ¿cómo se llama este ranchito?—preguntó el sar-
30 gento.

—Limón—contestó hosca la mujer, ya soplando las brasas del fogón y arrimando leña.

¿Qué... Palomo? What harm did my poor *Palomo* ever do to you?
¡Mira... chapetes Just look at those rosy cheeks

—¿Conque aquí es Limón? . . . ¡La tierra del famoso Demetrio Macías! . . . ¿lo oye, mi teniente? Estamos en Limón.

—¿En Limón? . . . Bueno, para mí . . . ¡plin!° . . . Ya sabe, sargento, si he de irme al infierno, nunca mejor que ahora . . . , que voy en buen caballo. ¡Mira no más qué cachetitos de morena! . . . ¡Un perón para morderlo!° . . .

—Usted ha de conocer al bandido ese, señora . . . Yo estuve junto con él en la Penitenciaría de Escobedo.

—Sargento, tráeme una botella de tequila; he decidido pasar la noche aquí en amable compañía con esta morenita . . . ¿El coronel? . . . ¿Qué me hablas tú del coronel a estas horas? . . . ¡Que vaya mucho a . . . !° Y si se enoja, pa mí . . . ¡plin! . . . Anda, sargento, dile al cabo que desensille y eche de cenar. Yo aquí me quedo . . . Oye, chatita, deja a mi sargento que fría los blanquillos y caliente las gordas; tú ven acá conmigo. Mira, esta carterita apretada de billetes es sólo para ti. Es mi gusto. ¡Figúrate! Ando un poco borrachito por eso, y por eso también hablo un poco ronco . . . ¡Como que en Guadalajara dejé la mitad de la campanilla y por el camino vengo escupiendo la otra mitad! . . . ¿Y qué le hace?° . . . Es mi gusto. Sargento, mi botella, mi botella de tequila. Chata, estás muy lejos; arrímate a echar un trago . . . ¿Cómo que no? . . . ¿Le tienes miedo a tu . . . marido . . . o lo que sea? . . . Si está metido en algún agujero dile que salga . . . , pa mí ¡plin! . . . Te aseguro que las ratas no me estorban.

Una silueta blanca llenó de pronto la boca oscura de la puerta.

—¡Demetrio Macías! —clamó el sargento despavorido, dando unos pasos atrás.

El teniente se puso de pie y enmudeció, quedóse frío e inmóvil como una estatua.

—¡Mátalos! —exclamó la mujer con la garganta seca.

pa(ra) . . . ¡plin! what do I care?

¡Mira . . . morderlo! Just look at the rosy cheeks that dark-skinned girl has! Like juicy pears for a fellow to bite into!

¡Que . . . a . . . ! Let him go to the devil!

¿Y . . . hace? What's the difference?

—¡Ah, dispense, amigo! ... Yo no sabía ... Pero yo respeto a los valientes de veras.

Demetrio se quedó mirándolos y una sonrisa insolente y despreciativa plegó sus líneas.

5 —Y no sólo los respeto, sino que también los quiero ... Aquí tiene la mano de un amigo ... Está bueno, Demetrio Macías, usted me desaira ... Es porque no me conoce, es porque me ve en este perro y maldito oficio ... ¡Qué quiere, amigo! ... ¡Es uno pobre, tiene familia numerosa que mantener! Sargento, vámonos; yo 10 respeto siempre la casa de un valiente, de un hombre de veras.

Luego que desaparecieron, la mujer abrazó estrechamente a Demetrio.

—¡Madre mía de Jalpa! ¡Qué susto! ¡Creí que a ti te habían tirado el balazo!

15 —Vete luego a la casa de mi padre —dijo Demetrio.

Ella quiso detenerlo; suplicó, lloró; pero él, apartándola dulcemente, repuso sombrío:

—Me late° que van a venir todos juntos.

—¿Por qué no los mataste?

20 —¡Seguro que no les tocaba todavía!°

Salieron juntos; ella con el niño en los brazos.

Ya a la puerta se apartaron en opuesta dirección.

La luna poblaba de sombras vagas la montaña.

En cada risco y en cada chaparro, Demetrio seguía mirando la 25 silueta dolorida de una mujer con su niño en los brazos.

Cuando después de muchas horas de ascenso volvió los ojos, en el fondo del cañón, cerca del río, se levantaban grandes llamaradas.

Su casa ardía ...

II

30 Todo era sombra todavía cuando Demetrio Macías comenzó a bajar al fondo del barranco. El angosto talud de una escarpa era

Me late I have a feeling
¡Seguro ... todavía! Their hour hasn't struck yet!

vereda, entre el peñascal veteado de enormes resquebrajaduras y la vertiente de centenares de metros, cortada como de un solo tajo.

Descendiendo con agilidad y rapidez, pensaba:

"Seguramente ahora sí van a dar con nuestro rastro los federales, y se nos vienen encima como perros. La fortuna es que no saben veredas, entradas ni salidas. Sólo que alguno de Moyahua anduviera con ellos de guía, porque los de Limón, Santa Rosa y demás ranchitos de la sierra son gente segura y nunca nos entregarían... En Moyahua está el cacique que me trae corriendo° por los cerros, y éste tendría mucho gusto en verme colgado de un poste del telégrafo y con tamaña lengua de fuera..."°

Y llegó al fondo del barranco cuando comenzaba a clarear el alba. Se tiró entre las piedras y se quedó dormido.

El río se arrastraba cantando en diminutas cascadas; los pajarillos piaban escondidos en los pitayos, y las chicharras monorrítmicas llenaban de misterio la soledad de la montaña.

Demetrio despertó sobresaltado, vadeó el río y tomó la vertiente opuesta del cañón. Como hormiga arriera ascendió la crestería, crispadas las manos en las peñas y ramazones, crispadas las plantas sobre las guijas de la vereda.

Cuando escaló la cumbre, el sol bañaba la altiplanicie en un lago de oro. Hacia la barranca se veían rocas enormes rebanadas; prominencias erizadas como fantásticas cabezas africanas; los pitayos como dedos anquilosados de coloso; árboles tendidos hacia el fondo del abismo. Y en la aridez de las peñas y de las ramas secas, albeaban las frescas rosas de San Juan como una blanca ofrenda al astro que comenzaba a deslizar sus hilos de oro de roca en roca.

Demetrio se detuvo en la cumbre; echó su diestra hacia atrás, tiró del cuerno que pendía a su espalda, lo llevó a sus labios gruesos, y por tres veces, inflando los carrillos, sopló en él. Tres silbidos contestaron la señal, más allá de la crestería frontera.

En la lejanía, de entre un cónico hacinamiento de cañas y paja

me . . . corriendo keeps chasing me
con . . . fuera with my tongue dangling out of my mouth

podrida, salieron, unos tras otros, muchos hombres de pechos y piernas desnudas, oscuros y repulidos como viejos bronces.

Vinieron presurosos al encuentro de Demetrio.

—¡Me quemaron mi casa! —respondió a las miradas interroga-
5 doras.

Hubo imprecaciones, amenazas, insolencias.

Demetrio los dejó desahogar; luego sacó de su camisa una botella, bebió un tanto, limpióla con el dorso de su mano y la pasó a su inmediato. La botella, en una vuelta de boca en boca, se
10 quedó vacía. Los hombres se relamieron.

—Si Dios nos da licencia —dijo Demetrio— mañana o esta misma noche les hemos de mirar la cara otra vez a los federales. ¿Qué dicen, muchachos, los dejamos conocer estas veredas?

Los hombres semidesnudos saltaron, dando grandes alaridos de
15 alegría. Y luego redoblaron las injurias, las maldiciones y las amenazas.

—No sabemos cuántos serán ellos —observó Demetrio, escudriñando los semblantes.

—Julián Medina, en Hostotipaquillo, con media docena de
20 pelados y con cuchillos afilados en el metate, les hizo frente a todos los cuicos y federales del pueblo, y se los echó... ¿Que tendrán algo los de Medina que a nosotros nos falte? —dijo uno de barba y cejas espesas y muy negras, de mirada dulzona; hombre macizo y robusto.

25 —Yo sólo les sé decir —agregó— que dejo de llamarme° Anastasio Montañés si mañana no soy dueño de un máuser, cartuchera, pantalones y zapatos. ¡De veras!... Mira, Codorniz, ¿voy que no me lo crees?° Yo traigo media docena de plomos adentro de mi cuerpo... Ai que diga mi compadre Demetrio° si no es cierto
30 ... Pero a mí me dan tanto miedo las balas, como una bolita de caramelo. ¿A que no me lo crees?°

—¡Que viva Antonio Montañés! —gritó el Manteca.

dejo de llamarme my name's not
¿voy (*or* **A**) **que ... crees?** I'll bet you don't believe it.
Ai ... Demetrio Let my pal Demetrio there tell you

—No —repuso aquél—; que viva Demetrio Macías, que es nuestro jefe, y vivan Dios del cielo y María Santísima.

—¡Viva Demetrio Macías! —gritaron todos.

Encendieron lumbre con zacate y leños secos, y sobre los carbones encendidos tendieron trozos de carne fresca. Se rodearon en torno de las llamas, sentados en cuclillas, olfateando con apetito la carne que se retorcía y crepitaba en las brasas.

Cerca de ellos estaba, en montón, la piel dorada de una res, sobre la tierra húmeda de sangre. De un cordel, entre dos huizaches, pendía la carne hecha cecina, oreándose al sol y al aire.

—Bueno —dijo Demetrio—; ya ven que aparte de mi treinta-treinta, no contamos más que con veinte armas. Si son pocos, les damos hasta no dejar uno; si son muchos, aunque sea un buen susto les hemos de sacar.°

Aflojó el ceñidor de su cintura y desató un nudo, ofreciendo del contenido a sus compañeros.

—¡Sal! —exclamaron con alborozo, tomando cada uno con la punta de los dedos algunos granos.

Comieron con avidez, y cuando quedaron satisfechos, se tiraron de barriga al sol y cantaron canciones monótonas y tristes, lanzando gritos estridentes después de cada estrofa.

III

Entre las malezas de la sierra durmieron los veinticinco hombres de Demetrio Macías, hasta que la señal del cuerno los hizo despertar. Pancracio la daba de lo alto de un risco de la montaña.

—¡Hora sí, muchachos, pónganse changos!° —dijo Anastasio Montañés, reconociendo los muelles de su rifle.

Pero transcurrió una hora sin que se oyera más que el canto de las cigarras en el herbazal y el croar de las ranas en los baches.

Cuando los albores de la luna se esfumaron en la faja débilmente rosada de la aurora, se destacó la primera silueta de un soldado en el filo más alto de la vereda. Y tras él aparecieron otros, y otros

aunque . . . sacar we'll attack them even if we only give them a good scare
pónganse changos get set

diez, y otros cien; pero todos en breve se perdían en la sombra. Asomaron los fulgores del sol, y hasta entonces pudo verse el despeñadero cubierto de gente: hombres diminutos en caballos de miniatura.

5 —¡Mírenlos qué bonitos! —exclamó Pancracio—. ¡Anden, muchachos, vamos a jugar con ellos!

Aquellas figuritas movedizas, ora se perdían en la espesura del chaparral, ora negreaban más abajo sobre el ocre de las peñas.

Distintamente se oían las voces de jefes y soldados.

10 Demetrio hizo una señal: crujieron los muelles y los resortes de los fusiles.

—¡Hora! —ordenó con voz apagada.

Veintiún hombres dispararon a un tiempo, y otros tantos federales cayeron de sus caballos. Los demás, sorprendidos, perma-
15 necían inmóviles, como bajorrelieves de las peñas.

Una nueva descarga, y otros veintiún hombres rodaron de roca en roca, con el cráneo abierto.

—¡Salgan, bandidos!... ¡Muertos de hambre!

—¡Mueran los ladrones nixtamaleros!°...

20 —¡Mueran los comevacas!...

Los federales gritaban a los enemigos, que, ocultos, quietos y callados, se contentaban con seguir haciendo gala de una puntería que ya los había hecho famosos.

—¡Mira, Pancracio —dijo el Meco, un individuo que sólo en
25 los ojos y en los dientes tenía algo de blanco—; ésta es para el que va a pasar detrás de aquel pitayo!... ¡Toma!... ¡Hijo de...! ¡En la pura calabaza! ¿Viste?... Hora pal que viene en el caballo tordillo... ¡Abajo, pelón!...

—Yo voy a darle una bañada al que va horita por el filo de la
30 vereda... Si no llegas al río, mocho infeliz, no quedas lejos°... ¿Qué tal?... ¿Lo viste?...

¡Mueran... nixtamaleros! Death to the corn-thieves!

Si... lejos. If you don't get to the river, my poor soldier-boy, you'll not be far from it.

—¡Hombre, Anastasio, no seas malo!... Empréstame tu carabina... ¡Ándale, un tiro no más!...

El Manteca, la Codorniz y los demás que no tenían armas las solicitaban, pedían como una gracia suprema que les dejaran hacer un tiro siquiera.

—¡Asómense si son tan hombres!

—Saquen la cabeza... ¡hilachos piojosos!°

De montaña a montaña los gritos se oían tan claros como de una acera a la del frente.

La Codorniz surgió de improviso, en cueros, con los calzones tendidos en actitud de torear a los federales.

Entonces comenzó una lluvia de proyectiles sobre la gente de Demetrio.

—¡Huy! ¡Huy! Parece que me echaron un panal de moscos en la cabeza —dijo Anastasio Montañés, ya tendido entre las rocas y sin atreverse a levantar los ojos.

—¡Codorniz, jijo de un...! ¡Hora adonde les dije! —rugió Demetrio.

Y, arrastrándose, tomaron nuevas posiciones.

Los federales comenzaron a gritar su triunfo y hacían cesar el fuego, cuando una nueva granizada de balas los desconcertó.

—¡Ya llegaron más! —clamaban los soldados.

Y presa de pánico, muchos volvieron grupas resueltamente, otros abandonaron las caballerías y se encaramaron, buscando refugio, entre las peñas. Fue preciso que los jefes hicieran fuego sobre los fugitivos para restablecer el orden.

—A los de abajo... A los de abajo —exclamó Demetrio, tendiendo su treinta-treinta hacia el hilo cristalino del río.

Un federal cayó en las mismas aguas, e indefectiblemente siguieron cayendo uno a uno a cada nuevo disparo. Pero sólo él tiraba hacia el río, y por cada uno de los que mataba, ascendían intactos diez o veinte a la otra vertiente.

—A los de abajo... A los de abajo —siguió gritando encolerizado.

hilachos piojosos lousy beggars

Los compañeros se prestaban ahora sus armas, y haciendo blancos cruzaban sendas apuestas.

—Mi cinturón de cuero si no le pego en la cabeza al del caballo prieto. Préstame tu rifle, Meco...

—Veinte tiros de máuser y media vara de chorizo porque me dejes tumbar al de la potranca mora... Bueno... ¡Ahora!... ¿Viste qué salto dio?... ¡Como venado!...

—¡No corran, mochos!... Vengan a conocer a su padre Demetrio Macías...

Ahora de éstos partían las injurias. Gritaba Pancracio, alargando su cara lampiña, inmutable como piedra, y gritaba el Manteca, contrayendo las cuerdas de su cuello y estirando las líneas de su rostro de ojos torvos de asesino.

Demetrio siguió tirando y advirtiendo del grave peligro a los otros; pero éstos no repararon en su voz desesperada sino hasta que sintieron el chicoteo de las balas por uno de los flancos.

—¡Ya me quemaron! —gritó Demetrio, y rechinó los dientes. —¡Hijos de...!

Y con prontitud se dejó resbalar hacia un barranco.

IV

Faltaron dos: Serapio el charamusquero y Antonio, el que tocaba los platillos en la Banda de Juchipila.

—A ver si se nos juntan más adelante —dijo Demetrio.

Volvían desazonados. Sólo Anastasio Montañés conservaba la expresión dulzona de sus ojos adormilados y su rostro barbado, y Pancracio la inmutabilidad repulsiva de su duro perfil de prognato.

Los federales habían regresado, y Demetrio recuperaba todos sus caballos, escondidos en la sierra.

De pronto, la Codorniz, que marchaba adelante, dio un grito: acababa de ver a los compañeros perdidos, pendientes de los brazos de un mezquite.

Eran ellos Serapio y Antonio. Los reconocieron, y Anastasio Montañés rezó entre dientes:

—Padre nuestro que estás en los cielos...

—Amén —rumorearon los demás, con la cabeza inclinada y el sombrero sobre el pecho.

Y apresurados tomaron el cañón de Juchipila, rumbo al Norte, sin descansar hasta ya muy entrada la noche.

La Codorniz no se apartaba un instante de Anastasio. Las siluetas de los ahorcados, con el cuello fláccido, los brazos pendientes, rígidas las piernas, suavemente mecidos por el viento, no se borraban de su memoria.

Otro día Demetrio se quejó mucho de la herida. Ya no pudo montar su caballo. Fue preciso conducirlo desde allí en una camilla improvisada con ramas de robles y haces de yerbas.

—Sigue desangrándose mucho, compadre Demetrio —dijo Anastasio Montañés. Y de un tirón arrancóse una manga de la camisa y la anudó fuertemente al muslo, arriba del balazo.

—Bueno —dijo Venancio—; eso le para la sangre y le quita la dolencia.

Venancio era barbero; en su pueblo sacaba muelas y ponía cáusticos y sanguijuelas. Gozaba de cierto ascendiente porque había leído *El judío errante* y *El sol de mayo*. Le llamaban *el dotor*, y él, muy pagado de su sabiduría, era hombre de pocas palabras.

Turnándose de cuatro en cuatro, condujeron la camilla por mesetas calvas y pedregosas y por cuestas empinadísimas.

Al mediodía, cuando la calina sofocaba y se obnubilaba la vista, con el canto incesante de las cigarras se oía el quejido acompasado y monocorde del herido.

En cada jacalito escondido entre las rocas abruptas, se detenían y descansaban.

—¡Gracias a Dios! ¡Un alma compasiva y una gorda copeteada de chile y frijoles nunca faltan! —decía Anastasio Montañés eructando.

Y los serranos, después de estrecharles fuertemente las manos encallecidas, exclamaban:

—¡Dios los bendiga! ¡Dios los ayude y los lleve por buen camino!... Ahora van ustedes; mañana correremos también nosotros, huyendo de la leva, perseguidos por estos condenados del gobierno, que nos han declarado guerra a muerte a todos los pobres; que nos roban nuestros puercos, nuestras gallinitas y hasta el maicito que tenemos para comer; que queman nuestras casas y se llevan nuestras mujeres, y que, por fin, donde dan con uno, allí lo acaban como si fuera perro del mal.

Cuando atardeció en llamaradas que tiñeron el cielo en vivísimos colores, pardearon unas casucas en una explanada, entre las montañas azules. Demetrio hizo que lo llevaran allí.

Eran unos cuantos pobrísimos jacales de zacate, diseminados a la orilla del río, entre pequeñas sementeras de maíz y frijol recién nacidos.

Pusieron la camilla en el suelo, y Demetrio, con débil voz, pidió un trago de agua.

En las bocas oscuras de las chozas se aglomeraron chomites incoloros, pechos huesudos, cabezas desgreñadas y, detrás, ojos brillantes y carrillos frescos.

Un chico gordinflón, de piel morena y reluciente, se acercó a ver al hombre de la camilla; luego una vieja, y después todos los demás vinieron a hacerle ruedo.

Una moza muy amable trajo una jícara de agua azul. Demetrio cogió la vasija entre sus manos trémulas y bebió con avidez.

—¿No quere más?

Alzó los ojos: la muchacha era de rostro muy vulgar, pero en su voz había mucha dulzura.

Se limpió con el dorso del puño el sudor que perlaba en su frente, y volviéndose de un lado, pronunció con fatiga:

—¡Dios se lo pague!

Y comenzó a tiritar con tal fuerza, que sacudía las yerbas y los pies de la camilla. La fiebre lo aletargó.

—Está haciendo sereno y eso es malo pa la calentura —dijo señá Remigia, una vieja enchomitada, descalza y con una garra de manta al pecho a modo de camisa.

Y los invitó a que metieran a Demetrio en su jacal.

Pancracio, Anastasio Montañés y la Codorniz se echaron a los pies de la camilla como perros fieles, pendientes de la voluntad del jefe.

Los demás se dispersaron en busca de comida.

Señá Remigia ofreció lo que tuvo: chile y tortillas.

—Afigúrense..., tenía güevos, gallinas y hasta una chiva parida; pero estos malditos federales me limpiaron. 5

Luego, puestas las manos en bocina, se acercó al oído de Anastasio y le dijo:

—¡Afigúrense..., cargaron hasta con la muchachilla de señá Nieves!... 10

V

La Codorniz, sobresaltado, abrió los ojos y se incorporó.

—¿Montañés, oíste?... ¡Un balazo!... Montañés, Montañés ... Despierta...

Le dio fuertes empellones, hasta conseguir que se removiera y dejara de roncar. 15

—¡Con un...! ¡Ya estás mordiendo!° ... Te digo que los muertos no se aparecen... —balbució Anastasio despertando a medias.

—¡Un balazo, Montañés!...

—Te duermes, Codorniz, o te meto una trompada... 20

—No, Anastasio; te digo que no es pesadilla... Ya no me he vuelto a acordar de los ahorcados. Es de veras un balazo; lo oí clarito...

—¿Dices que un balazo?... A ver, daca mi máuser...

Anastasio Montañés se restregó los ojos, estiró los brazos y las piernas con mucha flojera, y se puso en pie. 25

Salieron del jacal. El cielo estaba cuajado de estrellas y la luna ascendía como una fina hoz. De las casucas salió rumor confuso de mujeres asustadas, y se oyó el ruido de armas de los hombres que dormían afuera y despertaban también. 30

¡Con... mordiendo! What in the name of... Now you're at it again!

—¡Estúpido!... ¡Me has destrozado un pie!

La voz se oyó clara y distinta en las inmediaciones.

—¿Quién vive?...

El grito resonó de peña en peña, por crestones y hondonadas,
5 hasta perderse en la lejanía y en el silencio de la noche.

—¿Quién vive? —repitió con voz más fuerte Anastasio, haciendo ya correr el cerrojo de su máuser.

—¡Demetrio Macías! —respondieron cerca.

—¡Es Pancracio! —dijo la Codorniz regocijado. Y ya sin zozo-
10 bras dejó reposar en tierra la culata de su fusil.

Pancracio conducía a un mozalbete cubierto de polvo, desde el fieltro americano hasta los toscos zapatones. Llevaba una mancha de sangre fresca en su pantalón, cerca de un pie.

—¿Quién es este curro? —preguntó Anastasio.

15 —Yo estoy de centinela, oí ruido entre las yerbas y grité: "¿Quién vive?" "Carranzo", me respondió este vale... "¿Carranzo...? No conozco yo a ese gallo..." Y toma tu Carranzo: le metí un plomazo en una pata...

Sonriendo, Pancracio volvió su cara lampiña en solicitud de
20 aplausos.

Entonces habló el desconocido.

—¿Quién es aquí el jefe?

Anastasio levantó la cabeza con altivez, enfrentándosele.

El tono del mozo bajó un tanto.

25 —Pues yo también soy revolucionario. Los federales me cogieron de leva y entré a filas; pero en el combate de anteayer conseguí desertarme, y he venido, caminando a pie, en busca de ustedes.

—¡Ah, es federal!... —interrumpieron muchos, mirándolo con pasmo.

30 —¡Ah, es mocho! —dijo Anastasio Montañés—. ¿Y por qué no le metiste el plomo mejor en la mera chapa?

—¡Quién sabe qué mitote trai!° ¡Quesque quere hablar con Demetrio, que tiene que icirle quén sabe cuánto!... Pero eso no

¡Quién... trai! Who knows what he's up to?

le hace, pa todo hay tiempo como no arrebaten° —respondió Pancracio, preparando su fusil.

—Pero, ¿qué clase de brutos son ustedes? —profirió el desconocido.

Y no pudo decir más, porque un revés de Anastasio lo volteó con la cara bañada en sangre.

—¡Fusilen a ese mocho!...

—¡Hórquenlo!...

—¡Quémenlo..., es federal!...

Exaltados, gritaban, aullaban, preparando ya sus rifles.

—¡Chist..., chist..., cállense!... Parece que Demetrio habla —dijo Anastasio, sosegándolos.

En efecto, Demetrio quiso informarse de lo que ocurría e hizo que le llevaran el prisionero.

—¡Una infamia, mi jefe, mire usted..., mire usted! —pronunció Luis Cervantes, mostrando las manchas de sangre en su pantalón y su boca y su nariz abotagadas.

—Por eso, pues, ¿quién jijos de un... es usté? —interrogó Demetrio.

—Me llamo Luis Cervantes, soy estudiante de Medicina y periodista. Por haber dicho algo en favor de los revolucionarios, me persiguieron, me atraparon y fui a dar a un cuartel...

La relación que de su aventura siguió detallando en tono declamatorio, causó gran hilaridad a Pancracio y al Manteca.

—Yo he procurado hacerme entender, convencerlos de que soy un verdadero correligionario...

—¿Corre... qué? —inquirió Demetrio, tendiendo una oreja.

—Correligionario, mi jefe..., es decir, que persigo los mismos ideales y defiendo la misma causa que ustedes defienden.

Demetrio sonrió:

—¿Pos cuál causa defendemos nosotros?...

Luis Cervantes, desconcertado, no encontró qué contestar.

pa... arrebaten there's time for everything as long as you don't try to rush things

—¡Mi qué cara pone! ... ¿Pa qué son tantos brincos?° ... ¿Lo tronamos ya, Demetrio? —preguntó Pancracio, ansioso.

Demetrio llevó su mano al mechón de pelo que le cubría una oreja, se rascó largo rato, meditabundo; luego, no encontrando la 5 solución, dijo:

—Sálganse ... que ya me está doliendo otra vez ... Anastasio, apaga la mecha. Encierren a ése en el corral y me lo cuidan Pancracio y Manteca. Mañana veremos.

VI

Luis Cervantes no aprendía aún a discernir la forma precisa de 10 los objetos a la vaga tonalidad de las noches estrelladas, y buscando el mejor sitio para descansar, dio con sus huesos quebrantados sobre un montón de estiércol húmedo, al pie de la masa difusa de un huizache. Más por agotamiento que por resignación, se tendió cuan largo era y cerró los ojos resueltamente, dispuesto a dormir 15 hasta que sus feroces vigilantes le despertaran o el sol de la mañana le quemara las orejas. Algo como un vago calor a su lado, luego un respirar rudo y fatigoso, le hicieron estremecerse; abrió los brazos en torno, y su mano trémula dio con los pelos rígidos de un cerdo, que, incomodado seguramente por la vecindad, gruñó. 20 Inútiles fueron ya todos sus esfuerzos por atraer el sueño; no por el dolor del miembro lesionado, ni por el de sus carnes maguIladas, sino por la instantánea y precisa representación de su fracaso.

Sí; él no había sabido apreciar a su debido tiempo la distancia 25 que hay de manejar el escalpelo, fulminar latrofacciosos desde las columnas de un diario provinciano, a venir a buscarlos con el fusil en las manos a sus propias guaridas. Sospechó su equivocación, ya dado de alta como subteniente de caballería, al rendir la primera jornada. Brutal jornada de catorce leguas, que lo dejaba 30 con las caderas y las rodillas de una pieza, cual si todos sus huesos se hubieran soldado en uno. Acabólo de comprender ocho días

¡Mi ... brincos? Just look at that face! Why waste so much time?

después, al primer encuentro con los rebeldes. Juraría, la mano puesta sobre un Santo Cristo, que cuando los soldados se echaron los máuseres a la cara, alguien con estentórea voz había clamado a sus espaldas: "¡ Sálvese el que pueda!" Ello tan claro así, que su mismo brioso y noble corcel, avezado a los combates, había vuelto grupas y de estampida no había querido detenerse sino a distancia donde ni el rumor de las balas se escuchaba. Y era cabalmente a la puesta del sol, cuando la montaña comenzaba a poblarse de sombras vagorosas e inquietantes, cuando las tinieblas ascendían a toda prisa de la hondonada. ¿ Qué cosa más lógica podría ocurrírsele si no la de buscar abrigo entre las rocas, darles reposo al cuerpo y al espíritu y procurarse el sueño? Pero la lógica del soldado es la lógica del absurdo. Así, por ejemplo, a la mañana siguiente su coronel lo despierta a broncos puntapiés y le saca de su escondite con la cara gruesa a mojicones. Más todavía: aquello determina la hilaridad de los oficiales, a tal punto que, llorando de risa, imploran a una voz el perdón para el fugitivo. Y el coronel, en vez de fusilarlo, le larga un recio puntapié en las posaderas y le envía a la impedimenta como ayudante de cocina.

La injuria gravísima habría de dar sus frutos venenosos. Luis Cervantes cambia de chaqueta desde luego, aunque sólo *in mente* por el instante. Los dolores y las miserias de los desheredados alcanzan a conmoverlo; su causa es la causa sublime del pueblo subyugado que clama justicia, sólo justicia. Intima con el humilde soldado y, ¡ qué más!, una acémila muerta de fatiga en una tormentosa jornada le hace derramar lágrimas de compasión.

Luis Cervantes, pues, se hizo acreedor a la confianza de la tropa. Hubo soldados que le hicieron confidencias temerarias. Uno, muy serio, y que se distinguía por su temperancia y retraimiento, le dijo: "Yo soy carpintero; tenía mi madre, una viejita clavada en su silla por el reumatismo desde hacía diez años. A media noche me sacaron de mi casa tres gendarmes; amanecí en el cuartel y anochecí a doce leguas de mi pueblo ... Hace un mes pasé por allí con la tropa ... ¡ Mi madre estaba ya debajo de la tierra! ... No tenía más consuelo en esta vida ... Ahora no le hago falta a

nadie. Pero, por mi Dios que está en los cielos, estos cartuchos que aquí me cargan no han de ser para los enemigos... Y si se me hace el milagro (mi Madre Santísima de Guadalupe me lo ha de conceder), si me le junto a Villa..., juro por la sagrada alma de
5 mi madre que me la han de pagar estos federales".

Otro, joven, muy inteligente, pero charlatán hasta por los codos, dipsómano y fumador de marihuana, lo llamó aparte y, mirándolo a la cara fijamente con sus ojos vagos y vidriosos, le sopló al oído: "Compadre..., aquéllos..., los de allá del otro lado..., ¿com-
10 prendes?..., aquéllos cabalgan lo más granado de las caballerizas del Norte y del "interior", las guarniciones de sus caballos pesan de pura plata... Nosotros, ¡pst!..., en sardinas buenas para alzar cubos de noria..., ¿comprendes, compadre? Aquéllos reciben relucientes pesos fuertes; nosotros, billetes de celuloides de la fá-
15 brica del asesino... Dije..."

Y así todos, hasta un sargento segundo contó ingenuamente: "Yo soy voluntario, pero me he tirado una plancha. Lo que en tiempos de paz no se hace en toda una vida de trabajar como una mula, hoy se puede hacer en unos cuantos meses de correr la sierra
20 con un fusil a la espalda. Pero no con éstos, "mano"..., no con éstos..."

Y Luis Cervantes, que compartía ya con la tropa aquel odio solapado, implacable y mortal a las clases, oficiales y a todos los superiores, sintió que de sus ojos caía hasta la última telaraña y
25 vio claro el resultado final de la lucha.

¡Mas he aquí que hoy, al llegar apenas con sus correligionarios, en vez de recibirle con los brazos abiertos, lo encapillan en una zahurda!

Fue de día: los gallos cantaron en los jacales; las gallinas trepadas
30 en las ramas del huizache del corral, se removieron, abrían las alas y esponjaban las plumas y en un solo salto se ponían en el suelo.

Contempló a sus centinelas tirados en el estiércol y roncando. En su imaginación revivieron las fisonomías de los dos hombres de la víspera. Uno, Pancracio, agüerado, pecoso, su cara lampiña,
35 su barba saltona, la frente roma y oblicua, untadas las orejas al

cráneo y todo de un aspecto bestial. Y el otro, el Manteca, una piltrafa humana: ojos escondidos, mirada torva, cabellos muy lacios cayéndole a la nuca, sobre la frente y las orejas; sus labios de escrofuloso entreabiertos eternamente.

Y sintió una vez más que su carne se achinaba.

VII

Adormilado aún, Demetrio paseó la mano sobre los crespos mechones que cubrían su frente húmeda, apartados hacia una oreja, y abrió los ojos.

Distinta oyó la voz femenina y melodiosa que en sueños había escuchado ya, y se volvió a la puerta.

Era de día: los rayos del sol dardeaban entre los popotes del jacal. La misma moza que la víspera le había ofrecido un apastito de agua deliciosamente fría (sus sueños de toda la noche), ahora, igual de dulce y cariñosa, entraba con una olla de leche, desparramándose de espuma.

—Es de cabra, pero está regüena . . . Ándele no más; aprébela . . .

Agradecido, sonrió Demetrio, se incorporó y, tomando la vasija de barro, comenzó a dar pequeños sorbos, sin quitar los ojos de la muchacha.

Ella, inquieta, bajó los suyos.

—¿Cómo te llamas?

—Camila.

—Me cuadra el nombre, pero más la tonadita . . .

Camila se cubrió de rubor, y como él intentara asirla por un puño, asustada, tomó la vasija vacía y se escapó más que de prisa.

—No, compadre Demetrio —observó gravemente Anastasio Montañés—; hay que amansarlas primero . . . Yo tengo mucha experencia en eso . . .

—Me siento bien, compadre —dijo Demetrio haciéndose el sordo—; parece que me dieron fríos; sudé mucho y amanecí muy refrescado. Lo que me está fregando todavía es la maldita herida. Llame a Venancio para que me cure.

—¿Y qué hacemos, pues, con el curro que agarré anoche? —preguntó Pancracio.

—¡Cabal, hombre!... ¡No me había vuelto a acordar!...

Demetrio, como siempre, pensó y vaciló mucho antes de tomar una decisión.

—A ver, Codorniz, ven acá. Mira, pregunta por una capilla que hay como a tres leguas de aquí. Anda y róbale la sotana al cura.

—Pero ¿qué va a hacer, compadre? —preguntó Anastasio pasmado.

—Si este curro viene a asesinarme, es muy fácil sacarle la verdad. Yo le digo que lo voy a fusilar. La Codorniz se viste de padre y lo confiesa. Si tiene pecado, lo trueno; si no, lo dejo libre.

—¡Hum, cuánto requisito!... Yo lo quemaba y ya —exclamó Pancracio despectivo.

Por la noche regresó la Codorniz con la sotana del cura. Demetrio hizo que le llevaran el prisionero.

Luis Cervantes, sin dormir ni comer en dos días, entraba con el rostro demacrado y ojeroso, los labios descoloridos y secos.

Habló con lentitud y torpeza.

—Hagan de mí lo que quieran... Seguramente que me equivoqué con ustedes...

Hubo un prolongado silencio. Después:

—Creí que ustedes aceptarían con gusto al que viene a ofrecerles ayuda, pobre ayuda la mía, pero que sólo a ustedes mismos beneficia... ¿Yo qué me gano con que la revolución triunfe o no?

Poco a poco iba animándose, y la languidez de su mirada desaparecía por instantes.

—La revolución beneficia al pobre, al ignorante, al que toda su vida ha sido esclavo, a los infelices que ni siquiera saben que si lo son es porque el rico convierte en oro las lágrimas, el sudor y la sangre de los pobres...

—¡Bah!..., ¿y eso es como a modo de qué?° ... ¡Cuando ni a mí me cuadran los sermones! —interrumpió Pancracio.

—Yo he querido pelear por la causa santa de los desventurados

¿y... qué? and what does all that mean?

... Pero ustedes no me entienden..., ustedes me rechazan... ¡Hagan conmigo, pues, lo que gusten!

—Por lo pronto no más te pongo esta reata en el gaznate... ¡Mi qué rechonchito y qué blanco lo tienes!

—Sí, ya sé a lo que viene usted —repuso Demetrio con desabrimiento, rascándose la cabeza—. Lo voy a fusilar, ¿eh?...

Luego, volviéndose a Anastasio:

—Llévenselo..., y si quiere confesarse, tráiganle un padre...

Anastasio, impasible como siempre, tomó con suavidad el brazo de Cervantes.

—Véngase pa acá, curro...

Cuando después de algunos minutos vino la Codorniz ensotanado, todos rieron a echar las tripas.

—¡Hum, este curro es repicolargo! —exclamó—. Hasta se me figura que se rió de mí cuando comencé a hacerle preguntas.

—Pero ¿no cantó nada?

—No dijo más que lo de anoche...

—Me late que no viene a eso que usté teme, compadre —notó Anastasio.

—Bueno, pues denle de comer y ténganlo a una vista.°

VIII

Luis Cervantes, otro día, apenas pudo levantarse. Arrastrando el miembro lesionado, vagó de casa en casa buscando un poco de alcohol, agua hervida y pedazos de ropa usada. Camila, con su amabilidad incansable, se lo proporcionó todo.

Luego que comenzó a lavarse, ella se sentó a su lado, a ver curar la herida, con curiosidad de serrana.

—Oiga, ¿y quién lo insiñó a curar?... ¿Y pa qué jirvió la agua? ...¿Y los trapos, pa qué los ció?... ¡Mire, mire, cuánta curiosidá pa todo!° ... ¿Y eso que se echó en las manos?... ¡Pior! ... ¿Aguardiente de veras?... ¡Ande, pos si yo creiba que el aguardiente no más pal cólico era güeno!... ¡Ah!... ¿De moo

ténganlo... vista keep your eye on him
cuánta... todo! how careful you are about everything!

es que usté iba a ser dotor? ... ¡Ja, ja, ja! ... ¡Cosa de morirse uno de risa! ... ¿Y por qué no le regüelve mejor agua fría?° ... ¡Mi qué cuentos! ... ¡Quesque animales en el agua sin jervir! ... ¡Fuchi! ... ¡Pos cuando ni yo miro nada!° ...

5 Camila siguió interrogándole, y con tanta familiaridad, que de buenas a primeras comenzó a tutearlo.

Retraído a su propio pensamiento, Luis Cervantes no la escuchaba más.

"¿En dónde están esos hombres admirablemente armados y 10 montados, que reciben sus haberes en puros pesos duros de los que Villa está acuñando en Chihuahua? ¡Bah! Una veintena de encuerados y piojosos, habiendo quien cabalgara en una yegua decrépita, matadura de la cruz a la cola. ¿Sería verdad lo que la prensa del gobierno y él mismo habían asegurado, que los llamados revo- 15 lucionarios no eran sino bandidos agrupados ahora con un magnífico pretexto para saciar su sed de oro y de sangre? ¿Sería, pues, todo mentira lo que de ellos contaban los simpatizadores de la revolución? Pero si los periódicos gritaban todavía en todos los tonos triunfos y más triunfos de la federación, un pagador recién 20 llegado de Guadalajara había dejado escapar la especie de que los parientes y favoritos de Huerta abandonaban la capital rumbo a los puertos, por más que éste seguía aúlla que aúlla: "Haré la paz cueste lo que cueste". Por tanto, revolucionarios, bandidos o como quisiera llamárseles, ellos iban a derrocar al Gobierno; el mañana 25 les pertenecía; había que estar, pues, con ellos, sólo con ellos".

—No, lo que es ahora no me he equivocado —se dijo para sí, casi en voz alta.

—¿Qué estás diciendo? —preguntó Camila—; pos si yo creiba ya que los ratones te habían comido la lengua.

30 Luis Cervantes plegó las cejas y miró con aire hostil aquella especie de mono enchomitado, de tez broncínea, dientes de marfil, pies anchos y chatos.

—¿Oye, curro, y tú has de saber contar cuentos?

¿Y ... fría? Why don't you mix it with cold water?
¡Pos ... nada! Why, I can't see anything!

Luis hizo un gesto de aspereza y se alejó sin contestarla.

Ella, embelesada, le siguió con los ojos hasta que su silueta desapareció por la vereda del arroyo.

Tan abstraída así, que se estremeció vivamente a la voz de su vecina, la tuerta María Antonia, que, fisgoneando desde su jacal, le gritó:

—¡Epa, tú! ... Dale los polvos de amor ... A ver si ansina cai° ...

—¡Pior! ... Esa será usté° ...

—¡Si yo quisiera! ... Pero, ¡fuche!, les tengo asco a los curros ...

IX

—Señá Remigia, emprésteme unos blanquillos, mi gallina amaneció echada.° Allí tengo unos siñores que queren almorzar.

De la viva luz del sol a la penumbra del jacalucho, más turbia todavía por la densa humareda que se alzaba del fogón, los ojos de la vecina se ensancharon. Pero al cabo de breves segundos comenzó a percibir distintamente el contorno de los objetos y la camilla del herido en un rincón, tocando por su cabecera el cobertizo tiznado y brilloso.

Se acurrucó en cuclillas al lado de señá Remigia y, echando miradas furtivas adonde reposaba Demetrio, preguntó en voz baja:

—¿Cómo va el hombre? ... ¿Aliviado? ... ¡Qué güeno! ... ¡Mire, y tan muchacho! ... Pero en toavía está retedescolorido° ... ¡Ah! ... ¿De moo es que no le cierra el balazo? ... Oiga, señá Remigia, ¿no quere que le hagamos alguna lucha?°

Señá Remigia, desnuda arriba de la cintura, tiende sus brazos tendinosos y enjutos sobre la mano del metate y pasa y repasa su nixtamal.

A ... cai. Maybe then he'd fall for you.
¡Pior! ... usté. That's what you'd do, all right!
mi ... echada my hen's clucking and hatching this morning
Pero ... retedescolorido. But he still has a bad color.
¿no ... lucha? don't you think we ought to do something for him?

—Pos quién sabe si no les cuadre° —responde sin interrumpir la ruda tarea y casi sofocada— ellos train su dotor y por eso...

—Señá Remigia —entra otra vecina doblando su flaco espinazo para franquear la puerta—, ¿no tiene unas hojitas de laurel que 5 me dé pa hacerle un cocimiento a María Antonia?... Amaneció con el cólico...

Y como, a la verdad, sólo lleva pretexto para curiosear y chismorrear, vuelve los ojos hacia el rincón donde está el enfermo y con un guiño inquiere por su salud.

10 Señá Remigia baja los ojos para indicar que Demetrio está durmiendo...

—Ande, pos si aquí está usté también, señá Pachita..., no la había visto...

—Güenos días le dé Dios, ña Fortunata... ¿Cómo amane- 15 cieron?

—Pos María Antonia con su "superior"... y, como siempre, con el cólico...

En cuclillas, pónese cuadril a cuadril con señá Pachita.

—No tengo hojas de laurel, mi alma —responde señá Remigia 20 suspendiendo un instante la molienda; aparta de su rostro goteante algunos cabellos que caen sobre sus ojos y hunde luego las dos manos en un apaste, sacando un gran puñado de maíz cocido que chorrea una agua amarillenta y turbia—. Yo no tengo; pero vaya con° señá Dolores: a ella no le faltan nunca 25 yerbitas.

—Ña Dolores dende anoche se jue pa la cofradía. A sigún razón vinieron por ella pa que juera a sacar de su cuidado a la muchachilla de tía Matías.

—¡Ande, señá Pachita, no me lo diga!...

30 Las tres viejas forman animado corro y, hablando en voz muy baja, se ponen a chismorrear con vivísima animación.

—¡Cierto como haber Dios en los cielos!...

Pos... cuadre. Maybe they won't like it.
vaya con go to see

—¡Ah, pos si yo jui la primera que lo dije: "Marcelina está gorda y está gorda"! Pero naiden me lo quería creer...

—Pos pobre criatura... ¡Y pior si va resultando con que es de su tío Nazario!...

—¡Dios la favorezca!...

—¡No, qué tío Nazario ni qué ojo de hacha!° ... ¡Mal ajo pa los federales condenados!...

—¡Bah, pos aistá otra enfelizada más!...

El barullo de las comadres acabó por despertar a Demetrio. Asilenciáronse un momento, y a poco dijo señá Pachita, sacando del seno un palomo tierno que abría el pico casi sofocado ya:

—Pos la mera verdá, yo le traiba al siñor estas sustancias..., pero sigún razón está en manos de médico...

—Eso no le hace, señá Pachita...; es cosa que va por juera...

—Siñor, dispense la parvedá...; aquí le traigo este presente —dijo la vejarruca acercándose a Demetrio—. Pa las morragias de sangre no hay como estas sustancias...

Demetrio aprobó vivamente. Ya le habían puesto en el estómago unas piezas de pan mojado en aguardiente, y aunque cuando se las despegaron le vaporizó mucho el ombligo, sentía que aún le quedaba mucho calor encerrado.

—Ande, usté que sabe bien, señá Remigia —exclamaron las vecinas.

De un otate desensartó señá Remigia una larga y encorvada cuchilla que servía para apear tunas; tomó el pichón en una sola mano y, volviéndolo por el vientre, con habilidad de cirujano, lo partió por la mitad de un solo tajo.

—¡En el nombre de Jesús, María y José! —dijo señá Remigia echando una bendición. Luego, con rapidez, aplicó calientes y chorreando los dos pedazos del palomo sobre el abdomen de Demetrio.

—Ya verá cómo va a sentir mucho consuelo...

Obedeciendo las instrucciones de señá Remigia, Demetrio se inmovilizó, encogiéndose sobre un costado.

¡No . . . hacha! Her uncle Nazario, my eye!

Entonces seña Fortunata contó su cuita. Ella les tenía muy buena voluntad a los señores de la revolución. Hacía tres meses que los federales le robaron su única hija, y eso la tenía inconsolable y fuera de sí.

5 Al principio de la relación, la Codorniz y Anastasio Montañés, atejonados al pie de la camilla, levantaban la cabeza y, entreabierta la boca, escuchaban el relato; pero en tantas minucias se metió seña Fortunata, que a la mitad la Codorniz se aburrió y salió a rascarse al sol, y cuando terminaba solemnemente: "Espero de 10 Dios y María Santísima que ustedes no han de dejar vivo a uno de estos federales del infierno", Demetrio, vuelta la cara a la pared, sintiendo mucho consuelo con las substancias en el estómago, repasaba un itinerario para internarse en Durango, y Anastasio Montañés roncaba como un trombón.

X

15 —¿Por qué no llama al curro pa que lo cure, compadre Demetrio? —dijo Anastasio Montañés al jefe, que a diario sufría grandes calosfríos y calenturas—. Si viera, él se cura solo y anda ya tan aliviado que ni cojea siquiera.

Pero Venancio, que tenía dispuestos los botes de manteca y las 20 planchuelas de hilas mugrientas, protestó:

—Si alguien le pone mano, yo no respondo de las resultas.

—Oye, compa, ¡pero qué dotor ni qué naa eres tú!° . . . ¿Voy que ya hasta se te olvidó por qué viniste a dar aquí? —dijo la Codorniz.

25 —Sí, ya me acuerdo, Codorniz, de que andas con nosotros porque te robaste un reloj y unos anillos de brillantes —repuso muy exaltado Venancio.

La Codorniz lanzó una carcajada.

—¡Siquiera! . . . Pior que tú corriste de tu pueblo porque en-30 venenaste a tu novia.

—¡Mientes! . . .

¡pero . . . tú! you're not a doctor or anything else!

—Sí; le diste cantáridas pa...

Los gritos de protesta de Venancio se ahogaron entre las carcajadas estrepitosas de los demás.

Demetrio, avinagrado el semblante, les hizo callar; luego comenzó a quejarse, y dijo:

—A ver, traigan, pues, al estudiante.

Vino Luis Cervantes, descubrió la pierna, examinó detenidamente la herida y meneó la cabeza. La ligadura de manta se hundía en un surco de piel; la pierna, abotagada, parecía reventar. A cada movimiento, Demetrio ahogaba un gemido. Luis Cervantes cortó la ligadura, lavó abundantemente la herida, cubrió el muslo con grandes lienzos húmedos y lo vendó.

Demetrio pudo dormir toda la tarde y toda la noche. Otro día despertó muy contento.

—Tiene la mano muy liviana el curro —dijo.

Venancio, pronto observó:

—Está bueno; pero hay que saber que los curros son como la humedad, por dondequiera se filtran. Por los curros se ha perdido el fruto de las revoluciones.

Y como Demetrio creía a ojo cerrado en la ciencia del barbero, otro día, a la hora que Luis Cervantes lo fue a curar, le dijo:

—Oiga, hágalo bien pa que cuando me deje bueno y sano se largue ya a su casa o adonde le dé su gana.

Luis Cervantes, discreto, no respondió una palabra.

Pasó una semana, quince días; los federales no daban señales de vida. Por otra parte, el frijol y el maíz abundaban en los ranchos inmediatos; la gente tal odio tenía a los federales, que de buen grado proporcionaban auxilio a los rebeldes. Los de Demetrio, pues, esperaron sin impaciencia el completo restablecimiento de su jefe.

Durante muchos días, Luis Cervantes continuó mustio y silencioso.

—¡Que se me hace que usté está enamorado, curro! —le dijo Demetrio, bromista, un día, después de la curación y comenzando a encariñarse con él.

Poco a poco fue tomando interés por sus comodidades. Le preguntó si los soldados le daban su ración de carne y leche. Luis Cervantes tuvo que decir que se alimentaba sólo de lo que las buenas viejas del rancho querían darle y que la gente le seguía mirando como a un desconocido o a un intruso.

—Todos son buenos muchachos, curro —repuso Demetrio—; todo está en saberles el modo. Desde mañana no le faltará nada. Ya verá.

En efecto, esa misma tarde las cosas comenzaron a cambiar. Tirados en el pedregal, mirando las nubes crepusculares como gigantescos cuajarones de sangre, escuchaban algunos de los hombres de Macías la relación que hacía Venancio de amenos episodios de *El judío errante*. Muchos, arrullados por la meliflua voz del barbero, comenzaron a roncar; pero Luis Cervantes, muy atento, luego que aquél acabó su plática con extraños comentarios anticlericales, le dijo enfático:

—¡Admirable! ¡Tiene usted un bellísimo talento!

—No lo tengo malo —repuso Venancio convencido—; pero mis padres murieron y yo no pude hacer carrera.

—Es lo de menos. Al triunfo de nuestra causa, usted obtendrá fácilmente un título. Dos o tres semanas de concurrir a los hospitales, una buena recomendación de nuestro jefe Macías..., y usted, doctor... ¡Tiene tal facilidad, que todo sería un juego!

Desde esa noche, Venancio se distinguió de los demás, dejando de llamarle curro. Luisito por aquí y Luisito por allí.

XI

—Oye, curro, yo quería icirte una cosa... —dijo Camila una mañana, a la hora que Luis Cervantes iba por agua hervida al jacal para curar su pie.

La muchacha andaba inquieta de días atrás, y sus melindres y reticencias habían acabado por fastidiar al mozo, que, suspendiendo de pronto su tarea, se puso en pie y, mirándola cara a cara, le respondió:

—Bueno... ¿Qué cosa quieres decirme?

Camila sintió entonces la lengua hecha un trapo y nada pudo pronunciar; su rostro se encendió como un madroño, alzó los hombros y encogió la cabeza hasta tocarse el desnudo pecho. Después, sin moverse y fijando, con obstinación de idiota, sus ojos en la herida, pronunció con debilísima voz: 5

—¡Mira qué bonito viene encarnando ya! ... Parece botón de rosa de Castilla.

Luis Cervantes plegó el ceño con enojo manifiesto y se puso de nuevo a curarse sin hacer más caso de ella.

Cuando terminó, Camila había desaparecido. 10

Durante tres días no resultó la muchacha en parte alguna. Señá Agapita, su madre, era la que acudía al llamado de Luis Cervantes y era la que le hervía el agua y los lienzos. Él buen cuidado tuvo de no preguntar más. Pero a los tres días ahí estaba de nuevo Camila con más rodeos y melindres que antes. 15

Luis Cervantes, distraído, con su indiferencia envalentonó a Camila, que habló al fin:

—Oye, curro ... Yo quería icirte una cosa ... Oye, curro; yo quero que me repases *La Adelita* ... pa ... ¿A que no me adivinas pa qué? ... Pos pa cantarla muncho, muncho, cuando ustedes se vayan, cuando ya no estés tú aquí ..., cuando andes ya tan lejos, lejos ..., que ni más te acuerdes de mí ... 20

Sus palabras hacían en Luis Cervantes el efecto de una punta de acero resbalando por las paredes de una redoma.

Ella no lo advertía, y prosiguió tan ingenua como antes: 25

—¡Anda, curro, ni te cuento! ... Si vieras qué malo es el viejo que los manda a ustedes ... Ai tienes nomás lo que me sucedió con él° ... Ya sabes que no quere el tal Demetrio que naiden le haga la comida más que mi mamá y que naiden se la lleve más que yo ... Güeno; pos, l'otro día entré con el champurrao, y ¿qué te parece que hizo el viejo e porra?° Pos que me pepena de la mano y me la agarra juerte, juerte; luego comienza a pellizcarme las corvas ... ¡Ah, pero qué pliegue tan güeno le he echao! ... "¡Epa, 30

Ai ... él. For example, take what happened to me with him.
el ... porra the old fool

pior°! . . . ¡Estése quieto! . . . ¡Pior, viejo malcriado! . . . ¡Suélteme . . . , suélteme, viejo sin vergüenza!" Y que me doy el reculón y me le zafo, y que ai voy pa juera a toa carrera° . . . ¿Qué te parece no más curro?

5 Jamás había visto reír con tanto regocijo Camila a Luis Cervantes.

—Pero ¿de veras es cierto todo lo que me estás contando?

Profundamente desconcertada, Camila no podía responderle. Él volvió a reír estrepitosamente y a repetir su pregunta. Y ella, 10 sintiendo la inquietud y la zozobra más grandes, le respondió con voz quebrantada:

—Sí, es cierto . . . Y eso es lo que yo te quería icir . . . ¿Que no te ha dao coraje por eso, curro?

Una vez más Camila contempló con embeleso el fresco y radioso 15 rostro de Luis Cervantes, aquellos ojos glaucos de tierna expresión, sus carrillos frescos y rosados como los de un muñeco de porcelana, la tersura de una piel blanca y delicada que asomaba abajo del cuello y más arriba de las mangas de una tosca camiseta de lana, el rubio tierno de sus cabellos, rizados ligeramente.

20 —Pero, ¿qué diablos estás esperando, pues, boba? Si el jefe te quiere, ¿tú qué más pretendes? . . .

Camila sintió que de su pecho algo se levantaba, algo que llegaba hasta su garganta y en su garganta se anudaba. Apretó fuertemente sus párpados para exprimir sus ojos rasos; luego limpió con 25 el dorso de su mano la humedad de los carrillos y, como hacía tres días, con la ligereza del cervatillo, escapó.

XII

La herida de Demetrio había cicatrizado ya. Comenzaban a discutir los proyectos para acercarse al Norte, donde se decía que los revolucionarios habían triunfado en toda la línea de los fede- 30 rales. Un acontecimiento vino a precipitar las cosas. Una vez Luis

pior stop it

me doy . . . carrera. I struggled and shook myself free and ran off as fast as I could.

Cervantes, sentado en un picacho de la sierra, al fresco de la tarde, la mirada perdida a lo lejos, soñando, mataba el fastidio. Al pie del angosto crestón, alagartados entre los jarales y a orillas del río, Pancracio y el Manteca jugaban baraja. Anastasio Montañés, que veía el juego con indiferencia, volvió de pronto su rostro de negra barba y dulces ojos hacia Luis Cervantes, y le dijo:

—¿Por qué está triste, curro? ¿Qué piensa tanto? Venga, arrímese a platicar...

Luis Cervantes no se movió; pero Anastasio fue a sentarse amistosamente a su lado.

—A usté le hace falta la bulla de su tierra. Bien se echa de ver que es de zapato pintado y moñito en la camisa° ... Mire, curro: ai donde me ve aquí,° todo mugriento y desgarrado, no soy lo que parezco... ¿A que no me lo cree? ... Yo no tengo necesidad; soy dueño de diez yuntas de bueyes... ¡De veras! ... Ai que lo diga mi compadre Demetrio... Tengo mis diez fanegas de siembra... ¿A que no me lo cree? ... Mire, curro; a mí me cuadra mucho hacer repelar a los federales, y por eso me tienen mala voluntad. La última vez, hace ocho meses ya (los mismos que tengo de andar aquí), le metí un navajazo a un capitancito faceto (Dios me guarde), aquí, merito del ombligo° ... Pero, de veras, yo no tengo necesidad... Ando aquí por eso... y por darle la mano a mi compadre Demetrio.

—¡Moza de mi vida! —gritó el Manteca entusiasmado con un albur. Sobre la sota de espadas puso una moneda de veinte centavos de plata.

—¡Cómo cree que a mí nadita que me cuadra el juego,° curro! .. ¿Quiere usté apostar? ... ¡Ándele, mire; esta viborita de cuero suena todavía! —dijo Anastasio sacudiendo el cinturón y haciendo oír el choque de los pesos duros.

En éstas corrió Pancracio la baraja, vino la sota y se armó un al-

Bien . . . camisa. It's easy to see that you are the type that shines his shoes and wears embroidered shirts.
ai . . . aquí in spite of the way you see me here
merito del ombligo right in the stomach
!Cómo . . . juego Believe me, I don't like gambling at all

tercado. Jácara, gritos, luego injurias. Pancracio enfrentaba su rostro de piedra ante el del Manteca, que lo veía con ojos de culebra, convulso como un epiléptico. De un momento a otro llegaban a las manos. A falta de insolencias suficientemente incisivas, acudían
5 a nombrar padres y madres en el bordado más rico de indecencias.

Pero nada ocurrió; luego que se agotaron los insultos, suspendióse el juego, se echaron tranquilamente un brazo a la espalda y paso a paso se alejaron en busca de un trago de aguardiente.

—Tampoco a mí me gusta pelear con la lengua. Es eso feo,
10 ¿verdad, curro? ... De veras, mire, a mí naiden me ha mentao a mi familia... Me gusta darme mi lugar.° Por eso me verá que nunca ando chacoteando... Oiga, curro —prosiguió Anastasio, cambiando el acento de su voz, poniéndose una mano sobre la frente y de pie—, ¿qué polvareda se levanta allá, detrás de aquel
15 cerrito? ... ¡Caramba! ¡A poco son los mochos! ... ¡Y uno tan desprevenido! ... Véngase, curro; vamos a darles parte a los muchachos.

Fue motivo de gran regocijo.

—¡Vamos a toparlos! —dijo Pancracio.

20 —Sí, vamos a toparlos. ¡Qué pueden traer que no lleven!° ...

Pero el enemigo se redujo a un hatajo de burros y dos arrieros.

—Párenlos. Son arribeños y han de traer algunas novedades —dijo Demetrio.

Y las tuvieron de sensación. Los federales tenían fortificados los
25 cerros de El Grillo y La Bufa, de Zacatecas. Decíase que era el último reducto de Huerta, y todo el mundo auguraba la caída de la plaza. Las familias salían con precipitación rumbo al Sur; los trenes iban colmados de gente; faltaban carruajes y carretones, y por los caminos reales, muchos, sobrecogidos de pánico, marcha-
30 ban a pie y con sus equipajes a cuestas. Pánfilo Natera reunía su gente en Fresnillo, y a los federales "ya les venían muy anchos los pantalones".°

Me ... lugar. I like to be respected.
¡Qué ... lleven! What have they got that we don't have?
a ... pantalones the government soldiers were in a very bad way

—La caída de Zacatecas es el *Requiescat in pace* de Huerta —aseguró Luis Cervantes con extraordinaria vehemencia—. Necesitamos llegar antes del ataque a juntarnos con el general Natera.

Y reparando en el extrañamiento que sus palabras causaban en los semblantes de Demetrio y sus compañeros, se dio cuenta de que aún era un don nadie allí. 5

Pero otro día, cuando la gente salió en busca de buenas bestias para emprender de nuevo la marcha, Demetrio llamó a Luis Cervantes y le dijo: 10

—¿De veras quiere irse con nosotros, curro?... Usté es de otra madera, y la verdá, no entiendo cómo pueda gustarle esta vida. ¿Qué cree, que uno anda aquí por su puro gusto?... Cierto, ¿a qué negarlo?, a uno le cuadra el ruido; pero no sólo es eso... Siéntese, curro, siéntese, para contarle. ¿Sabe por qué me levantó? 15 ... Mire, antes de la revolución tenía yo hasta mi tierra volteada para sembrar, y si no hubiera sido por el choque con don Mónico, el cacique de Moyahua, a estas horas andaría yo con mucha priesa, preparando la yunta para las siembras... Pancracio, apéate dos botellas de cerveza, una para mí y otra para el curro... Por la señal 20 de la Santa Cruz... ¿Ya no hace daño, verdad?...

XIII

—Yo soy de Limón, allí, muy cerca de Moyahua, del puro cañón de Juchipila. Tenía mi casa, mis vacas y un pedazo de tierra para sembrar; es decir, que nada me faltaba. Pues, señor, nosotros los rancheros tenemos la costumbre de bajar al lugar cada ocho días. 25 Oye uno su misa, oye el sermón, luego va a la plaza, compra sus cebollas, sus jitomates y todas las encomiendas.° Después entra uno con los amigos a la tienda de Primitivo López a hacer las once. Se toma la copita; a veces es uno condescendiente y se deja cargar la mano,° y se le sube el trago, y le da mucho gusto, y ríe 30 uno, grita y canta, si le da su mucha gana. Todo está bueno, porque

y... encomiendas and tends to all his errands
y... mano and he drinks a little more than he should

no se ofende a nadie. Pero que comienzan a meterse con usté; que el policía pasa y pasa, arrima la oreja a la puerta; que al comisario o a los auxiliares se les ocurre quitarle a usté su gusto... ¡Claro, hombre, usté no tiene la sangre de horchata, usté lleva el alma en el cuerpo, a usté le da coraje, y se levanta y les dice su justo precio! Si entendieron, santo y bueno; a uno lo dejan en paz, y en eso paró todo. Pero hay veces que quieren hablar ronco y golpeado... y uno es lebroncito de por sí° ... y no le cuadra que nadie le pele los ojos° ... Y, sí señor; sale la daga, sale la pistola... ¡Y luego vamos a correr la sierra hasta que se les olvida el difuntito!

Bueno. ¿Qué pasó con don Mónico? ¡Faceto! muchísimo menos que con los otros. ¡Ni siquiera vio correr el gallo!° ... Una escupida en las barbas por entrometido, y pare usté de contar... Pues con eso ha habido para que me eche encima a la Federación. Usté ha de saber del chisme ese de México, donde mataron al señor Madero y a otro, a un tal Félix o Felipe Díaz, ¡qué sé yo!... Bueno; pues el dicho don Mónico fue en persona a Zacatecas a traer escolta para que me agarraran. Que dizque yo era maderista y que me iba a levantar. Pero como no faltan amigos, hubo quien me lo avisara a tiempo,° y cuando los federales vinieron a Limón, yo ya me había pelado. Después vino mi compadre Anastasio, que hizo una muerte, y luego Pancracio, la Codorniz y muchos amigos y conocidos. Después se nos han ido juntando más, y ya ve: hacemos la lucha como podemos.

—Mi jefe —dijo Luis Cervantes después de algunos minutos de silencio y meditación—, usted sabe ya que aquí cerca, en Juchipila, tenemos gente de Natera; nos conviene ir a juntarnos con ellos antes de que tomen Zacatecas. Nos presentamos con el general...

—No tengo genio para eso... A mí no me cuadra rendirle a nadie.

y ... sí and a fellow's quick-tempered himself
y ... ojos and he doesn't like to have anyone talk him down
¡Ni ... gallo! Nobody even got hurt!
hubo ... tiempo there was someone to let me know about it in time

—Pero usted, sólo con unos cuantos hombres por acá, no dejará de pasar por un cabecilla sin importancia alguna. La revolución gana indefectiblemente; luego que se acabe le dicen, como les dijo Madero a los que le ayudaron: "Amigos, muchas gracias; ahora vuélvanse a sus casas..."

—No quiero yo otra cosa, sino que me dejen en paz para volver a mi casa.

—Allá voy... No he terminado: "Ustedes, que me levantaron hasta la Presidencia de la República, arriesgando su vida, con peligro inminente de dejar viudas y huérfanos en la miseria, ahora que he conseguido mi objeto, váyanse a coger el azadón y la pala, a medio vivir, siempre con hambre y sin vestir, como estaban antes, mientras que nosotros, los de arriba, hacemos unos cuantos millones de pesos".

Demetrio meneó la cabeza y sonriendo se rascó.

—¡Luisito ha dicho una verdad como un templo! —exclamó con entusiasmo el barbero Venancio.

—Como decía —prosiguió Luis Cervantes—, se acaba la revolución, y se acabó todo. ¡Lástima de tanta vida segada, de tantas viudas y huérfanos, de tanta sangre vertida! Todo, ¿para qué? Para que unos cuantos bribones se enriquezcan y todo quede igual o peor que antes. Usted es desprendido, y dice: "Yo no ambiciono más que volver a mi tierra". Pero, ¿es de justicia privar a su mujer y a sus hijos de la fortuna que la Divina Providencia le pone ahora en sus manos? ¿Será justo abandonar a la Patria en estos momentos solemnes en que va a necesitar de toda la abnegación de sus hijos los humildes para que la salven, para que no la dejen caer de nuevo en manos de sus eternos detentadores y verdugos, los caciques? ... ¡No hay que olvidarse de lo más sagrado que existe en el mundo para el hombre: la familia y la patria!...

Macías sonrió y sus ojos brillaron.

—¿Qué, será bueno ir con Natera, curro?

—No sólo bueno —pronunció insinuante Venancio—, sino indispensable, Demetrio.

—Mi jefe —continuó Cervantes—, usted me ha simpatizado

desde que lo conocí, y lo quiero cada vez más, porque sé todo lo que vale. Permítame que sea enteramente franco. Usted no comprende todavía su verdadera, su alta y nobilísima misión. Usted, hombre modesto y sin ambiciones, no quiere ver el importantísimo papel que le toca en esta revolución. Mentira que usted ande por aquí por don Mónico, el cacique; usted se ha levantado contra el caciquismo que asola toda la nación. Somos elementos de un gran movimiento social que tiene que concluir por el engrandecimiento de nuestra patria. Somos instrumentos del destino para la reivindicación de los sagrados derechos del pueblo. No peleamos por derrocar a un asesino miserable, sino contra la tiranía misma. Eso es lo que se llama luchar por principios, tener ideales. Por ellos luchan Villa, Natera, Carranza; por ellos estamos luchando nosotros.

—Sí, sí; cabalmente lo que yo he pensado— dijo Venancio entusiasmadísimo.

—Pancracio, apéate otras dos cervezas...

XIV

—Si viera qué bien explica las cosas el curro, compadre Anastasio —dijo Demetrio, preocupado por lo que esa mañana había podido sacar en claro de las palabras de Luis Cervantes.

—Ya lo estuve oyendo —respondió Anastasio—. La verdad, es gente que, como sabe leer y escribir, entiende bien las cosas. Pero lo que a mí no se me alcanza, compadre, es eso de que usted vaya a presentarse con el señor Natera con tan poquitos que semos.

—¡Hum, es lo de menos! Desde hoy vamos a hacerlo ya de otro modo. He oído decir que Crispín Robles llega a todos los pueblos sacando cuantas armas y caballos encuentra; echa fuera de la cárcel a los presos, y en dos por tres tiene gente de sobra. Ya verá. La verdad, compadre Anastasio, hemos tonteado mucho. Parece a manera de mentira que este curro haya venido a enseñarnos la cartilla.

—¡Lo que es eso de saber leer y escribir!...

Los dos suspiraron con tristeza.

Luis Cervantes y muchos otros entraron a informarse de la fecha de salida.

—Mañana mismo nos vamos —dijo Demetrio sin vacilación.

Luego la Codorniz propuso traer música del pueblito inmediato y despedirse con un baile. Y su idea fue acogida con frenesí. 5

—Pos nos iremos —exclamó Pancracio y dio un aullido—; pero lo que es yo ya no me voy solo... Tengo mi amor y me lo llevo...

Demetrio dijo que él de muy buena gana se llevaría también a una mozuela que traía entre ojos, pero que deseaba mucho que ninguno de ellos dejara recuerdos negros, como los federales. 10

—No hay que esperar mucho; a la vuelta se arregla todo —pronunció en voz baja Luis Cervantes.

—¡Cómo! —dijo Demetrio—. ¿Pues no dicen que usté y Camila...? 15

—No es cierto, mi jefe; ella lo quiere a usted... pero le tiene miedo...

—¿De veras, curro?

—Sí; pero me parece muy acertado lo que usted dice: no hay que dejar malas impresiones... Cuando regresemos en triunfo, todo será diferente; hasta se lo agradecerán. 20

—¡Ah, curro!... ¡Es usté muy lanza! —contestó Demetrio, sonriendo y palmeándole la espalda.

Al declinar la tarde, como de costumbre, Camila bajaba por agua al río. Por la misma vereda y a su encuentro venía Luis Cervantes. 25

Camila sintió que el corazón se le quería salir°.

Quizá sin reparar en ella, Luis Cervantes, bruscamente, desapareció en un recodo de peñascos.

A esa hora, como todos los días, la penumbra apagaba en un tono mate las rocas calcinadas, los ramajes quemados por el sol y los musgos resecos. Soplaba un viento tibio en débil rumor, meciendo las hojas lanceoladas de la tierna milpa. Todo era igual; pero en las piedras, en las ramas secas, en el aire embalsamado y 30

Camila... salir. Camila felt her heart leap to her mouth.

en la hojarasca, Camila encontraba ahora algo muy extraño: como si todas aquellas cosas tuvieran mucha tristeza.

Dobló una peña gigantesca y carcomida, y dio bruscamente con Luis Cervantes, encaramado en una roca, las piernas pendientes y descubierta la cabeza.

—Oye, curro, ven a decirme adiós siquiera.

Luis Cervantes fue bastante dócil. Bajó y vino a ella.

—¡Orgulloso! ... ¿Tan mal te serví que hasta el habla me niegas? ...

—¿Por qué me dices eso, Camila? Tú has sido muy buena conmigo ... mejor que una amiga; me has cuidado como una hermana. Yo me voy muy agradecido de ti y siempre lo recordaré.

—¡Mentiroso! —dijo Camila transfigurada de alegría—. ¿Y si yo no te he hablado?

—Yo iba a darte las gracias esta noche en el baile.

—¿Cuál baile? ... Si hay baile, no iré yo ...

—¿Por qué no irás?

—Porque no puedo ver al viejo ese ... al Demetrio.

—¡Qué tonta! ... Mira, él te quiere mucho; no pierdas esta ocasión que no volverás a encontrar en toda tu vida. Tonta, Demetrio va a llegar a general, va a ser muy rico ... Muchos caballos, muchas alhajas, vestidos muy lujosos, casas elegantes y mucho dinero para gastar ... ¡Imagínate lo que serías al lado de él!

Para que no le viera los ojos, Camila los levantó hacia el azul del cielo. Una hoja seca se desprendió de las alturas del tajo y, balanceándose en el aire lentamente, cayó como mariposita muerta a sus pies. Se inclinó y la tomó en sus dedos. Luego, sin mirarlo a la cara, susurró:

—¡Ay, curro ... si vieras qué feo siento que tú me digas eso! ... Si yo a ti es al que quero ... pero a ti no más ... Vete, curro; vete, que no sé por qué me da tanta vergüenza ... ¡Vete, vete! ...

Y tiró la hoja desmenuzada entre sus dedos angustiosos y se cubrió la cara con la punta de su delantal.

Cuando abrió de nuevo los ojos, Luis Cervantes había desaparecido.

Ella siguió la vereda del arroyo. El agua parecía espolvoreada de finísimo carmín; en sus ondas se removían un cielo de colores y los picachos mitad luz y mitad sombra. Miríadas de insectos luminosos parpadeaban en un remanso. Y en el fondo de guijas lavadas se reprodujo con su blusa amarilla de cintas verdes, sus enaguas blancas sin almidonar, lamida la cabeza y estiradas las cejas y la frente; tal como se había ataviado para gustar a Luis.

Y rompió a llorar.

Entre los jarales las ranas cantaban la implacable melancolía de la hora.

Meciéndose en una rama seca, una torcaz lloró también.

XV

En el baile hubo mucha alegría y se bebió muy buen mezcal.

—Extraño a Camila —pronunció en voz alta Demetrio.

Y todo el mundo buscó con los ojos a Camila.

—Está mala, tiene jaqueca —respondió con aspereza señá Agapita, amoscada por las miradas de malicia que todos tenían puestas en ella.

Ya al acabarse el fandango, Demetrio, bamboleándose un poco, dio las gracias a los buenos vecinos que tan bien los habían acogido y prometió que al triunfo de la revolución a todos los tendría presentes, que "en la cama y en la cárcel se conoce a los amigos".

—Dios los tenga de su santa mano —dijo una vieja.

—Dios los bendiga y los lleve por buen camino —dijeron otras.

Y María Antonia, muy borracha:

—¡Que güelvan pronto ... pero repronto! ...

Otro día María Antonia, que aunque cacariza y con una nube en un ojo tenía muy mala fama, tan mala que se aseguraba que no había varón que no la hubiese conocido entre los jarales del río, le gritó así a Camila:

—¡Epa, tú! ... ¿Qué es eso? ... ¿Qué haces en el rincón con el rebozo liado a la cabeza? ... ¡Huy! ... ¿Llorando? ... ¡Mira qué ojos! ¡Vaya... no te apures!... No hay dolor que al alma llegue, que a los tres días no se acabe.°

Señá Agapita juntó las cejas, y quién sabe qué gruñó para sus adentros.

5 En verdad, las comadres estaban desazonadas por la partida de la gente, y los mismos hombres, no obstante díceres y chismes un tanto ofensivos, lamentaban que no hubiera ya quien surtiera el rancho de carneros y terneras para comer carne a diario. ¡Tan a gusto que se pasa uno la vida comiendo y bebiendo, durmiendo a 10 pierna tirante a la sombra de las peñas, mientras que las nubes se hacen y deshacen en el cielo!

—¡Mírenlos otra vez! Allá van —gritó María Antonia—; parecen juguetes de rinconera.

A lo lejos, allá donde la breña y el chaparral comenzaban a fun- 15 dirse en un solo plano aterciopelado y azuloso, se perfilaron en la claridad zafirina del cielo y sobre el filo de una cima los hombres de Macías en sus escuetos jamelgos. Una ráfaga de aire cálido llevó hasta los jacales los acentos vagos y entrecortados de *La Adelita.*

Camila, que a la voz de María Antonia había salido a verlos por 20 última vez, no pudo contenerse, y regresó ahogándose en sollozos.

María Antonia lanzó una carcajada y se alejó.

"A mi hija le han hecho mal de ojo"° rumoreó señá Agapita perpleja. Meditó mucho tiempo, y cuando lo hubo reflexionado bien, tomó una decisión: de una estaca clavada en un poste del 25 jacal, entre el Divino Rostro y la Virgen de Jalpa, descolgó un barzón de cuero crudo que servía a su marido para uncir la yunta y, doblándolo, propinó a Camila una soberbia golpiza para sacarle todo el daño.

En su caballo zaino, Demetrio se sentía rejuvenecido; sus ojos 30 recuperaban su brillo metálico peculiar, y en sus mejillas cobrizas de indígena de pura raza corría de nuevo la sangre roja y caliente.

Todos ensanchaban sus pulmones como para respirar los hori-

No... acabe. There's no sorrow no matter how great that lasts for more than three days.

A... ojo They've cast a spell over my daughter

zontes dilatados, la inmensidad del cielo, el azul de las montañas y el aire fresco, embalsamado de los aromas de la sierra. Y hacían galopar sus caballos, como si en aquel correr desenfrenado pretendieran posesionarse de toda la tierra. ¿Quién se acordaba ya del severo comandante de la policía, del gendarme gruñón y del cacique enfatuado? ¿Quién del mísero jacal, donde se vive como esclavo, siempre bajo la vigilancia del amo o del hosco y sañudo mayordomo, con la obligación imprescindible de estar de pie antes de salir el sol, con la pala y la canasta, o la mancera y el otate, para ganarse la olla de atole y el plato de frijoles del día?

Cantaban, reían y ululaban, ebrios de sol, de aire y de vida.

El Meco, haciendo cabriolas, mostraba su blanca dentadura, bromeaba y hacía payasadas.

—Oye, Pancracio —preguntó muy serio—; en carta que me pone mi mujer me notifica que izque ya tenemos otro hijo. ¿Cómo es eso? ¡Yo no la veo dende tiempos del siñor Madero!

—No, no es nada... ¡La dejaste enhuevada!

Todos ríen estrepitosamente. Sólo el Meco, con mucha gravedad e indiferencia, canta en horrible falsete:

> *Yo le daba un centavo*
> *y ella me dijo que no...*
> *Yo le daba medio*
> *y no lo quiso agarrar.*
> *Tanto me estuvo rogando*
> *hasta que me sacó un rial.*
> *¡Ay, qué mujeres ingratas,*
> *no saben considerar!*

La algarabía cesó cuando el sol los fue aturdiendo.

Todo el día caminaron por el cañón, subiendo y bajando cerros redondos, rapados y sucios como cabezas tiñosas, cerros que se sucedían interminablemente.

Al atardecer, en la lejanía, en medio de un lomerío azul, se esfumaron unas torrecillas acanteradas; luego la carretera polvorienta en blancos remolinos y los postes grises del telégrafo.

Avanzaron hacia el camino real y, a lo lejos, descubrieron el bulto de un hombre en cuclillas, a la vera. Llegaron hasta allí. Era un viejo haraposo y mal encarado. Con una navaja sin filo remendaba trabajosamente un guarache. Cerca de él pacía un borrico cargado de yerba.

Demetrio interrogó:

—¿Qué haces aquí, abuelito?

—Voy al pueblo a llevar alfalfa pa mi vaca.

—¿Cuántos son los federales?

—Sí..., unos cuantos; creo que no llegan a la docena.

El viejo soltó la lengua. Dijo que había rumores muy graves: que Obregón estaba ya sitiando a Guadalajara; Carrera Torres, dueño de San Luis Potosí, y Pánfilo Natera, en Fresnillo.

—Bueno —habló Demetrio—, puedes irte a tu pueblo; pero cuidado con ir a decir a nadie una palabra de lo que has visto, porque te trueno. Daría contigo aunque te escondieras en el centro de la tierra.

—¿Qué dicen, muchachos? —interrogó Demetrio cuando el viejo se había alejado.

—¡A darles!... ¡A no dejar un mocho vivo! —exclamaron todos a una.

Contaron los cartuchos y las granadas de mano que el Tecolote había fabricado con fragmentos de tubo de hierro y perillas de latón.

—Son pocos —observó Anastasio—; pero los vamos a cambiar por carabinas.

Y, ansiosos, se apresuraban a seguir delante, hincando las espuelas en los ijares enjutos de sus agotadas recuas.

La voz imperiosa de Demetrio los detuvo.

Acamparon a la falda de una loma, protegidos por espeso huizachal. Sin desensillar, cada uno fue buscando una piedra para cabecera.

XVI

A media noche, Demetrio Macías dio la orden de marcha.

El pueblo distaba una o dos leguas, y había que dar un albazo a los federales.

El cielo estaba nublado, brillaban una que otra estrella y, de vez en vez, en el parpadeo rojizo de un relámpago, se iluminaba vivamente la lejanía.

Luis Cervantes preguntó a Demetrio si no sería conveniente, para el mejor éxito del ataque, tomar un guía o cuando menos procurarse los datos topográficos del pueblo y la situación precisa del cuartel.

—No, curro —respondió Demetrio sonriendo y con un gesto desdeñoso—; nosotros caemos cuando ellos menos se lo esperen, y ya. Así lo hemos hecho muchas veces. ¿Ha visto cómo sacan la cabeza las ardillas por la boca del tusero cuando uno se los llena de agua? Pues igual de aturdidos van a salir estos mochitos infelices luego que oigan los primeros disparos. No salen más que a servirnos de blanco.

—¿Y si el viejo que ayer nos informó nos hubiera mentido? ¿Si en vez de veinte hombres resultaran cincuenta? ¿Si fuese un espía apostado por los federales?

—¡Este curro ya tuvo miedo!° —dijo Anastasio Montañés.

—¡Cómo que no es igual poner cataplasmas y lavativas a manejar un fusil! —observó Pancracio.

—¡Hum! —repuso el Meco—. Es ya mucha plática... ¡Pa una docena de ratas aturdidas!

—No va a ser hora cuando nuestras madres sepan si parieron hombres o qué° —agregó el Manteca.

Cuando llegaron a orillas del pueblito, Venancio se adelantó y llamó a la puerta de una choza.

—¿Dónde está el cuartel? —interrogó al hombre que salió, descalzo y con una garra de jorongo abrigando su pecho desnudo.

—El cuartel está abajito de la plaza, amo —contestó.

Mas como nadie sabía dónde era abajito de la plaza, Venancio

¡Este... miedo! The tenderfoot's afraid already!
No... qué This is not the time for our mothers to find out whether they had sons or something else.

lo obligó a que caminara a la cabeza de la columna y les enseñara el camino.

Temblando de espanto el pobre diablo, exclamó que era una barbaridad lo que hacían con él.

5 —Soy un pobre jornalero, siñor; tengo mujer y muchos hijos chiquitos.

—¿Y los que yo tengo serán perros? —repuso Demetrio.

Luego ordenó:

—Mucho silencio, y uno a uno por la tierra suelta a media calle.

10 Dominando el caserío, se alzaba la ancha cúpula cuadrangular de la iglesia.

—Miren, siñores, al frente de la iglesia está la plaza; caminan no más otro tantito pa abajo, y allí mero queda el cuartel.°

Luego se arrodilló, pidiendo que ya le dejaran regresar; pero 15 Pancracio, sin responderle, le dio un culatazo sobre el pecho y lo hizo seguir delante.

—¿Cuántos soldados están aquí? —inquirió Luis Cervantes.

—Amo, no quiero mentirle a su mercé; pero la verdá, la mera verdá, que son un titipuchal...

20 Luis Cervantes se volvió hacia Demetrio que fingía no haber escuchado.

De pronto desembocaron en una plazoleta.

Una estruendosa descarga de fusilería los ensordeció. Estremeciéndose, el caballo zaino de Demetrio vaciló sobre las piernas, 25 dobló las rodillas y cayó pataleando. El Tecolote lanzó un grito agudo y rodó del caballo, que fue a dar a media plaza, desbocado.

Una nueva descarga, y el hombre guía abrió los brazos y cayó de espaldas, sin exhalar una queja.

Anastasio Montañés levantó rápidamente a Demetrio y se lo 30 puso en ancas. Los demás habían retrocedido ya y se amparaban en las paredes de las casas.

—Señores, señores —habló un hombre del pueblo, sacando la cabeza de un zaguán grande—, lléguenles por la espalda de la

caminan . . . cuartel just walk a bit farther down the street and the barracks are right there

capilla... allí están todos. Devuélvanse por esta misma calle, tuerzan sobre su mano zurda, luego darán con un callejoncito, y sigan otra vez adelante a caer en la mera espalda de la capilla.

En ese momento comenzaron a recibir una nutrida lluvia de tiros de pistola. Venían de las azoteas cercanas.

—¡Hum —dijo el hombre—, ésas no son arañas que pican!... Son los curros... Métanse aquí mientras se van... Esos le tienen miedo hasta a su sombra.

—¿Qué tantos son los mochos? —preguntó Demetrio.

—No estaban aquí más que doce; pero anoche traiban mucho miedo y por telégrafo llamaron a los de delantito. ¡Quién sabe los que serán!... Pero no le hace que sean muchos. Los más han de ser de leva, y todo es que uno haga por voltearse y dejan a los jefes solos. A mi hermano le tocó la leva condenada y aquí lo train. Yo me voy con ustedes, le hago una señal y verán cómo todos se vienen de este lado. Y acabamos no más con los puros oficiales. Si el siñor quisiera darme una armita...

—Rifle no queda, hermano; pero esto de algo te ha de servir —dijo Anastasio Montañés tendiéndole al hombre dos granadas de mano.

El jefe de los federales era un joven de pelo rubio y bigotes retorcidos, muy presuntuoso. Mientras no supo a ciencia cierta el número de los asaltantes, se había mantenido callado y prudente en extremo; pero ahora que los acababan de rechazar con tal éxito que no les habían dado tiempo para contestar un tiro siquiera, hacía gala de valor y temeridad inauditos. Cuando todos los soldados apenas se atrevían a asomar sus cabezas detrás de los pretiles del pórtico, él, a la pálida claridad del amanecer, destacaba airosamente su esbelta silueta y su capa dragona, que el aire hinchaba de vez en vez.

—¡Ah, me acuerdo del cuartelazo!...

Como su vida militar se reducía a la aventura en que se vio envuelto como alumno de la Escuela de Aspirantes al verificarse la traición al presidente Madero, siempre que un motivo propicio se presentaba, traía a colación la hazaña de la Ciudadela.

—Teniente Campos —ordenó enfático—, baje usted con diez hombres a chicotearme a esos bandidos que se esconden... ¡Canallas!... ¡Sólo son bravos para comer vacas y robar gallinas!

En la puertecilla del caracol apareció un paisano. Llevaba el aviso de que los asaltantes estaban en un corral, donde era facilísimo cogerlos inmediatamente.

Eso informaban los vecinos prominentes del pueblo, apostados en las azoteas y listos para no dejar escapar al enemigo.

—Yo mismo voy a acabar con ellos —dijo con impetuosidad el oficial. Pero pronto cambió de opinión. De la puerta misma del caracol retrocedió:

—Es posible que esperen refuerzos, y no será prudente que yo desampare mi puesto. Teniente Campos, va usted y me los coge vivos a todos, para fusilarlos hoy mismo al mediodía, a la hora que la gente esté saliendo de la misa mayor. ¡Ya verán los bandidos qué ejemplares sé poner!... Pero si no es posible, teniente Campos, acabe con todos. No me deje uno solo vivo. ¿Me ha entendido?

Y, satisfecho, comenzó a dar vueltas, meditando la redacción del parte oficial que rendiría. "Señor Ministro de la Guerra, general don Aureliano Blanquet.—México.—Hónrome, mi General, en poner en el superior conocimiento de usted que en la madrugada del día... una partida de quinientos hombres al mando del cabecilla H... osó atacar esta plaza. Con la violencia que el caso demandaba, me fortifiqué en las alturas de la población. El ataque comenzó al amanecer, durando más de dos horas un nutrido fuego. No obstante la superioridad numérica del enemigo, logré castigarlos severamente, inflingiéndole completa derrota. El número de muertos fue el de veinte y mayor el de heridos, a juzgar por las huellas de sangre que dejaron en su precipitada fuga. En nuestras filas tuvimos la fortuna de no contar una sola baja.—Me honro en felicitar a usted, señor Ministro, por el triunfo de las armas del Gobierno. ¡Viva el señor general don Victoriano Huerta! ¡Viva México!"

—Y luego —siguió pensando— mi ascenso seguro a "mayor".

Y se apretó las manos con regocijo, en el mismo momento en que un estallido lo dejó con los oídos zumbando.

XVII

—¿De modo es que si por este corral pudiéramos atravesar, saldríamos derecho al callejón? —preguntó Demetrio.

—Sí; sólo que del corral sigue una casa, luego otro corral y una tienda más adelante —respondió el paisano. 5

Demetrio, pensativo, se rascó la cabeza. Pero su decisión fue pronta.

—¿Puedes conseguir un barretón, una pica, algo así como para agujerear la pared? 10

—Sí, hay todo . . . ; pero . . .

—¿Pero qué? . . . ¿En dónde están?

—Cabal que ai están los avíos,° pero todas esas casas son del patrón, y . . .

Demetrio, sin acabar de escucharlo, se encaminó hacia el cuarto 15 señalado como depósito de la herramienta.

Todo fue obra de breves minutos.

Luego que estuvieron en el callejón, uno tras otro, arrimados a las paredes, corrieron hasta ponerse detrás del templo.

Había que saltar primero una tapia, en seguida el muro posterior 20 de la capilla.

"Obra de Dios", pensó Demetrio. Y fue el primero que la escaló.

Cual monos, siguieron tras él los otros, llegando arriba con las manos estriadas de tierra y de sangre. El resto fue más fácil: esca- 25 lones ahuecados en la mampostería les permitió salvar con ligereza el muro de la capilla; luego la cúpula misma los ocultaba de la vista de los soldados.

—Párense tantito —dijo el paisano—; voy a ver dónde anda mi hermano. Yo les hago la señal . . . , después sobre las clases, ¿eh? 30

Sólo que no había en aquel momento quien reparara ya más en él.

Cabal . . . avíos Well, the tools are right there

Demetrio contempló un instante el negrear de los capotes a lo largo del pretil, en todo el frente y por los lados, en las torres apretadas de gente, tras la baranda de hierro.

Se sonrió con satisfacción, y volviendo la cara a los suyos, exclamó:

—¡Hora! . . .

Veinte bombas estallaron a un tiempo en medio de los federales, que, llenos de espanto, se irguieron con los ojos desmesuradamente abiertos. Mas antes de que pudieran darse cuenta cabal del trance, otras veinte bombas reventaban con fragor, dejando un reguero de muertos y heridos.

—¡Tovía no! . . . ¡Tovía no! . . . Tovía no veo a mi hermano . . . —imploraba angustiado el paisano.

En vano un viejo sargento increpa a los soldados y los injuria, con la esperanza de una reorganización salvadora. Aquello no es más que una correría de ratas dentro de la trampa. Unos van a tomar la puertecilla de la escalera y allí caen acribillados a tiros por Demetrio; otros se echan a los pies de aquella veintena de espectros de cabeza y pechos oscuros como de hierro, de largos calzones blancos desgarrados, que les bajan hasta los guaraches. En el campanario algunos luchan por salir, de entre los muertos que han caído sobre ellos.

—¡Mi jefe! —exclama Luis Cervantes alarmadísimo—. ¡Se acabaron las bombas y los rifles están en el corral! ¡Qué barbaridad! . . .

Demetrio sonríe, saca un puñal de larga hoja reluciente. Instantáneamente brillan los aceros en las manos de sus veinte soldados; unos largos y puntiagudos, otros anchos como la palma de la mano, y muchos pesados como marrazos.

—¡El espía! —clama en son de triunfo Luis Cervantes—. ¡No se los dije!

—¡No me mates, padrecito! —implora el viejo sargento a los pies de Demetrio, que tiene su mano armada en alto.

El viejo levanta su cara de indígena llena de arrugas y sin una cana. Demetrio reconoce al que la víspera los engañó.

En un gesto de pavor, Luis Cervantes vuelve bruscamente el rostro. La lámina de acero tropieza con las costillas, que hacen *crac, crac,* y el viejo cae de espaldas con los brazos abiertos y los ojos espantados.

—¡A mi hermano, no! . . . ¡No lo maten, es mi hermano! —grita loco de terror el paisano que ve a Pancracio arrojarse sobre un federal.

Es tarde. Pancracio, de un tajo, le ha rebanado el cuello, y como de una fuente borbotan dos chorros escarlata.

—¡Mueran los juanes! . . . ¡Mueran los mochos! . . .

Se distinguen en la carnicería Pancracio y el Manteca, rematando a los heridos. Montañés deja caer su mano, rendido ya; en su semblante persiste su mirada dulzona, en su impasible rostro brillan la ingenuidad del niño y la amoralidad del chacal.

—Acá queda uno vivo —grita la Codorniz.

Pancracio corre hacia él. Es el capitancito rubio de bigote borgoñonés, blanco como la cera, que, arrimado a un rincón cerca de la entrada al caracol, se ha detenido por falta de fuerzas para descender.

Pancracio lo lleva a empellones al pretil. Un rodillazo en las caderas y algo como un saco de piedras que cae de veinte metros de altura sobre el atrio de la iglesia.

—¡Qué bruto eres! —exclama la Codorniz—, si la malicio, no te digo nada.° ¡Tan buenos zapatos que le iba yo a avanzar!

Los hombres, inclinados ahora, se dedican a desnudar a los que traen mejores ropas. Y con los despojos se visten, y bromean y ríen muy divertidos.

Demetrio, echando a un lado los largos mechones que le han caído sobre la frente, cubriéndole los ojos, empapados en sudor, dice:

—¡Ahora con los curros!

si . . . nada if I had suspected what you were going to do I never would have told you about him

XVIII

Demetrio llegó con cien hombres a Fresnillo el mismo día que Pánfilo Natera iniciaba el avance de sus fuerzas sobre la plaza de Zacatecas.

El jefe zacateco lo acogió cordialmente.

—¡Ya sé quién es usted y qué gente trae! ¡Ya tengo noticia de la cuereada que han dado ustedes a los federales desde Tepic hasta Durango!

Natera estrechó efusivamente la mano de Macías, en tanto que Luis Cervantes peroraba:

—Con hombres como mi general Natera y mi coronel Macías, nuestra patria se verá siempre llena de gloria.

Demetrio entendió la intención de aquellas palabras cuando oyó repetidas veces a Natera llamarle "mi coronel".

Hubo vino y cerveza. Demetrio chocó muchas veces su vaso con el de Natera. Luis Cervantes brindó "por el triunfo de nuestra causa, que es el triunfo sublime de la Justicia; porque pronto veamos realizados los ideales de redención de este nuestro pueblo sufrido y noble, y sean ahora los mismos hombres que han regado con su propia sangre la tierra los que cosechen los frutos que legítimamente les pertenecen".

Natera volvió un instante su cara adusta hacia el parlanchín, y dándole luego la espalda, se puso a platicar con Demetrio.

Poco a poco, uno de los oficiales de Natera se había acercado, fijándose con insistencia en Luis Cervantes. Era joven, de semblante abierto y cordial.

—¿Luis Cervantes?...

—¿El señor Solís?

—Desde que entraron ustedes creí conocerlo... Y, ¡vamos!, ahora lo veo y aún me parece mentira.

—Y no lo es...

—¿De modo que...? Pero vamos a tomar una copa; venga usted...

—¡Bah! —prosiguió Solís ofreciendo asiento a Luis Cervantes—. ¿Pues desde cuándo se ha vuelto usted revolucionario?

—Dos meses corridos.

—¡Ah, con razón habla todavía con ese entusiasmo y esa fe con que todos estamos aquí al principio!

—¿Usted los ha perdido ya?

—Mire, compañero, no le extrañen confidencias de buenas a primeras. Da tanta gana de hablar con gente de sentido común, por acá, que cuando uno suele encontrarla se le quiere con esa misma ansiedad con que se quiere un jarro de agua fría después de caminar con la boca seca horas y más horas bajo los rayos del sol... Pero, francamente, necesito ante todo que usted me explique... No comprendo cómo el corresponsal de *El País* en tiempo de Madero, el que escribía furibundos artículos en *El Regional,* el que usaba con tanta prodigalidad del epíteto de bandidos para nosotros, milite en nuestras propias filas ahora.

—¡La verdad de la verdad, me han convencido!—repuso enfático Cervantes.

—¿Convencido?...

Solís dejó escapar un suspiro; llenó los vasos y bebieron.

—¿Se ha cansado, pues, de la revolución?—preguntó Luis Cervantes esquivo.

—¿Cansado?... Tengo veinticinco años y, usted lo ve, me sobra salud... ¿Desilusionado? Puede ser.

—Debe tener sus razones...

—"Yo pensé una florida pradera al remate de un camino... Y me encontré un pantano". Amigo mío: hay hechos y hay hombres que no son sino pura hiel... Y esa hiel va cayendo gota a gota en el alma y todo lo amarga, todo lo envenena. Entusiasmo, esperanzas, ideales, alegrías..., ¡nada! Luego no le queda más: o se convierte usted en un bandido igual a ellos, o desaparece de la escena, escondiéndose tras las murallas de un egoísmo impenetrable y feroz.

A Luis Cervantes le torturaba la conversación; era para él un sacrificio oír frases tan fuera de lugar y tiempo. Para eximirse, pues, de tomar parte activa en ella, invitó a Solís a que menudamente refiriera los hechos que le habían conducido a tal estado de desencanto.

—¿Hechos? ... Insignificancias, naderías: gestos inadvertidos para los más; la vida instantánea de una línea que se contrae, de unos ojos que brillan, de unos labios que se pliegan; el significado fugaz de una frase que se pierde. Pero hechos, gestos y expresiones que agrupados en su lógica y natural expresión, constituyen e integran la mueca pavorosa y grotesca a la vez de una raza... ¡De una raza irredenta!...

Apuró un nuevo vaso de vino, hizo una larga pausa y prosiguió:

—Me preguntará que por qué sigo entonces en la revolución. La revolución es el huracán y el hombre que se entrega a ella no es ya el hombre, es la miserable hoja seca arrebatada por el vendaval...

Interrumpió a Solís la presencia de Demetrio Macías, que se acercó.

—Nos vamos, curro...

Alberto Solís, con fácil palabra y acento de sinceridad profunda, lo felicitó efusivamente por sus hechos de armas, por sus aventuras, que le habían hecho famoso, siendo conocidas hasta por los mismos hombres de la poderosa División del Norte.

Y Demetrio, encantado, oía el relato de sus hazañas, compuestas y aderezadas de tal suerte, que él mismo no las conociera. Por lo demás, aquello tan bien sonaba a sus oídos, que acabó por contarlas más tarde en el mismo tono y aun por creer que así habíanse realizado.

—¡Qué hombre tan simpático es el general Natera! —observó Luis Cervantes cuando regresaba al mesón—. En cambio, el capitancillo Solís... ¡qué lata!...

Demetrio Macías, sin escucharlo, muy contento, le oprimió un brazo y le dijo en voz baja:

—Ya soy coronel de veras, curro... Y usted, mi secretario...

Los hombres de Macías también hicieron muchas amistades nuevas esa noche, y "por el gusto de habernos conocido", se bebió harto mezcal y aguardiente. Como no todo el mundo congenia y a veces el alcohol es mal consejero, naturalmente hubo sus diferencias; pero todo se arregló en buena forma y fuera de la cantina, de la fonda o del lupanar, sin molestar a los amigos.

A la mañana siguiente amanecieron algunos muertos°: una vieja prostituta con un balazo en el ombligo y dos reclutas del coronel Macías con el cráneo agujereado.

Anastasio Montañés le dio cuenta a su jefe, y éste, alzando los hombros, dijo:

—¡Psch! ... Pos que los entierren ...

XIX

—Allí vienen ya los gorrudos—clamaron con azoro los vecinos de Fresnillo cuando supieron que el asalto de los revolucionarios a la plaza de Zacatecas había sido un fracaso.

Volvía la turba desenfrenada de hombres requemados, mugrientos y casi desnudos, cubierta la cabeza con sombreros de palma de alta copa cónica y de inmensa falda que les ocultaba medio rostro.

Les llamaban los gorrudos. Y los gorrudos regresaban tan alegremente como habían marchado días antes a los combates, saqueando cada pueblo, cada hacienda, cada ranchería y hasta el jacal más miserable que encontraban a su paso.

—¿Quién me merca esta maquinaria? —pregonaba uno, enrojecido y fatigado de llevar la carga de su "avance".

Era una máquina de escribir nueva, que a todos atrajo con los deslumbrantes reflejos del niquelado.

La "Oliver," en una sola mañana, había tenido cinco propietarios, comenzando por valer diez pesos, depreciándose uno o dos a cada cambio de dueño. La verdad era que pesaba demasiado y nadie podía soportarla más de media hora.

—Doy peseta por ella —ofreció la Codorniz.

—Es tuya —respondió el dueño dándosela prontamente y con temores ostensibles de que aquél se arrepintiera.

La Codorniz, por veinticinco centavos, tuvo el gusto de tomarla en sus manos y de arrojarla luego contra las piedras, donde se rompió ruidosamente.

Fue como una señal: todos los que llevaban objetos pesados o

amanecieron . . . muertos in the morning there were a few dead

molestos comenzaron a deshacerse de ellos, estrellándolos contra las rocas. Volaron los aparatos de cristal y porcelana; gruesos espejos, candelabros de latón, finas estatuillas, tibores y todo lo redundante del "avance" de la jornada, quedó hecho añicos por el camino.

Demetrio, que no participaba de aquella alegría, ajena del todo al resultado de las operaciones militares, llamó aparte a Montañés y a Pancracio y les dijo:

—A éstos les falta nervio. No es tan trabajoso tomar una plaza. Miren, primero se abre uno así . . . , luego se va juntando, se va juntando . . . , hasta que ¡zas! . . . ¡Y ya!°

Y, en un gesto amplio, abría sus brazos nervudos y fuertes; luego los aproximaba poco a poco, acompañando el gesto a la palabra, hasta estrecharlos contra su pecho.

Anastasio y Pancracio encontraban tan sencilla y tan clara la explicación, que contestaron convencidos:

—¡Esa es la mera verdá! . . . ¡A éstos les falta ñervo! . . .

La gente de Demetrio se alojó en un corral.

—¿Se acuerda de Camila, compadre Anastasio? —exclamó suspirando Demetrio, tirado boca arriba en el estiércol, donde todos, acostados ya, bostezaban de sueño.

—¿Quién es esa Camila, compadre?

—La que me hacía de comer allá, en el ranchito . . .

Anastasio hizo un gesto que quería decir: "Esas cosas de mujeres no me interesan a mí".

—No se me olvida —prosiguió Demetrio hablando y con el cigarro en la boca—. Iba yo muy retemalo. Acababa de beberme un jarro de agua azul muy fresquecita. "¿No quere más?", me preguntó la prietilla . . . Bueno, pos me quedé rendido del calenturón, y too fue estar viendo una jícara de agua azul y oír la vocecita: "¿No quere más?" . . . Pero una voz, compadre, que me sonaba en las orejas como organillo de plata . . . Pancracio, tú, ¿qué dices? ¿No vamos al ranchito?

¡Y ya! And that's all there is to it!

— Mire, compadre Demetrio, ¿a que no me lo cree? Yo tengo mucha experiencia en eso de las viejas... ¡Las mujeres!... Pa un rato... ¡Y mi' qué rato!... ¡Pa las lepras y rasguños con que me han marcao el pellejo! ¡Mal ajo pa ellas!° Son el enemigo malo. De veras, compadre, ¿voy que no me lo cree?... Por eso verá que ni... Pero yo tengo mucha experiencia en eso.

—¿Qué día vamos al ranchito, Pancracio?—insistió Demetrio, echando una bocanada de humo gris.

—Usté no más dice... Ya sabe que allí dejé a mi amor...

—Tuyo... y no —pronunció la Codorniz amodorrado.

—Tuya... y mía también. Güeno es que seas compadecido y nos la vayas a trair de veras—rumoreó el Manteca.

—Hombre, sí, Pancracio; traite a la tuerta María Antonia, que por acá hace mucho frío —gritó a lo lejos el Meco.

Y muchos prorrumpieron en carcajadas, mientras el Manteca y Pancracio iniciaban su torneo de insolencias y obscenidades.

XX

¡Que viene Villa!

La noticia se propagó con la velocidad del relámpago.

¡Ah, Villa!... La palabra mágica. El gran hombre que se esboza; el guerrero invicto que ejerce a distancia ya su gran fascinación de boa.

—¡Nuestro Napoleón mexicano!— exclama Luis Cervantes.

Sí, "el Aguila azteca, que ha clavado su pico de acero sobre la cabeza de la víbora Victoriano Huerta"... Así dije en un discurso en Ciudad Juárez— habló en tono un tanto irónico Alberto Solís, el ayudante de Natera.

Los dos sentados en el mostrador de una cantina, apuraban sendos vasos de cerveza.

Y los gorrudos de bufandas al cuello, de gruesos zapatones de vaqueta y encallecidas manos de vaquero, comiendo y bebiendo sin cesar, sólo hablaban de Villa y sus tropas.

¡Mal... ellas! Curses on them!

Los de Natera hacían abrir tamaña boca de admiración a los de Macías.°

¡Oh Villa! ... ¡Los combates de Ciudad Juárez, Tierra Blanca, Chihuahua, Torreón!

Pero los hechos vistos y vividos no valían nada. Había que oír la narración de sus proezas portentosas, donde, a renglón seguido de un acto de sorprendente magnanimidad, venía la hazaña más bestial. Villa es el indomable señor de la sierra, la eterna víctima de todos los Gobiernos, que lo persiguen como una fiera; Villa es la reencarnación de la vieja leyenda: el bandido-providencia, que pasa por el mundo con la antorcha luminosa de un ideal: ¡robar a los ricos para hacer ricos a los pobres! Y los pobres le forjan una leyenda que el tiempo se encargará de embellecer para que viva de generación en generación.

—Pero sí sé decirle, amigo Montañés —dijo uno de los de Natera—, que si usted le cae bien a mi general Villa, le regala una hacienda; pero si le choca ..., ¡no más lo manda fusilar! ...

¡Ah, las tropas de Villa! Puros hombres norteños, muy bien puestos, de sombrero tejano, traje de kaki nuevecito y calzado de los Estados Unidos de a cuatro dólares.

Y cuando esto decían los hombres de Natera, se miraban entre sí desconsolados, dándose cuenta cabal de sus sombrerazos de soyate podridos por el sol y la humedad y de las garras de calzones y camisas que medio cubrían sus cuerpos sucios y empiojados.

—Porque ahí no hay hambre ... Traen sus carros apretados de bueyes, carneros, vacas. Furgones de ropa; trenes enteros de parque y armamento, y comestibles para que reviente el que quiera.

Luego se hablaba de los aeroplanos de Villa.

—¡Ah, los airoplanos! Abajo, así de cerquita, no sabe usted qué son; parecen canoas, parecen chalupas; pero que comienzan a subir, amigo, y es un ruidazo que lo aturde. Luego algo como un automóvil que va muy recio. Y haga usté de cuenta un pájaro grande, muy grande, que parece de repente que ni se bulle siquiera. Y aquí va lo mero bueno: adentro de ese pájaro, un gringo lleva

Los ... Macías. Natera's men made Macías' men gape with admiration.

miles de granadas. ¡Afigúrese lo que será eso! Llega la hora de pelear, y como quien les riega maíz a las gallinas, allí van puños y puños de plomo pal enemigo... Y aquello se vuelve un camposanto: muertos por aquí, muertos por allí, y ¡muertos por todas partes!

Y como Anastasio Montañés preguntara a su interlocutor si la gente de Natera había peleado ya junta con la de Villa, se vino a cuenta de que todo lo que con tanto entusiasmo estaban platicando sólo de oídas lo sabían, pues que nadie de ellos le había visto jamás la cara a Villa.

—¡Hum..., pos se me hace que de hombre a hombre todos semos iguales!° ... Lo que es pa mí naiden es más hombre que otro. Pa peliar, lo que uno necesita es no más tantita vergüenza. ¡Yo, qué soldado ni qué nada había de ser!° Pero, oiga, ai donde me mira tan desgarrao° ... ¿Voy que no me lo cree? ... Pero, de veras, yo no tengo necesidá...

—¡Tengo mis diez yuntas de bueyes! ... ¿A que no me lo cree? —dijo la Codorniz a espaldas de Anastasio, remedándolo y dando grandes risotadas.

XXI

El atronar de la fusilería aminoró y fue alejándose. Luis Cervantes se animó a sacar la cabeza de su escondrijo, en medio de los escombros de unas fortificaciones, en lo más alto del cerro.

Apenas se daba cuenta de cómo había llegado hasta allí. No supo cuándo desaparecieron Demetrio y sus hombres de su lado. Se encontró solo de pronto, y luego, arrebatado por una avalancha de infantería, lo derribaron de la montura, y cuando, todo pisoteado, se enderezó, uno de a caballo lo puso a grupas. Pero, a poco, caballo y montados dieron en tierra, y él, sin saber de su fusil, ni del revólver, ni de nada, se encontró en medio de la blanca hu-

pos... iguales! well, it seems to me that as far as men go we're all just alike!

¡Yo... ser! I wasn't cut out to be a soldier or anything else for that matter!

ai... desgarrao even though you see me dressed in rags

mareda y del silbar de los proyectiles. Y aquel hoyanco y aquellos pedazos de adobes amontonados se le habían ofrecido como abrigo segurísimo.

—¡Compañero!...

5 —¡Compañero!...

—Me tiró el caballo; se me echaron encima; me han creído muerto y me despojaron de mis armas... ¿Qué podía yo hacer? —explicó apenado Luis Cervantes.

—A mí nadie me tiró... Estoy aquí por precaución..., 10 ¿sabe?...

El tono festivo de Alberto Solís ruborizó a Luis Cervantes.

—¡Caramba! —exclamó aquél—. ¡Qué machito es su jefe! ¡Qué temeridad y qué serenidad! No sólo a mí, sino a muchos bien quemados nos dejó con tamaña boca abierta.°

15 Luis Cervantes, confuso, no sabía qué decir.

—¡Ah! ¿No estaba usted allí? ¡Bravo! ¡Buscó lugar seguro a muy buena hora!... Mire, compañero; venga para explicarle. Vamos allí, detrás de aquel picacho. Note que de aquella laderita, al pie del cerro, no hay más vía accesible que la que tenemos de- 20 lante; a la derecha la vertiente está cortada a plomo y toda maniobra es imposible por ese lado; punto menos por la izquierda: el ascenso es tan peligroso, que dar un solo paso en falso es rodar y hacerse añicos por las vivas aristas de las rocas. Pues bien; una parte de la brigada Moya nos tendimos en la ladera, pecho a tierra, 25 resueltos a avanzar sobre la primera trinchera de los federales. Los proyectiles pasaban zumbando sobre nuestras cabezas; el combate era ya general; hubo un momento en que dejaron de foguearnos. Nos supusimos que se les atacaba vigorosamente por la espalda. Entonces nosotros nos arrojamos sobre la trinchera. ¡Ah, compa- 30 ñero, fíjese!... De media ladera abajo es un verdadero tapiz de cadáveres. Las ametralladoras lo hicieron todo; nos barrieron materialmente; unos cuantos pudimos escapar. Los generales estaban lívidos y vacilaban en ordenar una nueva carga con el refuerzo in-

nos... abierta he left us gasping with astonishment

mediato que nos vino. Entonces fue cuando Demetrio Macías, sin esperar ni pedir órdenes a nadie, gritó:

—¡Arriba, muchachos! ...

—¡Qué bárbaro!—clamé asombrado.

—Los jefes, sorprendidos, no chistaron. El caballo de Macías, cual si en vez de pezuñas hubiese tenido garras de águila, trepó sobre estos peñascos. "¡Arriba, arriba!", gritaron sus hombres, siguiendo tras él, como venados, sobre las rocas, hombres y bestias hechos uno. Sólo un muchacho perdió pisada y rodó al abismo; los demás aparecieron en brevísimos instantes en la cumbre, derribando trincheras y acuchillando soldados. Demetrio lazaba las ametralladoras, tirando de ellas cual si fuesen toros bravos. Aquello no podía durar. La desigualdad numérica los habría aniquilado en menos tiempo del que gastaron en llegar allí. Pero nosotros nos aprovechamos del momentáneo desconcierto, y con rapidez vertiginosa nos echamos sobre las posiciones y los arrojamos de ellas con la mayor facilidad. ¡Ah, qué bonito soldado es su jefe!

De lo alto del cerro se veía un costado de la Bufa, con su crestón, como testa empenachada de altivo rey azteca. La vertiente, de seiscientos metros, estaba cubierta de muertos, con los cabellos enmarañados, manchadas las ropas de tierra y de sangre, y en aquel hacinamiento de cadáveres calientes, mujeres haraposas iban y venían como famélicos coyotes, esculcando y despojando.

En medio de la humareda blanca de la fusilería y los negros borbotones de los edificios incendiados, refulgían al claro sol casas de grandes puertas y múltiples ventanas, todas cerradas; calles en amontonamiento, sobrepuestas y revueltas en vericuetos pintorescos, trepando a los cerros circunvecinos. Y sobre el caserío risueño se alzaba una alquería de esbeltas columnas y las torres y cúpulas de las iglesias.

—¡Qué hermosa es la Revolución, aun en su misma barbarie! —pronunció Solís conmovido. Luego, en voz baja y con vaga melancolía:

—Lástima que lo que falta no sea igual. Hay que esperar un

poco. A que no haya combatientes, a que no se oigan más disparos que los de las turbas entregadas a las delicias del saqueo; a que resplandezca diáfana, como una gota de agua, la psicología de nuestra raza, condensada en dos palabras: ¡robar, matar! . . . ¡Qué chasco, amigo mío, si los que venimos a ofrecer todo nuestro entusiasmo, nuestra misma vida por derribar a un miserable asesino, resultásemos los obreros de un enorme pedestal donde pudieran levantarse cien o doscientos mil monstruos de la misma especie! . . . ¡Pueblo sin ideales, pueblo de tiranos! . . . ¡Lástima de sangre!

Muchos federales fugitivos subían, huyendo de soldados de grandes sombreros de palma y anchos calzones blancos.

Pasó silbando una bala.

Alberto Solís, que, cruzados los brazos, permanecía absorto después de sus últimas palabras, tuvo un sobresalto repentino y dijo:

—Compañero, maldito lo que me simpatizan estos mosquitos zumbadores.° ¿Quiere que nos alejemos un poco de aquí?

Fue la sonrisa de Luis Cervantes, tan despectiva, que Solís, amoscado, se sentó tranquilamente en una peña.

Su sonrisa volvió a vagar siguiendo las espirales de humo de los rifles y la polvareda de cada casa derribada y de cada techo que se hundía. Y creyó haber descubierto un símbolo de la revolución en aquellas nubes de humo y en aquellas nubes de polvo que fraternalmente ascendían, se abrazaban, se confundían y se borraban en la nada.

—¡Ah—clamó de pronto—, ahora sí! . . .

Y su mano tendida señaló la estación de los ferrocarriles. Los trenes resoplando furiosos, arrojando espesas columnas de humo, los carros colmados de gente que escapaba a todo vapor.

Sintió un golpecito seco en el vientre, y como si las piernas se le hubiesen vuelto de trapo, resbaló de la piedra. Luego le zumbaron los oídos . . . Después, oscuridad y silencio eternos . . .

maldito . . . zumbadores I'll be darned if I like the way these humming mosquitoes take after me!

SEGUNDA PARTE

I

Al champaña que ebulle en burbujas donde se descompone la luz de los candiles, Demetrio Macías prefiere el límpido tequila de Jalisco.

Hombres manchados de tierra, de humo y de sudor; de barbas crespas y alborotadas cabelleras, cubiertos de andrajos mugrientos, se agrupan en torno de las mesas de un restaurante.

—Yo maté dos coroneles —clama con voz ríspida y gutural un sujeto pequeño y gordo, de sombrero galoneado, cotona de gamuza y mascada solferina al cuello—. ¡No podían correr de tan tripones: se tropezaban con las piedras, y para subir al cerro, se ponían como jitomates y echaban tamaña lengua!... "No corran tanto, mochitos —les grité—; párense, no me gustan las gallinas asustadas... ¡Párense, pelones, que no les voy a hacer nada!... ¡Están dados!" ¡Ja!, ¡ja!, ¡ja!... La comieron los muy° ... ¡Paf, paf! ¡Uno para cada uno... y de veras descansaron!

—A mí se me jue uno de los meros copetones° —habló un soldado de rostro renegrido, sentado en un ángulo del salón, entre el muro y el mostrador, con las piernas alargadas y el fusil entre ellas—. ¡Ah, cómo traiba oro el condenado! No más le hacían visos los galones en las charreteras y en la mantilla.° ¿Y yo?... ¡El muy burro lo dejé pesar! Sacó el paño y me hizo la contraseña, y yo me quedé nomás abriendo la boca. ¡Pero apenas me

La... muy. The stupid fools, they certainly fell for it!
A... copetones One of their big shots got away from me
No... mantilla. The gold braid on his shoulder straps and his cape was simply dazzling.

dio campo de hacerme de la esquina, cuando aistá a bala y bala!°
...Lo dejé que acabara un cargador... ¡Hora voy yo!... ¡Madre
mía de Jalpa, que no le jierre a este jijo de... la mala palabra!
¡Nada, nomás dio el estampido!... ¡Traiba muy buen cuaco! Me
5 pasó por los ojos como un relámpago... Otro probe que venía
por la misma calle me la pagó°... ¡Qué maroma lo he hecho dar!

Se arrebatan las palabras de la boca, y mientras ellos refieren
con mucho calor sus aventuras, mujeres de tez aceitunada, ojos
blanquecinos y dientes de marfil, con revólveres a la cintura, ca-
10 nanas apretadas de tiros cruzados sobre el pecho, grandes sombreros de palma a la cabeza, van y vienen como perros callejeros
entre los grupos.

Una muchacha de carrillos teñidos de carmín, de cuello y brazos
muy trigueños y de burdísimo continente, da un salto y se pone
15 sobre el mostrador de la cantina, cerca de la mesa de Demetrio.

Éste vuelve la cara hacia ella y choca con unos ojos lascivos,
bajo una frente pequeña y entre dos bandos de pelo hirsuto.

La puerta se abre de par en par, y, boquiabiertos y deslumbrados,
uno tras otro, penetran Anastasio Montañés, Pancracio, la Codor-
20 niz y el Meco.

Anastasio da un grito de sorpresa y se adelanta a saludar al
charro pequeño y gordo, de sombrero galoneado y mascada solferina.

Son viejos amigos que ahora se reconocen. Y se abrazan tan
25 fuerte que la cara se les pone negra.

—Compadre Demetrio, tengo el gusto de presentarle al güero
Margarito... ¡Un amigo de veras!... ¡Ah, cómo quiero yo a
este güero! Ya lo conocerá, compadre... ¡Es reteacabao!... ¿Te
acuerdas, güero, de la penitenciaría de Escobedo, allá en Jalisco?
30 ... ¡Un año juntos!

Demetrio, que permanecía silencioso y huraño en medio de la

¡Pero... bala! But scarcely did he give me time to get around the corner when he began shooting at me!

Otro... pagó. Another poor fellow that was coming along the same street got it.

alharaca general, sin quitarse el puro de entre los labios rumoreó, tendiéndole la mano:

—Servidor...

—¿Usted se llama, pues, Demetrio Macías?—preguntó intempestivamente la muchacha que sobre el mostrador estaba meneando las piernas y tocaba con sus zapatos de vaqueta la espalda de Demetrio.

—A la orden—le contestó éste, volviendo apenas la cara.

Ella, indiferente, siguió moviendo las piernas descubiertas, haciendo ostentación de sus medias azules.

—¡Eh, Pintada!... ¿Tú por acá?... Anda, baja, ven a tomar una copa—le dijo el güero Margarito.

La muchacha aceptó en seguida la invitación y con mucho desparpajo se abrió lugar, sentándose enfrente de Demetrio.

—¿Conque usté es el famoso Demetrio Macías que tanto se lució en Zacatecas? —preguntó la Pintada.

Demetrio inclinó la cabeza asintiendo, en tanto que el güero Margarito lanzaba una alegre carcajada y decía:

—¡Diablo de Pintada tan lista!... ¡Ya quieres estrenar general!°...

Demetrio, sin comprender, levantó los ojos hacia ella; se miraron cara a cara como dos perros desconocidos. Demetrio no pudo sostener la mirada furiosamente provocativa de la muchacha y bajó los ojos.

Oficiales de Natera, desde sus sitios, comenzaron a bromear a la Pintada con dicharachos obscenos.

Pero ella, sin inmutarse, dijo:

—Mi general Natera le va a dar a usté su aguilita... ¡Ándele, chóquela!...

Y tendió su mano hacia Demetrio y lo estrechó con fuerza varonil.

Demetrio, envanecido por las felicitaciones que comenzaron a lloverle, mandó que sirvieran champaña.

¡Diablo... general! You're a wise one, Pintada! Now you want to sport a general!

—No, yo no quiero vino ahora, ando malo —dijo el güero Margarito al mesero—; tráeme sólo agua con hielo.

—Yo quiero de cenar; con tal de que no sea chile ni frijoles, lo que jaiga—pidió Pancracio.

5 Siguieron entrando oficiales y poco a poco se llenó el restaurante. Menudearon las estrellas y las barras en sombreros de todas formas y matices; grandes pañuelos de seda al cuello, anillos de gruesos brillantes y pesadas leopoldinas de oro.

—Oye, mozo —gritó el güero Margarito—, te he pedido agua 10 con hielo... Entiende que no te pido limosna... Mira este fajo de billetes: te compro a ti y... a la más vieja de tu casa, ¿entiendes?... No me importa saber si se acabó, ni por qué se acabó... Tú sabrás de dónde me la traes... ¡Mira que soy muy corajudo! ... Te digo que no quiero explicaciones, sino agua con hielo... 15 ¿Me la traes o no me la traes?... ¿Ah, no?... Pues toma...

El mesero cae al golpe de una sonora bofetada.

—Así soy yo, mi general Macías; mire cómo ya no me queda pelo de barba en la cara. ¿Sabe por qué? Pues porque soy muy corajudo, y cuando no tengo en quien descansar, me arranco los 20 pelos hasta que se me baja el coraje. ¡Palabra de honor, mi general; si no lo hiciera así, me moriría del puro berrinche!

—Es muy malo eso de comerse uno solo sus corajes—afirma, muy serio, uno de sombrero de petate como cobertizo de jacal—. Yo, en Torreón, maté a una vieja que no quiso venderme un plato 25 de enchiladas. Estaban de pleito. No cumplí mi antojo, pero siquiera descansé.

—Yo maté a un tendajonero en el Parral porque me metió en un cambio dos billetes de Huerta —dijo otro de estrellita, mostrando en sus dedos negros y callosos, piedras de luces refulgentes.

30 —Yo, en Chihuahua, maté a un tío porque me lo topaba siempre en la mesma mesa y a la mesma hora, cuando yo iba a almorzar... ¡Me chocaba mucho!... ¡Qué queren ustedes!...

—¡Hum!... Yo maté...

El tema es inagotable.

35 A la madrugada, cuando el restaurante está lleno de alegría y

cuando con las hembras norteñas de caras oscuras y cenicientas se revuelven jovencitas pintarrajeadas de los suburbios de la ciudad, Demetrio saca su repetición de oro incrustado de piedras y pide la hora a Anastasio Montañés.

Anastasio ve la carátula, luego saca la cabeza por una ventanilla y, mirando al cielo estrellado, dice: 5

—Ya van muy colgadas las cabrillas,° compadre; no dilata en amanecer.

Fuera del restaurante no cesan los gritos, las carcajadas y las canciones de los ebrios. Pasan soldados a caballo desbocado, azotando las aceras. Por todos los rumbos de la ciudad se oyen disparos de fusiles y pistolas. 10

Y por en medio de la calle caminan, rumbo al hotel, Demetrio y la Pintada, abrazados y dando tumbos.

II

—¡Qué brutos! —exclamó la Pintada riendo a carcajadas. 15

¿Pos de dónde son ustedes? Si eso de que los soldados vayan a parar a los mesones es cosa que ya no se usa. ¿De dónde vienen? Llega uno a cualquer parte y no tiene más que escoger la casa que le cuadre y ésa agarra sin pedirle licencia a naiden. Entonces ¿pa quén jue la revolución? ¿Pa los catrines? Si ahora nosotros vamos a ser los meros catrines... A ver, Pancracio, presta acá tu marrazo ... ¡Ricos... tales!° ... Todo lo han de guardar debajo de siete llaves. 20

Hundió la punta de acero en la hendidura de un cajón y, haciendo palanca con el mango rompió la chapa y levantó astillada la cubierta del escritorio. 25

Las manos de Anastasio Montañés, de Pancracio y de la Pintada se hundieron en el montón de cartas, estampas, fotografías y papeles desparramados por la alfombra.

Pancracio manifestó su enojo de no encontrar algo que le com- 30

Ya ... cabrillas The Pleiades are very low in the sky
¡Ricos ... tales! The rich ... such people!

placiera, lanzando al aire con la punta del guarache un retrato encuadrado, cuyo cristal se estrelló en el candelabro del centro.

Sacaron las manos vacías de entre los papeles, profiriendo insolencias.

Pero la Pintada, incansable, siguió descerrajando cajón por cajón, hasta no dejar hueco sin escudriñar.

No advirtieron el rodar silencioso de una pequeña caja forrada de terciopelo gris, que fue a parar a los pies de Luis Cervantes.

Este, que veía todo con aire de profunda indiferencia, mientras que Demetrio, despatarrado sobre la alfombra, parecía dormir, atrajo con la punta del pie la cajita, se inclinó, rascóse un tobillo y con ligereza la levantó.

Se quedó deslumbrado: dos diamantes en una montadura de filigrana. Con prontitud la ocultó en el bolsillo.

Cuando Demetrio despertó, Luis Cervantes le dijo:

—Mi general, vea usted qué diabluras han hecho los muchachos. ¿No sería conveniente evitarles esto?

—No, curro... ¡Pobres!... Es el único gusto que les queda después de ponerle la barriga a las balas.°

—Sí, mi general; pero siquiera que no lo hagan aquí... Mire usted, eso nos desprestigia, y lo que es peor, desprestigia nuestra causa...

Demetrio clavó sus ojos de aguilucho en Luis Cervantes. Se golpeó los dientes con las uñas de dos dedos y dijo:

—No se ponga colorado... ¡Mire, a mí no me cuente!°... Ya sabemos que lo tuyo, tuyo, y lo mío, mío. A usted le tocó la cajita, bueno; a mí el reloj de repetición.

Y ya los dos en muy buena armonía, se mostraron sus "avances".

La Pintada y sus compañeros, entretanto, registraban el resto de la casa.

La Codorniz entró en la sala con una chiquilla de doce años, ya marcada con manchas cobrizas en la frente y en los brazos. Sorprendidos los dos, se mantuvieron atónitos, contemplando los

después... balas after exposing themselves to bullets

¡Mire... cuente! Say, don't talk to me!

montones de libros sobre la alfombra, mesas y silas, los espejos descolgados con sus vidrios rotos, grandes marcos de estampas y retratos destrozados, muebles y bibelots hechos pedazos. Con ojos ávidos, la Codorniz buscaba su presa, suspendiendo la respiracion.

Afuera, en un ángulo del patio y entre el humo sofocante, el Manteca cocía elotes, atizando las brasas con libros y papeles que alzaban vivas llamaradas.

—¡Ah —gritó de pronto la Codorniz—, mira lo que me jallé!... ¡Qué sudaderos pa mi yegua!...

Y de un tirón arrancó una cortina de peluche, que se vino al suelo con todo y galería sobre el copete finamente tallado de un sillón.

—¡Mira, tú... cuánta vieja encuerada! —clamó la chiquilla de la Codorniz, divertidísima con las láminas de un lujoso ejemplar de la *Divina Comedia*—. Ésta me cuadra y me la llevo.

Y comenzó a arrancar los grabados que más llamaban su atención. Demetrio se incorporó y tomó asiento al lado de Luis Cervantes. Pidió cerveza, alargó una botella a su secretario, y de un solo trago apuró la suya. Luego, amodorrado, entrecerró los ojos y volvió a dormir.

—Oiga —habló un hombre a Pancracio en el zaguán—, ¿a qué hora se le puede hablar al general?

—No se le puede hablar a ninguna; amaneció crudo —respondió Pancracio—. ¿Qué quiere?

—Que me venda unos de esos libros que están quemando.

—Yo mesmo se los puedo vender.

—¿A cómo los da?

Pancracio, perplejo, frunció las cejas:

—Pos los que tengan monitos, a cinco centavos, y los otros... se los doy de pilón si me merca todos.

El interesado volvió por los libros en una canasta pizcadora.

—¡Demetrio, hombre, Demetrio, despierta ya —gritó la Pintada—, ya no duermas como puerco gordo! ¡Mira quién está aquí! ... ¡El güero Margarito! ¡No sabes tú todo lo que vale este güero!

—Yo lo aprecio a usted mucho, mi general Macías, y vengo a decirle que le tengo mucha voluntad y me gustan mucho sus modales. Así es que si no lo tiene a mal, yo me paso a su brigada.

—¿Qué grado tiene? —inquirió Demetrio.

5 —Capitán primero, mi general.

—Véngase, pues... Aquí lo hago mayor.

El güero Margarito era un hombrecillo redondo, de bigotes retorcidos, ojos azules muy malignos que se le perdían entre los carrillos y la frente cuando se reía. Ex mesero del Delmónico de 10 Chihuahua, ostentaba ahora tres barras de latón amarillo, insignias de su grado en la división del Norte.

El güero colmó de elogios a Demetrio y a sus hombres, y con esto bastó para que una caja de cerveza se vaciara en un santiamén.

La Pintada apareció de pronto en medio de la sala, luciendo un 15 espléndido traje de seda de riquísimos encajes.

—¡No más las medias se te olvidaron! —exclamó el güero Margarito desternillándose de risa.

La muchacha de la Codorniz prorrumpió también en carcajadas.

Pero a la Pintada nada se le dio; hizo una mueca de indiferencia, 20 se tiró en la alfombra y con los pies hizo saltar las zapatillas de raso blanco, moviendo muy a gusto los dedos desnudos, entumecidos por la opresión del calzado, y dijo:

—¡Epa, tú, Pancracio! ... Anda a traerme unas medias azules de mis "avances".

25 La sala se iba llenando de nuevos amigos y viejos compañeros de campaña. Demetrio, animándose, comenzaba a referir menudamente algunos de sus más notables hechos de armas.

—Pero ¿qué ruido es ése? —preguntó sorprendido por el afinar de cuerdas y latones en el patio de la casa.

30 —Mi general —dijo solemnemente Luis Cervantes—, es un banquete que le ofrecemos sus viejos amigos y compañeros para celebrar el hecho de armas de Zacatecas y el merecido ascenso de usted a general.

III

—Le presento a usted, mi general Macías, a mi futura —pronunció enfático Luis Cervantes, haciendo entrar al comedor a una muchacha de rara belleza.

Todos se volvieron hacia ella, que abría sus grandes ojos azules con azoro. 5

Tendría apenas catorce años; su piel era fresca y suave como un pétalo de rosa; sus cabellos rubios, y la expresión de sus ojos con algo de maligna curiosidad y mucho de vago temor infantil.

Luis Cervantes reparó en que Demetrio clavaba su mirada de ave de rapiña en ella y se sintió satifecho. 10

Se le abrió sitio entre el güero Margarito y Luis Cervantes, enfrente de Demetrio.

Entre los cristales, porcelanas y búcaros de flores, abundaban las botellas de tequila.

El Meco entró sudoroso y renegando, con una caja de cervezas a cuestas. 15

—Ustedes no conocen todavía a este güero —dijo la Pintada reparando en que él no quitaba los ojos de la novia de Luis Cervantes—. Tiene mucha sal, y en el mundo no he visto gente más acabada que él. 20

Le lanzó una mirada lúbrica y añadió:

—¡Por eso no lo puedo ver ni pintado!°

Rompió la orquesta una rumbosa marcha taurina.

Los soldados bramaron de alegría.

—¡Qué menudo, mi general!... Le juro que en mi vida he comido otro más bien guisado —dijo el güero Margarito, e hizo reminiscencias del Delmónico de Chihuahua. 25

—¿Le gusta de veras, güero? —repuso Demetrio—. Pos que le sirvan hasta que llene.

—Ese es mi mero gusto —confirmó Anastasio Montañés—, y eso es lo bonito; de que a mí me cuadra un guiso,° como, como, hasta que lo eructo. 30

¡Por... pintado! That's why I can't stand the sight of him!
de... guiso if I like a stew

Siguió un ruido de bocazas y grandes tragantadas. Se bebió copiosamente.

Al final, Luis Cervantes, tomó una copa de champaña y se puso de pie:

—Señor general...

—¡Hum! —interrumpió la Pintada—. Hora va de discurso, y eso es cosa que a mí me aburre mucho. Voy mejor al corral, al cabo ya no hay que comer.

Luis Cervantes ofreció el escudo de paño negro con una aguilita de latón amarillo, en un brindis que nadie entendió, pero que todos aplaudieron con estrépito.

Demetrio tomó en sus manos la insignia de su nuevo grado y, muy encendido, la mirada brillante, relucientes los dientes, dijo con mucha ingenuidad:

—¿Y qué voy a hacer ahora yo con este zopilote?

—Compadre —pronunció trémulo y en pie Anastasio Montañés—, yo no tengo que decirle...

Transcurrieron minutos enteros; las malditas palabras no querían acudir al llamado del compadre Anastasio. Su cara enrojecida perlaba el sudor en su frente, costrosa de mugre. Por fin se resolvió a terminar su brindis:

—Pos yo tengo que decirle... sino que ya sabe que soy su compadre...

Y como todos habían aplaudido a Luis Cervantes, el propio Anastasio, al acabar, dio la señal, palmoteando con mucha gravedad.

Pero todo estuvo bien y su torpeza sirvió de estímulo. Brindaron el Manteca y la Codorniz.

Llegaba su turno al Meco, cuando se presentó la Pintada dando fuertes voces de júbilo. Chasqueando la lengua, pretendía meter al comedor una bellísima yegua de un negro azabache.

—¡Mi "avance"! ¡Mi "avance"! —clamaba palmoteando el cuello enarcado del soberbio animal.

La yegua se resistía al franquear la puerta; pero un tirón del cabestro y un latigazo en el anca la hicieron entrar con brío y estrépito.

Los soldados, embebecidos, contemplaban con mal reprimida envidia la rica presa.

—¡Yo no sé qué carga esta diabla de Pintada que siempre nos gana los mejores "avances"!° —clamó el güero Margarito—. Así la verán desde que se nos juntó en Tierra Blanca.

—Epa, tú, Pancracio, anda a traerme un tercio de alfalfa pa mi yegua —ordenó secamente la Pintada.

Luego tendió la soga hacia un soldado.

Una vez más llenaron los vasos y las copas. Algunos comenzaban a doblar el cuello y a entrecerrar los ojos; la mayoría gritaba jubilosa.

Y entre ellos la muchacha de Luis Cervantes, que había tirado todo el vino en un pañuelo, tornaba de una parte a la otra sus grandes ojos azules, llenos de azoro.

—Muchachos —gritó de pie el güero Margarito, dominando con su voz aguda y gutural el vocerío—, estoy cansado de vivir y me han dado ganas° ahora de matarme. La Pintada ya me hartó ... y este querubincito del cielo no arrienda siquiera a verme ...

Luis Cervantes notó que las últimas palabras iban dirigidas a su novia, y con gran sorpresa vino a cuentas de que el pie que sentía entre los de la muchacha no era de Demetrio, sino del güero Margarito.

Y la indignación hirvió en su pecho.

—¡Fíjense, muchachos —prosiguió el güero con el revólver en lo alto—; me voy a pegar un tiro en la merita frente!

Y apuntó al gran espejo del fondo, donde se veía de cuerpo entero.

—¡No te buigas, Pintada! ...

¡Yo ... "avances"! I don't know what this she-devil's got, but she always beats us to the best loot!

me ... ganas I feel like

El espejo se estrelló en largos y puntiagudos fragmentos. La bala había pasado rozando los cabellos de la Pintada, que ni pestañeó siquiera.

IV

Al atardecer despertó Luis Cervantes, se restregó los ojos y se incorporó. Se encontraba en el suelo duro, entre los tiestos del huerto. Cerca de él respiraban ruidosamente, muy dormidos, Anastasio Montañés, Pancracio y la Codorniz.

Sintió los labios hinchados y la nariz dura y seca; se miró sangre en las manos y en la camisa, e instantámeamente hizo memoria de lo ocurrido. Pronto se puso de pie y se encaminó hacia una recámara; empujó la puerta repetidas veces, sin conseguir abrirla. Mantúvose indeciso algunos instantes.

Porque todo era cierto; estaba seguro de no haber soñado. De la mesa del comedor se había levantado con su compañera, la condujo a la recámara; pero antes de cerrar la puerta, Demetrio, tambaleándose de borracho, se precipitó tras ellos. Luego la Pintada siguió a Demetrio, y comenzaron a forcejear. Demetrio, con los ojos encendidos como una brasa y hebras cristalinas en los burdos labios, buscaba con avidez a la muchacha. La Pintada, a fuertes empellones, lo hacía retroceder.

—¡Pero tú qué! ... ¿Tú qué? ... —ululaba Demetrio irritado.

La Pintada metió la pierna entre las de él, hizo palanca y Demetrio cayó de largo, fuera del cuarto.

Se levantó furioso.

—¡Auxilio! ... ¡Auxilio! ... ¡Que me mata! ...

La Pintada cogía vigorosamente la muñeca de Demetrio y desviaba el cañón de su pistola.

La bala se incrustó en los ladrillos. La Pintada seguía berreando. Anastasio Montañés llegó detrás de Demetrio y lo desarmó. Éste, como toro a media plaza, volvió sus ojos extraviados. Le rodeaban Luis Cervantes, Anastasio, el Manteca y otros muchos.

—¡Infelices! . . . ¡Me han desarmado! . . . ¡Como si pa ustedes se necesitaran armas!

Y abriendo los brazos, en brevísimos instantes volteó de narices sobre el enladrillado al que alcanzó.

¿Y después? Luis Cervantes no recordaba más. Seguramente que allí se habían quedado bien aporreados y dormidos. Seguramente que su novia, por miedo a tanto bruto, había tomado la sabia providencia de encerrarse.

"Tal vez esa recámara comunique con la sala y por ella pueda entrar", pensó.

A sus pasos despertó la Pintada, que dormía cerca de Demetrio, sobre la alfombra y al pie de un confidente colmado de alfalfa y maíz donde la yegua negra cenaba.

—¿Qué busca? —preguntó la muchacha—. ¡Ah, sí; ya sé lo que quiere! . . . ¡Sinvergüenza! . . . Mire, encerré a su novia porque ya no podía aguantar a este condenado de Demetrio. Coja la llave, allí está sobre la mesa.

En vano Luis Cervantes buscó por todos los escondrijos de la casa.

—A ver, curro, cuénteme cómo estuvo eso de esa muchacha.

Luis Cervantes, muy nervioso, seguía buscando la llave.

—No coma ansia, hombre, allá se la voy a dar. Pero cuénteme . . . A mí me divierten mucho estas cosas. Esa currita es igual a usté . . . No es pata rajada como nosotros.

—No tengo qué contar . . . Es mi novia y ya.

—¡Ja, ja, ja! . . . ¡Su novia y . . . no! Mire, curro, adonde usté va yo ya vengo.° Tengo el colmillo duro. A esa pobre la sacaron de su casa entre el Manteca y el Meco; eso ya lo sabía . . . ; pero usté les ha de haber dado por ella . . . algunas mancuernillas chapeadas . . . alguna estampita milagrosa del Señor de la Villita . . . ¿Miento, curro? . . . ¡Que los hay, los hay!° . . . ¡El trabajo es dar con ellos! . . . ¿Verdad?

adonde . . . vengo I know what you're up to.

¡Que . . . hay! As to whether there are people like that or not, there certainly are!

La Pintada se levantó a darle la llave; pero tampoco la encontró y se sorprendió mucho.

Estuvo largo rato pensativa.

De repente salió a toda carrera hacia la puerta de la recámara, aplicó un ojo a la cerradura y allí se mantuvo inmóvil hasta que su vista se hizo a la oscuridad del cuarto. De pronto, y sin quitar los ojos, murmuró:

—¡Ah, güero . . . jijo de un . . . ! ¡Asómese no más, curro!

Y se alejó, lanzando una sonora carcajada.

—¡Si le digo que en mi vida he visto hombre más acabado que éste!

Otro día por la mañana, la Pintada espió el momento en que el güero salía de la recámara a darle de almorzar a su caballo.

—¡Criatura de Dios! . . . ¡Anda, vete a tu casa! . . . Estos hombres son capaces de matarte! . . . ¡Anda, corre! . . .

Y sobre la chiquilla de grandes ojos azules y semblante de virgen, que sólo vestía camisón y medias, echó la frazada piojosa del Manteca; la cogió de la mano y la puso en la calle.

—¡Bendito sea Dios! —exclamó—. Ahora sí . . . ¡Cómo quiero yo a este güero!

V

Como los potros que relinchan y retozan a los primeros truenos de mayo, así van por la sierra los hombres de Demetrio.

—¡A Moyahua, muchachos!

—A la tierra de Demetrio Macías.

—¡A la tierra de don Mónico el cacique!

El paisaje se aclara, el sol asoma en una faja escarlata sobre la diafanidad del cielo.

Vanse destacando las cordilleras como monstruos alagartados, de angulosa vertebradura; cerros que parecen testas de colosales ídolos aztecas, caras de gigantes, muecas pavorosas y grotescas, que ora hacen sonreír, ora dejan un vago terror, algo como presentimiento de misterio.

A la cabeza de la tropa va Demetrio Macías con su Estado

Mayor: el coronel Anastasio Montañés, el teniente coronel Pancracio y los mayores Luis Cervantes y el güero Margarito.

Siguen en segunda fila la Pintada y Venancio, que la galantea con muchas finezas, recitándole poéticamente versos desesperados de Antonio Plaza.

Cuando los rayos del sol bordearon los pretiles del caserío, de cuatro en fondo y tocando los clarines, comenzaron a entrar a Moyahua.

Cantaban los gallos a ensordecer, ladraban con alarma los perros; pero la gente no dio señales de vida en parte alguna.

La Pintada azuzó su yegua negra y de un salto se puso codo a codo con Demetrio. Muy ufana, lucía vestido de seda y grandes arracadas de oro; el azul pálido del talle acentuaba el tinte aceitunado de su rostro y las manchas cobrizas de la avería. Perniabierta, su falda se remangaba hasta la rodilla y se veían sus medias deslavadas y con muchos agujeros. Llevaba revólver al pecho y una cartuchera cruzada sobre la cabeza de la silla.

Demetrio también vestía de gala: sombrero galoneado, pantalón de gamuza con botonadura de plata y chamarra bordada de hilo de oro.

Comenzó a oírse el abrir forzado de las puertas. Los soldados, diseminados ya por el pueblo, recogían armas y monturas por todo el vecindario.

—Nosotros vamos a hacer la mañana a casa de don Mónico —pronunció con gravedad Demetrio, apeandose y tendiendo las riendas de su caballo a un soldado—. Vamos a almorzar con don Mónico... un amigo que me quiere mucho...

Su Estado Mayor sonríe con risa siniestra.

Y, arrastrando ruidosamente las espuelas por las banquetas, se encaminaron hacia un caserón pretencioso, que no podía ser sino albergue de cacique.

—Está cerrada a piedra y cal —dijo Anastasio Montañés empujando con toda su fuerza la puerta.

—Pero yo sé abrir —repuso Pancracio abocando prontamente su fusil al pestillo.

—No, no —dijo Demetrio—; toca primero.

Tres golpes con la culata del rifle, otros tres y nadie responde. Pancracio se insolenta y no se atiene a más órdenes. Dispara, salta la chapa y se abre la puerta.

Vense extremos de faldas, piernas de niños, todos en dispersión hacia el interior de la casa.

—¡Quiero vino! ... ¡Aquí, vino! ... —pide Demetrio con voz imperiosa, dando fuertes golpes sobre la mesa.

—Siéntense, compañeros.

Una señora asoma, luego otra y otra, y entre las faldas negras aparecen cabezas de niños asustados. Una de las mujeres, temblando, se encamina hacia un aparador, saca copas y botellas y sirve vino.

—¿Qué armas tienen?—inquiere Demetrio con aspereza.

—¿Armas? ... —contesta la señora, la lengua hecha trapo—. ¿Pero qué armas quieren ustedes que tengan unas señoras solas y decentes?

—¡Ah, solas! ... ¿Y don Mónico? ...

—No está aquí, señores ... Nosotras sólo rentamos la casa ... Al señor don Mónico no más de nombre lo conocemos.

Demetrio manda que se practique un cateo.

—No, señores, por favor ... Nosotras mismas vamos a traerles lo que tenemos; pero, por el amor de Dios, no nos falten al respeto. ¡Somos niñas solas y decentes!

—¿Y los chamacos? —inquiere Pancracio brutalmente—. ¿Nacieron de la tierra?

Las señoras desaparecen con precipitación y vuelven momentos después con una escopeta astillada, cubierta de polvo y de telarañas, y una pistola de muelles enmohecidas y descompuestas.

Demetrio se sonríe.

—Bueno, a ver el dinero ...

—¿Dinero? ... Pero ¿qué dinero quieren ustedes que tengan unas pobres niñas solas?

Y vuelven sus ojos suplicatorios hacia el más cercano de los soldados; pero luego los aprietan con horror: ¡han visto al sayón que está crucificando a Nuestro Señor Jesucristo en el vía crucis de la parroquia!... ¡Han visto a Pancracio!...

Demetrio ordena el cateo.

A un tiempo se precipitan otra vez las señoras, y al instante vuelven con una cartera apolillada, con unos cuantos billetes de los de la emisión de Huerta.

Demetrio sonríe, y ya sin más consideraciones, hace entrar a su gente.

Como perros hambrientos que han olfateado su presa, la turba penetra, atropellando a las señoras, que pretenden defender la entrada con sus propios cuerpos. Unas caen desvanecidas, otras huyen; los chicos dan gritos.

Pancracio se dispone a romper la cerradura de un gran ropero, cuando las puertas se abren solas y de dentro saltà un hombre con un fusil en las manos.

—¡Don Mónico! —exclaman sorprendidos.

—¡Hombre, Demetrio!... ¡No me haga nada!... ¡No me perjudique!... ¡Soy su amigo, don Demetrio!...

Demetrio Macías se ríe socarronamente y le pregunta si a los amigos se les recibe con el fusil en las manos.

Don Mónico, confuso, aturdido, se echa a sus pies, le abraza las rodillas, le besa los pies:

—¡Mi mujer!... ¡Mis hijos!... ¡Amigo don Demetrio!...

Demetrio, con mano trémula, vuelve el revólver a la cintura.

Una silueta dolorida ha pasado por su memoria. Una mujer con su hijo en los brazos, atravesando por las rocas de la sierra a media noche y a la luz de la luna...

Una casa ardiendo...

—¡Vámonos!... ¡Afuera todos! —clama sombríamente.

Su Estado Mayor obedece; don Mónico y las señoras le besan las manos y lloran de agradecimiento.

En la calle la turba está esperando alegre y dicharachera el permiso del general para saquear la casa del cacique.

—Yo sé muy bien dónde tienen escondido el dinero, pero no lo digo —pronuncia un muchacho con un cesto bajo el brazo.

—¡Hum, yo ya sé! —repone una vieja que lleva un costal para recoger "lo que Dios le quiera dar"—. Está en un altito; allí hay muchos triques y entre los triques una petaquilla con dibujos de concha... ¡Allí mero está lo güeno!° ...

5 —No es cierto —dice un hombre—; no son tan tarugos para dejar así la plata. A mi modo de ver, la tienen enterrada en el pozo en un tenate de cuero.

Y el gentío se remueve, unos con sogas para hacer sus fardos, otros con bateas; las mujeres extienden sus delantales o el extremo 10 de sus rebozos, calculando lo que les puede caber. Todos, dando las gracias a su Divina Majestad, esperan su buena parte de saqueo.

Cuando Demetrio anuncia que no permitirá nada y ordena que todos se retiren, con gesto desconsolado la gente del pueblo lo obedece y se disemina luego; pero entre la soldadesca hay un sordo 15 rumor de desaprobación y nadie se mueve de su sitio.

Demetrio, irritado, repite que se vayan.

Un mozalbete de los últimos reclutados, con algún aguardiente en la cabeza, se ríe y avanza sin zozobra hacia la puerta.

Pero antes de que pueda franquear el umbral, un disparo ins- 20 tantáneo lo hace caer como los toros heridos por la puntilla.

Demetrio, con la pistola humeante en las manos, inmutable, espera que los soldados se retiren.

—Que se le pegue fuego a la casa —ordenó a Luis Cervantes cuando llegan al cuartel.

25 Y Luis Cervantes, con rara solicitud, sin transmitir la orden, se encargó de ejecutarla personalmente.

Cuando dos horas después la plazuela se ennegrecía de humo y de la casa de don Mónico se alzaban enormes lenguas de fuego, nadie comprendió el extraño proceder del general.

VI

30 Se habían alojado en una casona sombría, propiedad del mismo cacique de Moyahua.

Sus predecesores en aquella finca habían dejado ya su rastro

¡Allí ... güeno! Right in there is where the valuables are!

vigoroso en el patio, convertido en estercolero; en los muros, desconchados hasta mostrar grandes manchones de adobe crudo; en los pisos, demolidos por las pezuñas de las bestias; en el huerto, hecho un reguero de hojas marchitas y ramajes secos. Se tropezaba, desde el entrar, con pies de muebles, fondos y respaldos de sillas, todo sucio de tierra y bazofia.

A las diez de la noche, Luis Cervantes bostezó muy aburrido y dijo adiós al güero Margarito y a la Pintada, que bebían sin descanso en una banca de la plaza.

Se encaminó al cuartel. El único cuarto amueblado era la sala. Entró, y Demetrio, que estaba tendido en el suelo, los ojos claros y mirando al techo, dejó de contar las vigas y volvió la cara.

—¿Es usted, curro?... ¿Qué trae?... Ande, entre, siéntese.

Luis Cervantes fue primero a despabilar la vela, tiró luego de un sillón sin respaldo y cuyo asiento de mimbres había sido substituído con un áspero cotense. Chirriaron las patas de la silla y la yegua prieta de la Pintada bufó y se removió en la sombra, describiendo con su anca redonda y tersa una gallarda curva.

Luis Cervantes se hundió en el asiento y dijo:

—Mi general, vengo a darle cuenta de la comisión... Aquí tiene...

—Hombre, curro... ¡si yo no quería eso!... Moyahua casi es mi tierra... ¡Dirán que por eso anda uno aquí!... —respondió Demetrio mirando el saco apretado de monedas que Luis le tendía.

Este dejó el asiento para venir a ponerse en cuclillas al lado de Demetrio. Tendió un sarape en el suelo y sobre él vació el talego de hidalgos relucientes como ascuas de oro.

—En primer lugar, mi general, esto lo sabemos sólo usted y yo... Y por otra parte, ya sabe que al buen sol hay que abrirle la ventana... Hoy nos está dando de cara; pero ¿mañana?... Hay que ver siempre adelante. Una bala, el reparo de un caballo, hasta un ridículo resfrío... ¡y una viuda y unos huérfanos en la miseria!... ¿El Gobierno? ¡Ja, ja, ja!... Vaya usted con Carranza, con Villa o con cualquier otro de los jefes principales y hábleles de su familia... Si le responden con un puntapié... donde usted ya sabe, diga que le fue de perlas... Y hacen bien, mi general; nosotros no nos hemos levantado en armas para que un tal Carranza o un tal Villa lleguen a presidentes de la República; nosotros peleamos en defensa de los sagrados derechos del pueblo, pisoteados por el vil cacique... Y así como ni Villa, ni Carranza, ni ningún otro han de venir a pedir nuestro consentimiento para pagarse los servicios que le están prestando a la patria, tampoco nosotros tenemos necesidad de pedirle licencia a nadie.

Demetrio se medio incorporó, tomó una botella cerca de su cabecera, empinó y luego, hinchando los carrillos, lanzó una bocanada a lo lejos.

—¡Qué pico largo es usted, curro!

Luis sintió un vértigo. La cerveza regada parecía avivar la fermentación del basurero donde reposaban: un tapiz de cáscaras de naranjas y plátanos, carnosas cortezas de sandía, hebrosos núcleos de mangos y bagazos de caña, todo revuelto con hojas enchiladas de tamales y todo húmedo de deyecciones.

Los dedos callosos de Demetrio iban y venían sobre las brillantes monedas a cuenta y cuenta.

Repuesto ya, Luis Cervantes sacó un botecito de fosfatina Falliéres y volcó dijes, anillos, pendientes y otras muchas alhajas de valor.

—Mire, mi general; si, como parece, esta bola va a seguir, si la Revolución no se acaba, nosotros tenemos ya lo suficiente para irnos a brillarla° una temporada fuera del país.

Demetrio meneó la cabeza negativamente.

—¿No haría usted eso? ... Pues ¿a qué nos quedaríamos ya? ... ¿Qué causa defenderíamos ahora?

—Eso es cosa que yo no puedo explicar, curro; pero siento que no es cosa de hombres...

—Escoja, mi general —dijo Luis Cervantes mostrando las joyas puestas en fila.

—Déjelo todo para usted... De veras, curro... ¡Si viera que no

para ... brillarla to go and live in fine style

le tengo amor al dinero! . . . ¿Quiere que le diga la verdad? Pues yo, con que no me falte el trago y con traer una chamaquita que me cuadre, soy el hombre más feliz del mundo.

—¡Ja, ja, ja! . . . ¡Qué mi general! . . . Bueno, ¿y por qué se aguanta a esa sierpe de la Pintada? 5

—Hombre, curro, me tiene harto; pero así soy. No me animo a decírselo . . . No tengo valor para despacharla a . . . Yo soy así, ése es mi genio. Mire, de que me cuadra una mujer, soy tan boca de palo, que si ella no comienza . . . , yo no me animo a nada.

Y suspiró. 10

—Ahí está Camila, la del ranchito . . . La muchachita es fea; pero si viera cómo me llena el ojo . . .

—El día que usted quiera, nos la vamos a traer, mi general.

Demetrio guiñó los ojos con malicia.

—Le juro que se la hago buena,° mi general . . . 15

—¿De veras, curro? . . . Mire, si me hace esa valedura, pa usté es el reló con todo y leopoldina de oro,° ya que le cuadra tanto.

Los ojos de Luis Cervantes resplandecieron. Tomó el bote de fosfatina, ya bien lleno, se puso en pie y, sonriendo, dijo:

—Hasta mañana, mi general . . . Que pase buena noche. 20

VII

—¿Yo qué sé? Lo mismo que ustedes saben. Me dijo el general: "Codorniz, ensilla tu caballo y mi yegua mora. Vas con el curro a una comisión." Bueno, así fue: salimos de aquí a mediodía y, ya anocheciendo, llegamos al ranchito. Nos dio posada la tuerta María Antonia . . . Que cómo estás tanto,° Pancracio . . . En la 25 madrugada me despertó el curro: "Codorniz, Codorniz, ensilla las bestias. Me dejas mi caballo y te vuelves con la yegua del general otra vez para Moyahua. Dentro de un rato te alcanzo."

se . . . buena I'll do it right for you
el . . . oro both the watch and the gold chain
Que . . . tanto She asked about you a lot

Y ya estaba el sol alto cuando llegó con Camila en la silla. La apeó y la montamos en la yegua mora.

—Bueno, y ella, ¿qué cara venía poniendo? —preguntó uno.

—¡Hum, pos no le paraba la boca de tan contenta! . . .

5 —¿Y el curro?

—Callado como siempre; igual a como es él.

—Yo creo —opinó con mucha gravedad Venancio— que si Camila amaneció en la cama de Demetrio, sólo fue por una equivocación. Bebimos mucho . . . ¡Acuérdense! . . . Se nos subieron

10 los espíritus alcohólicos a la cabeza y todos perdimos el sentido.

—¡Qué espíritus alcohólicos ni qué!° . . . Fue cosa convenida entre el curro y el general.

—¡Claro! . . . Pa mí el tal curro no es más que un . . .

—A mí no me gusta hablar de los amigos en ausencia —dijo

15 el güero Margarito—; pero sí sé decirles que de dos novias que le he conocido, una ha sido para . . . mí y la otra para el general . . .

Y prorrumpieron en carcajadas.

Luego que la Pintada se dio cuenta cabal de lo sucedido, fue muy cariñosa a consolar a Camila.

20 —¡Pobrecita de ti, platícame cómo estuvo eso!

Camila tenía los ojos hinchados de llorar.

—¡Me mintió, me mintió! . . . Fue al rancho y me dijo: "Camila, vengo no más por ti. ¿Te sales conmigo?" ¡Hum, dígame si yo no tendría ganas de salirme con él! De quererlo, lo quero

25 y lo requero . . . ¡Míreme tan encanijada sólo por estar pensando en él! Amanece y ni ganas del metate . . . Me llama mi mamá al almuerzo, y la gorda se me hace trapo en la boca . . . ¡Y aquella pinción! . . . ¡Y aquella pinción! . . .

Y comenzó a llorar otra vez, y para que no se oyeran sus sollo-

30 zos se tapaba la boca y la nariz con un extremo del rebozo.

—Mira, yo te voy a sacar de esta apuración. No seas tonta, ya no llores. Ya no pienses en el curro . . . ¿Sabes lo que es ese curro? . . . ¡Palabra! . . . ¡Te digo que no más para eso lo trae el general! . . . ¡Qué tonta! . . . Bueno, ¿quieres volver a tu casa?

¡Qué . . . qué! Alcoholic spirits, baloney!

—¡La Virgen de Jalpa me ampare!... ¡Me mataría mi mamá a palos!

—No te hace nada. Vamos haciendo una cosa. La tropa tiene que salir de un momento a otro; cuando Demetrio te diga que te prevengas para irnos, tú le respondes que tienes muchas dolencias de cuerpo, y que estás como si te hubieran dado de palos, y te estiras y bostezas muy seguido. Luego te tientas la frente y dices: "Estoy ardiendo en calentura." Entonces yo le digo a Demetrio que nos deje a las dos, que yo me quedo a curarte y que luego que estés buena nos vamos a alcanzarlo. Y lo que hacemos es que yo te pongo en tu casa buena y sana.

VIII

Ya el sol se había puesto y el caserío se envolvía en la tristeza gris de sus calles viejas y en el silencio de terror de sus moradores, recogidos a muy buena hora, cuando Luis Cervantes llegó a la tienda de Primitivo López a interrumpir una juerga que prometía grandes sucesos. Demetrio se emborrachaba allí con sus viejos camaradas. El mostrador no podía contener más gente. Demetrio, la Pintada y el güero Margarito habían dejado afuera sus caballos; pero los demás oficiales se habían metido brutalmente con todo y cabalgaduras. Los sombreros galoneados de cóncavas y colosales faldas se encontraban en vaivén constante; caracoleaban las ancas de las bestias, y sin cesar removían sus finas cabezas de ojazos negros, narices palpitantes y orejas pequeñas. Y en la infernal alharaca de los borrachos se oía el resoplar de los caballos, su rudo golpe de pezuñas en el pavimento y, de vez en vez, un relincho breve y nervioso.

Cuando Luis Cervantes llegó, se comentaba un suceso banal. Un paisano, con un agujerito negruzco y sanguinolento en la frente, estaba tendido boca arriba en medio de la carretera. Las opiniones, divididas al principio, ahora se unificaban bajo una justísima reflexión del güero Margarito. Aquel pobre diablo que yacía bien muerto era el sacristán de la iglesia. Pero, ¡tonto!... La culpa había sido suya... ¿Pues a quién se le ocurre, señor, vestir pantalón, chaqueta y gorrita? ¡Pancracio no puede ver un catrín enfrente de él!

Ocho músicos "de viento", las caras rojas y redondas como soles, desorbitados los ojos, echando los bofes por los latones desde la
5 madrugada, suspenden su faena al mandato de Cervantes.

—Mi general —dijo éste abriéndose paso entre los montados—, acaba de llegar un propio de urgencia. Le ordenan a usted que salga inmediatamente a perseguir a los orozquistas.

Los semblantes, ensombrecidos un momento, brillaron de ale-
10 gría.

—¡A Jalisco, muchachos! —gritó el güero Margarito dando un golpe seco sobre el mostrador.

—¡Aprevénganse, tapatías de mi alma, que allá voy yo! ° —gritó la Codorniz arriscándose el sombrero.

15 Todo fue regocijo y entusiasmo. Los amigos de Demetrio, en la excitación de la borrachera, le ofrecieron incorporarse a las filas. Demetrio no podía hablar de gusto. "¡Ah, ir a batir a los orozquistas!... ¡Habérselas al fin con hombres de veras!... ¡Dejar de matar federales como se matan liebres o guajolotes!"

20 —Si yo pudiera coger vivo a Pascual Orozco —dijo el güero Margarito—, le arrancaba la planta de los pies y lo hacía caminar veinticuatro horas por la sierra...

—¿Qué, ése fue el que mató al señor Madero? —preguntó el Meco.

25 No —repuso el güero con solemnidad—; pero a mí me dio una cachetada cuando fui mesero del Delmónico en Chihuahua.

—Para Camila, la yegua mora —ordenó Demetrio a Pancracio, que estaba ya ensillando.

—Camila no se puede ir —dijo la Pintada con prontitud.

30 —¿Quién te pide a ti tu parecer? —repuso Demetrio con aspereza.

—¿Verdá, Camila, que amaneciste con mucha dolencia de cuerpo y te sientes acalenturada ahora?

¡Aprevénganse... yo! Get ready, you darling Jaliscan girls. I'm on my way!

—Pos yo..., pos yo..., lo que diga don Demetrio...

—¡Ah, qué guaje!... Di que no, di que no... —pronunció a su oído la Pintada con gran inquietud.

—Pos es que ya le voy cobrando voluntá°..., ¿lo cree?... —contestó Camila también muy quedo. 5

La Pintada se puso negra y se le inflamaron los carrillos; pero no dijo nada y se alejó a montar la yegua que le estaba ensillando el güero Margarito.

IX

El torbellino del polvo, prolongado a buen trecho a lo largo de 10 la carretera, rompíase bruscamente en masas difusas y violentas, y se destacaban pechos hinchados, crines revueltas, narices trémulas, ojos ovoides, impetuosos, patas abiertas y como encogidas al impulso de la carrera. Los hombres, de rostro de bronce y dientes de marfil, ojos flameantes, blandían los rifles o los cruzaban sobre 15 las cabezas de las monturas.

Cerrando la retaguardia, y al paso, venían Demetrio y Camila; ella trémula aún, con los labios blancos y secos; él, malhumorado por lo insulso de la hazaña. Ni tales orozquistas, ni tal combate. Unos cuantos federales dispersos, un pobre diablo de cura con un 20 centenar de ilusos, todos reunidos bajo la vetusta bandera de "Religión y Fueros". El cura se quedaba allí bamboleándose, pendiente de un mezquite, y en el campo, un reguero de muertos que ostentaban en el pecho un escudito de bayeta roja y un letrero: "¡Detente! ¡El Sagrado Corazón de Jesús está conmigo!" 25

—La verdá es que yo ya me pagué hasta de más mis sueldos atrasados° —dijo la Codorniz mostrando los relojes y anillos de oro que se habían extraído de la casa cural.

—Así siquiera pelea uno con gusto —exclamó el Manteca entreverando insolencias entre cada frase—. ¡Ya sabe uno por qué 30 arriesga el cuero!

Y cogía fuertemente con la misma mano que empuñaba las

Pos... voluntá. Well, to tell the truth, I'm beginning to like him.

La... atrasados The fact is that I collected even more than my back pay

riendas un reluciente resplandor que le había arrancado al Divino Preso de la iglesia.

Cuando la Codorniz, muy perito en la materia, examinó codiciosamente el "avance" del Manteca, lanzó una carcajada solemne:

—¡Tu resplandor es de hoja de lata!...

—¿Por qué vienes cargando con esa roña? —preguntó Pancracio al güero Margarito, que llegaba de los últimos con un prisionero.

—¿Saben por qué? Porque nunca he visto bien a bien la cara que pone un prójimo cuando se le aprieta una reata en el pescuezo.

El prisionero, muy gordo, respiraba fatigado; su rostro estaba encendido, sus ojos inyectados y su frente goteaba. Lo traían atado de las muñecas y a pie.

—Anastasio, préstame tu reata; mi cabestro se revienta con este gallo... Pero, ahora que lo pienso mejor, no... Amigo federal, te voy a matar de una vez; vienes penando mucho. Mira, los mezquites están muy lejos todavía y por aquí no hay telégrafo siquiera para colgarte de algún poste.

Y el güero Margarito sacó su pistola, puso el cañón sobre la tetilla izquierda del prisionero y paulatinamente echó el gatillo atrás.

El federal palideció como cadáver, su cara se afiló y sus ojos vidriosos se quebraron. Su pecho palpitaba tumultuosamente y todo su cuerpo se sacudía como por un gran calosfrío.

El güero Margarito mantuvo así su pistola durante segundos eternos. Y sus ojos brillaron de un modo extraño, y su cara regordeta, de inflados carrillos, se encendía de una sensación de suprema voluptuosidad.

—¡No, amigo federal! —dijo lentamente retirando el arma y volviéndola a su funda—, no te quiero matar todavía... Vas a seguir como mi asistente... ¡Ya verás si soy hombre de mal corazón!

Y guiñó malignamente sus ojos a sus inmediatos.

El prisionero había embrutecido; sólo hacía movimientos de deglución; su boca y su garganta estaban secas.

Camila, que se había quedado atrás, picó el ijar de su yegua y alcanzó a Demetrio.

—¡Ah, qué malo es el hombre ese Margarito!... ¡Si viera lo que viene haciendo con un preso!

Y refirió lo que acababa de presenciar.

Demetrio contrajo las cejas, pero nada contestó.

La Pintada llamó a Camila a distancia.

—Oye, tú, ¿qué chismes le trais a Demetrio?... El güero Margarito es mi mero amor... ¡Pa que te lo sepas! °... Y ya sabes... Lo que haiga con él, hay conmigo, ¡Ya te lo aviso!...

Y Camila, muy asustada, fue a reunirse con Demetrio.

X

La tropa acampó en una planicie, cerca de tres casitas alineadas que, solitarias, recortaban sus blancos muros sobre la faja purpúrea del horizonte.

Demetrio y Camila fueron hacia ellas.

Dentro del corral, un hombre en camisa y calzón blanco, de pie, chupaba con avidez un gran cigarro de hoja; cerca de él, sentado sobre una losa, otro desgranaba maíz, frotando mazorcas entre sus dos manos, mientras que una de sus piernas, seca y retorcida, remataba en algo como pezuña de chivo, se sacudía a cada instante para espantar a las gallinas.

—Date priesa, Pifanio —dijo el que estaba parado—; ya se metió el sol y todavía no bajas al agua a las bestias.

Un caballo relinchó fuera y los dos hombres alzaron la cabeza azorados.

Demetrio y Camila asomaban tras la barda del corral.

—No más quiero alojamiento para mí y para mi mujer —les dijo Demetrio tranquilizándoles.

Y como les explicara que él era el jefe de un cuerpo de ejército que iba a pernoctar en las cercanías, el hombre que estaba en pie, y que era el amo, con mucha solicitud los hizo entrar. Y corrió por un apaste de agua y una escoba, pronto a barrer y regar el

¡Pa... sepas! Get this straight!

mejor rincón de la troje para alojar decentemente a tan honorables huéspedes.

—Anda, Pifanio; desensilla los caballos de los señores.

El hombre que desgranaba se puso trabajosamente en pie. Vestía 5 unas garras de camisa y chaleco, una piltrafa de pantalón, abierto en dos alas, cuyos extremos, levantados, pendían de la cintura.

Anduvo, y su paso marcó un compás grotesco.

—Pero ¿puedes tú trabajar, amigo? —le preguntó Demetrio sin dejarlo quitar las monturas.

10 —¡Pobre —gritó el amo desde el interior de la troje—, le falta la juerza! ... ¡Pero viera qué bien desquita el salario! ... ¡Trabaja dende que Dios amanece! ... ¡Que ha que se metió el sol° ..., y mírelo, no para todavía!

Demetrio salió con Camila a dar una vuelta por el campamento. 15 La planicie, de dorados barbechos, rapada hasta de arbustos, se dilataba inmensa en su desolación. Parecían un verdadero milagro los tres grandes fresnos enfrente de las casitas, sus cimas verdinegras, redondas y ondulosas, su follaje rico, que descendía hasta besar el suelo.

20 —¡Yo no sé qué siento por acá que me da tanta tristeza! —dijo Demetrio.

—Sí —contestó Camila—; lo mismo a mí.

A orillas de un arroyuelo, Pifanio estaba tirando rudamente de la soga de un bambilete. Una olla enorme se volcaba sobre un 25 montón de hierba fresca, y a las postreras luces de la tarde cintilaba el chorro de cristal desparramándose en la pila. Allí bebían ruidosamente una vaca flaca, un caballo matado y un burro.

Demetrio reconoció al peón cojitranco y le preguntó:

—¿Cuánto ganas diario, amigo?

30 —Diez y seis centavos, patrón ...

Era un hombrecillo rubio, escrofuloso, de pelo lacio y ojos zarcos. Echó pestes del patrón, del rancho y de la perra suerte.

—Desquitas bien el sueldo, hijo —le interrumpió Demetrio con

¡Que ... sol The sun set quite a while ago

mansedumbre—. A reniega y reniega, pero a trabaja y trabaja.°

Y volviéndose a Camila.

—Siempre hay otros más pencos que nosotros los de la sierra, ¿verdad?

—Sí —contestó Camila.

Y siguieron caminando.

El valle se perdió en la sombra y las estrellas se escondieron.

Demetrio estrechó a Camila amorosamente por la cintura, y quién sabe qué palabras susurró a su oído.

—Sí —contestó ella débilmente.

Porque ya le iba cobrando "voluntá".

Demetrio durmió mal, y muy temprano se echó fuera de la casa.

"A mí me va a suceder algo" pensó.

Era un amanecer silencioso y de discreta alegría. Un tordo piaba tímidamente en el fresno; los animales removían las basuras del rastrojo en el corral; gruñía el cerdo su somnolencia. Asomó el tinte anaranjado del sol, y la última estrellita se apagó.

Demetrio, paso a paso, iba al campamento.

Pensaba en su yunta: dos bueyes prietos, nuevecitos, de dos años de trabajo apenas, en sus dos fanegas de labor bien abonadas. La fisonomía de su joven esposa se reprodujo fielmente en su memoria: aquellas líneas dulces y de infinita mansedumbre para el marido, de indomables energías y altivez para el extraño. Pero cuando pretendió reconstruir la imagen de su hijo, fueron vanos todos sus esfuerzos; lo había olvidado.

Llegó al campamento. Tendidos entre los surcos, dormían los soldados, y revueltos con ellos, los caballos echados, caída la cabeza y cerrados los ojos.

—Están muy estragadas las remudas, compadre Anastasio; es bueno que nos quedemos a descansar un día siquiera.

—¡Ay, compadre Demetrio! ... ¡Qué ganas ya de la sierra! Si viera ..., ¿a que no me lo cree? ... pero naditita que me jallo

A . . . trabaja. You grumble and grumble but you keep on working.

por acá... ¡Una tristeza y una murria!... ¡Quién sabe qué le hará a uno falta!° ...

—¿Cuántas horas se hacen de aquí a Limón?

—No es cosa de horas: son tres jornadas muy bien hechas, com-
5 padre Demetrio.

—¡Si viera!... ¡Tengo ganas de ver a mi mujer!

No tardó mucho la Pintada en ir a buscar a Camila:

—¡Ujule, újule!... Sólo por eso que ya Demetrio te va a largar. A mí, a mí mero me lo dijo... Va a traer a su mujer de veras...
10 Y es muy bonita, muy blanca... ¡Unos chapetes!... Pero si tú no te queres ir, pué que hasta te ocupen: tienen una criatura y tú la puedes cargar...

Cuando Demetrio regresó, Camila, llorando, se lo dijo todo.

—No le hagas caso a esa loca... Son mentiras, son mentiras...
15 Y como Demetrio no fue a Limón ni se volvió a acordar de su mujer, Camila estuvo muy contenta y la Pintada se volvió un alacrán.

XI

Antes de la madrugada salieron rumbo a Tepatitlán. Diseminados por el camino real y por los barbechos, sus siluetas ondulaban
20 vagamente al paso monótono y acompasado de las caballerías, esfumándose en el tono perla de la luna en menguante, que bañaba todo el valle.

Se oía lejanísimo ladrar de perros.

—Hoy a mediodía llegamos a Tepatitlán, mañana a Cuquío, y
25 luego..., a la sierra —dijo Demetrio.

—¿No sería bueno, mi general —observó a su oído Luis Cervantes—, llegar primero a Aguascalientes?

—¿Qué vamos a hacer allá?

—Se nos están agotando los fondos...
30 —¡Cómo!... ¿Cuarenta mil pesos en ocho días?

pero... falta! but nothing strikes me right here. I feel sad and I'm bored. I have no idea what it is that I miss.

—Sólo en esta semana hemos reclutado cerca de quinientos hombres, y en anticipos y gratificaciones se nos ha ido todo —repuso muy bajo Luis Cervantes.

—No; vamos derecho a la sierra... Ya veremos...

—¡Sí, a la sierra! —clamaron muchos.

—¡A la sierra!... ¡A la sierra!... No hay como la sierra.

La planicie seguía oprimiendo sus pechos; hablaron de la sierra con entusiasmo y delirio, y pensaron en ella como en la deseada amante a quien se ha dejado de ver por mucho tiempo.

Clareó el día. Después, una polvareda de tierra roja se levantó hacia el oriente, en una inmensa cortina de púrpura incendiada.

Luis Cervantes templó la brida de su caballo y esperó a la Codorniz.

—¿En qué quedamos, pues, Codorniz?°

—Ya le dije, curro: doscientos por el puro reló.

—No, yo te compro a bulto: relojes, anillos y todas las alhajitas. ¿Cuánto?

La Codorniz vaciló, se puso descolorido; luego dijo con ímpetu:

—Deque dos mil papeles por todo.

Pero Luis Cervantes se dejó traicionar; sus ojos brillaron con tan manifiesta codicia, que la Codorniz volvió sobre sus pasos y exclamó pronto:

—No, mentiras, no vendo nada... El puro reló, y eso porque ya debo los doscientos pesos a Pancracio, que anoche me ganó otra vez.

Luis Cervantes sacó cuatro flamantes billetes de "dos caritas" y los puso en manos de la Codorniz.

—De veras —le dijo—, me intereso al lotecito... Nadie te dará más de lo que yo te dé.

Cuando comenzó a sentirse el sol, el Manteca gritó de pronto:

—Güero Margarito, ya tu asistente quiere pelar gallo. Dice que ya no puede andar.

El prisionero se había dejado caer, exhausto, en medio del camino.

¿En... Codorniz? Well, what's the last word on our deal, Codorniz?

—¡Calla! —clamó el güero Margarito retrocediendo—. ¿Conque ya te cansaste, simpático? ¡Pobrecito de ti! Voy a comprar un nicho de cristal para guardarte en una rinconera de mi casa, como Niño Dios. Pero es necesario llegar primero al pueblo, y para esto te voy a ayudar.

Y sacó el sable y descargó sobre el infeliz repetidos golpes.

—A ver la reata, Pancracio —dijo luego, brillantes y extraños los ojos.

Pero como la Codorniz le hiciera notar que ya el federal no movía ni pie ni mano, dio una gran carcajada y dijo:

—¡Qué bruto soy!... ¡Ahora que lo tenía enseñado a no comer!...

—Ahora sí, ya llegamos a Guadalajara chiquita —dijo Venancio descubriendo el caserío risueño de Tepatitlán, suavemente recostado en una colina.

Entraron regocijados; a las ventanas asomaban rostros sonrosados y bellos ojos negros.

Las escuelas quedaron convertidas en cuarteles. Demetrio se alojó en la sacristía de una capilla abandonada.

Después los soldados se desperdigaron, como siempre, en busca de "avances", so pretexto de recoger armas y caballos.

Por la tarde, algunos de los de la escolta de Demetrio estaban tumbados en el atrio de la iglesia rascándose la barriga. Venancio, con mucha gravedad, pecho y espaldas desnudos, espulgaba su camisa.

Un hombre se acercó a la barda, pidiendo la venia de hablarle al jefe.

Los soldados levantaron la cabeza, pero ninguno le respondió.

—Soy viudo, señores; tengo nueve criaturas y no vivo más que de mi trabajo... ¡No sean ingratos con los pobres!...

—Por mujer no te apures, tío —dijo el Meco, que con un cabo de vela se embadurnaba los pies—; ai traimos a la Pintada, y te la pasamos al costo.

El hombre sonrió amargamente.

—No más que tiene una maña —observó Pancracio, boca arriba

y mirando el azul del cielo—: apenas mira un hombre, y luego luego se prepara.

Rieron a carcajadas; pero Venancio, muy grave, indicó la puerta de la sacristía al paisano.

Este, tímidamente, entró y expuso a Demetrio su queja. Los soldados acababan de "limpiarlo". Ni un grano de maíz le habían dejado.

—Pos ¿pa qué se dejan?° —le respondió Demetrio con indolencia.

Luego el hombre insistió con lamentos y lloriqueos, y Luis Cervantes se dispuso a echarlo fuera insolentemente. Pero Camila intervino:

—¡Ande, don Demetrio, no sea usté también mal alma; déle una orden pa que le devuelvan su maíz!...

Luis Cervantes tuvo que obedecer; escribió unos renglones, y Demetrio, al calce, puso un garabato.

—¡Dios se lo pague, niña!... Dios se lo ha de dar de su santísima gloria°... Diez fanegas de maíz, apenas pa comer este año —clamó el hombre, llorando de agradecimiento. Y tomó el papel y a todos les besó las manos.

XII

Iban llegando ya a Cuquío, cuando Anastasio Montañés se acercó a Demetrio y le dijo:

—Ande, compadre, ni le he contado... ¡Qué travieso es de veras el güero Margarito! ¿Sabe lo que hizo ayer con el hombre que vino a darle la queja de que le habíamos sacado su maíz para nuestros caballos? Bueno, pos con la orden que usté le dio fue al cuartel. "Sí, amigo, le dijo el güero; entra para acá; es muy justo devolverte lo tuyo. Entra, entra... ¿Cuántas fanegas te robamos? ... ¿Diez? ¿Pero estás seguro de que no son más que diez?... Sí, eso es; como quince, poco más o menos... ¿No serían veinte? ... Acuérdate bien... Eres muy pobre, tienes muchos hijos que

Pos... dejan? Well, why should they leave it?
Dios... gloria. God will grant you a place in Heaven.

mantener. Sí, es lo que digo, como veinte; ésas deben haber sido... Pasa por acá; no te voy a dar ni quince, ni veinte. Tú no más vas contando... Una, dos, tres... Y luego que ya no quieras, me dices: ya". Y saca el sable y le ha dado una cintareada que lo hizo 5 pedir misericordia.

La Pintada se caía de risa.

Y Camila, sin poderse contener, dijo:

—¡Viejo condenado, tan mala entraña!... ¡Con razón no lo puedo ver!

10 Instantáneamente se demudó el rostro de la Pintada.

—¿Y a ti te da tos por eso?°

Camila tuvo miedo y adelantó su yegua.

La Pintada disparó la suya y rapidísima, al pasar atropellando a Camila la cogió de la cabeza y le deshizo la trenza.

15 Al empellón, la yegua de Camila se encabritó y la muchacha abandonó las riendas por quitarse los cabellos de la cara; vaciló, perdió el equilibrio y cayó en un pedregal, rompiéndose la frente.

Desmorecida de risa, la Pintada, con mucha habilidad, galopó a 20 detener la yegua desbocada.

¡Ándale, curro, ya te cayó trabajo!°— dijo Pancracio luego que vio a Camila en la misma silla de Demetrio, con la cara mojada de sangre.

Luis Cervantes, presuroso, acudió con sus materiales de cura-25 ción; pero Camila, dejando de sollozar, se limpió los ojos y dijo con voz apagada:

—¿De usté?... ¡Aunque me estuviera muriendo!... ¡Ni agua!...

En Cuquío recibió Demetrio un propio.

30 —Otra vez a Tepatitlán, mi general—dijo Luis Cervantes pasando rápidamente sus ojos por el oficio—. Tendrá que dejar allí la gente, y usted a Lagos, a tomar el tren de Aguascalientes.

Hubo protestas calurosas; algunos serranos juraron que ellos

¿Y... eso? And what's that to you?

¡Ándale... trabajo! Come, Tenderfoot, here's a job for you!

no seguirían ya en la columna, entre gruñidos, quejas y rezongos.

Camila lloró toda la noche, y otro día, por la mañana, dijo a Demetrio que ya le diera licencia de volverse a su casa.

—¡Si le falta voluntá!° ... —contestó Demetrio hosco.

—No es eso, don Demetrio; voluntá se la tengo y mucha ..., pero ya lo ha estado viendo ... ¡Esa mujer! ...

—No se apure, hoy mismo la despacho. Ya lo tengo bien pensado.

Camila dejó de llorar.

Todos estaban ensillando ya. Demetrio se acercó a la Pintada y le dijo en voz muy baja:

—Tú ya no te vas con nosotros.

—¿Qué dices? —inquirió ella sin comprender.

—Que te quedas aquí o te largas adonde te dé la gana, pero no con nosotros.

—¿Qué estás diciendo? —exclamó ella con asombro—. ¿Es decir, que tú me corres? ¡Ja!, ¡ja!, ¡ja! ... Pues que ... ¡tal serás tú si te andas creyendo de los chismes de esa ... !°

Y la Pintada insultó a Camila, a Demetrio, a Luis Cervantes y a cuantos le vinieron a las mientes, con tal energía y novedad, que la tropa oyó injurias e insolencias que no había sospechado siquiera.

Demetrio esperó largo rato con paciencia; pero como ella no diera trazas de acabar, con mucha calma dijo a un soldado:

—Echa fuera a esa borracha.

—¡Güero Margarito! ¡Güero de mi vida! ¡Ven a defenderme de estos ... ! ¡Anda, güerito de mi corazón! ... ¡Ven a enseñarles que tú eres hombre de veras y ellos no son más que unos hijos de ... !

Y gesticulaba, pateaba y daba de gritos.

El güero Margarito apareció. Acababa de levantarse; sus ojos azules se perdían bajo unos párpados hinchados y su voz estaba ronca. Se informó del sucedido y, acercándose a la Pintada, le dijo con mucha gravedad:

¡Si ... voluntá! If you don't like me, all right!
¡tal ... esa! You're a fool if you go on believing the lies that that woman tells you!

—Sí, me parece muy bien que ya te largues mucho a la... ¡A todos nos tienes hartos!°

El rostro de la Pintada se granitificó. Quiso hablar, pero sus músculos estaban rígidos.

5 Los soldados reían divertidísimos; Camila, muy asustada, contenía la respiración.

La Pintada paseó sus ojos en torno. Y todo fue en un abrir y cerrar de ojos: se inclinó, sacó una hoja aguda y brillante de entre la media y la pierna y se lanzó sobre Camila.

10 Un grito estridente y un cuerpo que se desploma arrojando sangre a borbotones.

—Mátenla —gritó Demetrio fuera de sí.

Dos soldados se arrojaron sobre la Pintada que, esgrimiendo el puñal, no les permitió tocarla.

15 —¡Ustedes no, infelices!... Mátame tú, Demetrio. Se adelantó, entregó su arma, irguió el pecho y dejó caer los brazos.

Demetrio puso en alto el puñal tinto en sangre; pero sus ojos se nublaron, vaciló, dio un paso atrás.

Luego con voz apagada y ronca, gritó:

20 —¡Lárgate!... ¡Pero luego!...

Nadie se atrevió a detenerla.

Se alejó muda y sombría, paso a paso.

Y el silencio y la estupefacción lo rompió la voz aguda y gutural del güero Margarito:

25 —¡Ah, qué bueno!... ¡Hasta que se me despegó esta chinche!°...

XIII

En la medianía del cuerpo
una daga me metió,
sin saber por qué
30 *ni por qué sé yo...*

Sí... hartos! Yes, it's a good idea for you to clear out of here. We've all had enough of you.

¡Hasta... chinche! At last I'm rid of that louse!

El sí sabía,
pero yo no...

Y de aquella herida mortal
mucha sangre me salió,
sin saber por qué
ni por qué sé yo...
El sí lo sabía,
pero yo no...

Caída la cabeza, las manos cruzadas sobre la montura, Demetrio tarareaba con melancólico acento la tonadilla obsesionante.

Luego callaba; largos minutos se mantenía en silencio y pesaroso.

—Ya verá cómo llegando a Lagos le quito esa murria, mi general. Allí hay muchachas bonitas para darnos gusto —dijo el güero Margarito.

—Ahora sólo tengo gana de ponerme una borrachera —contestó Demetrio.

Y se alejó otra vez de ellos, espoleando su caballo, como si quisiera abandonarse todo a su tristeza.

Después de muchas horas de caminar, hizo venir a Luis Cervantes:

—Oiga, curro, ahora que lo estoy pensando, yo ¿qué pitos voy a tocar° a Aguascalientes?

—A dar su voto, mi general, para Presidente provisional de la República.

—¿Presidente provisional?... Pos entonces, ¿qué... tal es, pues, Carranza?... La verdad, yo no entiendo estas políticas...

Llegaron a Lagos. El güero apostó a que esa noche haría reír a Demetrio a carcajadas.

Arrastrando las espuelas, las chivarras caídas abajo de la cintura, entró Demetrio a "El Cosmopolita", con Luis Cervantes, el güero Margarito y sus asistentes.

—¿Por qué corren, curros?... ¡No sabemos comer gente! —exclamó el güero.

yo... tocar what am I supposed to do

Los paisanos, sorprendidos en el mismo momento de escapar, se detuvieron; unos, con disimulo, regresaron a sus mesas a seguir bebiendo y charlando, y otros, vacilantes, se adelantaron a ofrecer sus respetos a los jefes.

5 —¡Mi general! ... ¡Mucho gusto! ... ¡Señor mayor! ...

—¡Eso es! ... Así me gustan los amigos, finos y decentes —dijo el güero Margarito.

—Vamos, muchachos —agregó, sacando su pistola jovialmente—; ahí les va un buscapiés para que lo toreen.°

10 Una bala rebotó en el cemento, pasando entre las patas de las mesas y las piernas de los señoritos, que saltaron asustados como dama a quien se le ha metido un ratón bajo la falda.

Pálidos, sonríen para festejar debidamente al señor mayor. Demetrio despliega apenas sus labios, mientras que el acompaña-
15 miento lanza carcajadas a pierna tendida.

—Güero —observa la Codorniz—, a ése que va saliendo le prendió la avispa°; mira cómo cojea.

El güero, sin parar mientes ni volver siquiera la cara hacia el herido, afirma con entusiasmo que a treinta pasos de distancia
20 y al descubrir le pega a un cartucho de tequila.

—A ver, amigo, párese —dice al mozo de la cantina. Luego, de la mano lo lleva a la cabecera del patio del hotel y le pone un cartucho lleno de tequila en la cabeza.

El pobre diablo resiste, quiere huir, espantado, pero el güero
25 prepara su pistola y apunta.

—¡A tu lugar ... tasajo! O de veras te meto una calentita.°

El güero se vuelve a la pared opuesta, levanta su arma y hace puntería. El cartucho se estrella en pedazos, bañando de tequila la cara del muchacho, descolorido como un muerto.

30 —¡Ahora va de veras! —clama, corriendo a la cantina por un nuevo cartucho, que vuelve a colocar sobre la cabeza del mancebo.

ahí . . . toreen there's a foot-chaser for you to dodge
le . . . avispa got stung
O . . . calentita. Or I'll really give you a hot one.

Torna a su sitio, da una vuelta vertiginosa sobre los pies, y al descubrir, dispara.

Sólo que ahora se ha llevado una oreja en vez del cartucho.

Y apretándose el estómago de tanto reír, dice al muchacho:

—Toma, chico, esos billetes. ¡Es cualquier cosa! Eso se quita con tantita árnica y aguardiente...

Después de beber mucho alcohol y cerveza, habla Demetrio:

—Pague, güero... Ya me voy...

—No traigo ya nada, mi general; pero no hay cuidado por eso... ¿Qué tanto se te debe, amigo?

—Ciento ochenta pesos, mi jefe —responde amablemente el cantinero.

El güero salta prontamente el mostrador, y en dos manotadas derriba todos los frascos, botellas y cristalería.

—Ai le pasas la cuenta a tu padre Villa, ¿sabes?

Y sale dando estrepitosas carcajadas.

—Oiga, amigo, ¿dónde queda el barrio de las muchachas? —pregunta tambaleándose de borracho, a un sujeto pequeño, correctamente vestido, que está cerrando la puerta de una sastrería.

El interpelado se baja de la banqueta atentamente para dejar libre el paso.

El güero se detiene y lo mira con impertinencia y curiosidad:

—Oiga, amigo, ¡qué chiquito y qué bonito es usted! ... ¿Cómo que no? ... ¿Entonces yo soy mentiroso? ... Bueno, así me gusta ... ¿Usted sabe bailar los enanos? ... ¿Que no sabe? ... ¡Resabe! ... ¡Yo lo conocí a usted en un circo! ¡Le juro que sí sabe y muy rebién! ... ¡Ahora lo verá! ...

El güero saca su pistola y comienza a disparar hacia los pies del sastre, que, muy gordo y muy pequeño, a cada tiro da un saltito.

—¿Ya ve cómo sí sabe bailar los enanos?

Y echando los brazos a espaldas de sus amigos, se hace conducir hacia el arrabal de gente alegre, marcando su paso a balazos en los focos de las esquinas, en las puertas y en las casas del poblado. Demetrio lo deja y regresa al hotel, tarareando entre los dientes:

En la medianía del cuerpo
una daga me metió,
sin saber por qué
ni por qué sé yo...

XIV

Humo de cigarro, olor penetrante de ropas sudadas, emanaciones alcohólicas y el respirar de una multitud: hacinamiento peor que el de un carro de cerdos. Predominan los de sombrero tejano, toquilla de galón y vestidos de kaki.

—Caballeros, un señor decente me ha robado mi petaca en la estación de Silao. Los ahorros de toda mi vida de trabajo. No tengo para darle de comer a mi niño.

La voz era aguda, chillona y plañidera; pero se extinguía a corta distancia en el vocerío que llenaba el carro.

—¿Qué dice esa vieja? —preguntó el güero Margarito entrando en busca de un asiento.

—Que una petaca... que un niño decente... —respondió Pancracio, que ya había encontrado las rodillas de unos paisanos para sentarse.

Demetrio y los demás se abrían paso a fuerza de codos. Y como los que soportaban a Pancracio prefirieran abandonar los asientos y seguir de pie, Demetrio y Luis Cervantes los aprovecharon gustosos.

Una señora que venía parada desde Irapuato con un niño en brazos sufrió un desmayo. Un paisano se aprontó a tomar en sus manos a la criatura. El resto no se dio por entendido: las hembras de tropa ocupaban dos o tres asientos cada una con maletas, perros, gatos y cotorras. Al contrario, los de sombrero tejano rieron mucho de la robustez de muslos y laxitud de pechos de la desmayada.

—Caballeros, un señor decente me ha robado mi petaca en la estación de Silao... Los ahorros de toda mi vida de trabajo... No tengo ahora ni para darle de comer a mi niño...

La vieja habla de prisa y automáticamente, suspira y solloza.

Sus ojos, muy vivos, se vuelven de todos lados. Y aquí recoge un billete, y más allá otro. Le llueven en abundancia.

Acaba una colecta y adelanta unos cuantos asientos:

—Caballeros, un señor decente me ha robado mi petaca en la estación de Silao...

El efecto de sus palabras es seguro e inmediato.

¡Un señor decente! ¡Un señor decente que se roba una petaca! ¡Eso es incalificable! Eso despierta un sentimiento de indignación general. ¡Oh, es lástima que ese señor decente no esté a la mano para que lo fusilen siquiera cada uno de los generales que van allí!

—Porque a mí no hay cosa que me dé tanto coraje como un curro ratero —dice uno reventando de dignidad.

—¡Robar a una pobre señora!

—¡Robar a una infeliz mujer que no puede defenderse!

Y todos manifiestan el enternecimiento de su corazón de palabra y de obra: una insolencia para el ladrón y un bilimbique de cinco pesos para la víctima.

—Yo, la verdad les digo, no creo que sea malo matar, porque cuando uno mata lo hace siempre con coraje; ¿pero robar?... —clama el güero Margarito.

Todos parecen asentir ante tan graves razones; pero tras breve silencio y momentos de reflexión, un coronel aventura su parecer:

—La verdá es que todo tiene sus "asigunes".° ¿Para qué es más que la verdá? La puritita verdá es que yo he robao... y si digo que todos los que venimos aquí hemos hecho lo mesmo, se me afigura que no echo mentiras...

—¡Hum, pa las máquinas de coser que yo me robé en México! —exclamó con ánimo un mayor—. Junté más de quinientos pesos con ser que vendí hasta a cincuenta centavos máquina.

—Yo me robé en Zacatecas unos caballos tan finos, que dije acá pa mí: "Lo que es de este hecho ya te armaste,° Pascual Mata; no te vuelves a apurar por nada en los días que de vida te quedan" —dijo un capitán desmolado y ya blanco de canas—. Lo malo fue

La... "asigunes". The fact is that everything has its own peculiar circumstances.

Lo... armaste As far as this job goes, you're set for life

que mis caballos le cuadraron a mi general Limón y él me los robó a mí.

—¡Bueno! ¡A qué negarlo, pues! Yo también he robado —asintió el güero Margarito—; pero aquí están mis compañeros que digan cuánto he hecho de capital. Eso sí, mi gusto es gastarlo todo con las amistades. Para mí es más contento ponerme una papalina con todos los amigos que mandarles un centavo a las viejas de mi casa...

El tema del "yo robé", aunque parece inagotable, se va extinguiendo cuando en cada banca aparecen tendidos de naipes, que atraen a jefes y oficiales como la luz a los mosquitos.

Las peripecias del juego pronto lo absorben todo y caldean el ambiente más y más; se respira el cuartel, la cárcel y hasta la zahurda.

Y dominando el barullo general, se escucha, allá en el otro carro: "Caballeros, un señor decente me ha robado mi petaca..."

Las calles de Aguascalientes se habían convertido en basureros. La gente de kaki se removía, como las abejas a la boca de una colmena, en las puertas de los restaurantes, fonduchos y mesones, en las mesas de comistrajos y puestos al aire libre, donde al lado de una batea de chicharrones rancios se alzaba un montón de quesos mugrientos.

El olor de las frituras abrió el apetito de Demetrio y sus acompañantes. Penetraron a fuerza de empellones a una fonda, y una vieja desgreñada y asquerosa les sirvió en platos de barro huesos de cerdos nadando en un caldillo claro de chile y tres tortillas correosas y quemadas. Pagaron dos pesos por cada uno, y al salir Pancracio aseguró que tenía más hambre que antes de haber entrado.

—Ahora sí —dijo Demetrio— vamos a tomar consejo de mi general Natera.

Y siguieron una calle hacia la casa que ocupaba el jefe norteño.

Un revuelto y agitado grupo de gentes les detuvo el paso en una bocacalle. Un hombre que se perdía entre la multitud clamaba en sonsonete y con acento uncioso algo que parecía un rezo. Se acercaron hasta descubrirlo. El hombre, de camisa y calzón blanco, repetía: "Todos los buenos católicos que recen con devoción esta oración a Cristo Crucificado se verán libres de tempestades, de pestes, de guerras y de hambres..."

—Este sí que la acertó° —dijo Demetrio sonriendo.

El hombre agitaba en alto un puñado de impresos y decía:

—Cincuenta centavos la oración a Cristo Crucificado, cincuenta centavos...

Luego desaparecía un instante para levantarse de nuevo con un colmillo de víbora, una estrella de mar, un esqueleto de pescado. Y con el mismo acento rezandero, ponderaba las propiedades medicinales y raras virtudes de cada cosa.

La Codorniz, que no le tenía fe a Venancio, pidió al vendedor que le extrajera una muela; el güero Margarito compró un núcleo negro de cierto fruto que tiene la propiedad de librar a su poseedor tan bien del rayo como de cualquier "malhora", y Anastasio Montañés una oración a Cristo Crucificado, que cuidadosamente dobló y con gran piedad guardó en el pecho.

—¡Cierto como hay Dios, compañero; sigue la bola! ¡Ahora Villa contra Carranza! —dijo Natera.

Y Demetrio, sin responderle, con los ojos muy abiertos, pedía más explicaciones.

—Es decir —insistió Natera—, que la Convención desconoce a Carranza como Primer Jefe y va a elegir un presidente provisional de la República... ¿Entiende, compañero?

Demetrio inclinó la cabeza en señal de asentimiento.

—¿Qué dice de eso, compañero? —interrogó Natera.

Demetrio se alzó de hombros.

—Se trata, a lo que parece, de seguir peleando. Bueno, pos a darle°; ya sabe, mi general, que por mi lado no hay portillo.

—Bien, ¿y de parte de quién se va a poner?

Demetrio, muy perplejo, se llevó las manos a los cabellos y se rascó breves instantes.

Este ... acertó This fellow's certainly got the right idea
Bueno ... darle All right, let's go to it

—Mire, a mí no me haga preguntas, que no soy escuelante... La aguilita que traigo en el sombrero usté me la dió... Bueno, pos ya sabe que no más me dice: "Demetrio, haces esto y esto y esto... ¡y se acabó el cuento!"

TERCERA PARTE

I

"El Paso, Tex., mayo 16 de 1915.

Muy estimado Venancio:

Hasta ahora puedo contestar° su grata de enero del corriente año debido a que mis atenciones profesionales absorben todo mi tiempo. Me recibí en diciembre pasado, como usted lo sabe. Lamento la suerte de Pancracio y del Manteca; pero no me extraña que después de una partida de naipes se hayan apuñalado. ¡Lástima: eran unos valientes! Siento en el alma no poder comunicarme con el güero Margarito para hacerle presente mi felicitación más calurosa, pues el acto más noble y más hermoso de su vida fue ése . . . ¡ el de suicidarse!

Me parece difícil, amigo Venancio, que pueda usted obtener el título de médico que ambiciona tanto aquí en los Estados Unidos, por más que haya reunido suficiente oro y plata para comprarlo. Yo le tengo estimación, Venancio, y creo que es muy digno de mejor suerte. Ahora bien, me ocurre una idea que podría favorecer nuestros mutuos intereses y las ambiciones justas que usted tiene por cambiar de posición social. Si usted y yo nos asociáramos, podríamos hacer un negocio muy bonito. Cierto que por el momento yo no tengo fondos de reserva, porque todo lo he agotado en mis estudios y en mi recepción; pero cuento con algo que vale mucho más que el dinero: mi conocimiento perfecto de esta plaza, de sus necesidades y de los negocios seguros que pueden empren-

Hasta . . . contestar Only now am I able to answer

derse. Podríamos establecer un restaurante netamente mexicano, apareciendo usted como el propietario y repartiéndonos las utilidades a fin de cada mes. Además, algo relativo a lo que tanto nos interesa: su cambio de esfera social. Yo me acuerdo que usted toca bastante bien la guitarra, y creo fácil, por medio de mis recomendaciones y de los conocimientos musicales de usted, conseguirle el ser admitido como miembro de la Salvation Army, sociedad respetabilísima que le daría a usted mucho carácter.

No vacile, querido Venancio; véngase con los fondos y podemos hacernos ricos en muy poco tiempo. Sírvase dar mis recuerdos afectuosos al General, a Anastasio y demás amigos.

Su amigo que lo aprecia,

Luis Cervantes".

Venancio acabó de leer la carta por centésima vez, y, suspirando, repitió su comentario:

—¡Este curro de veras que la supo hacer! °

—Porque lo que yo no podré hacerme entrar en la cabeza —observó Anastasio Montañés— es eso de que tengamos que seguir peleando... ¿Pos no acabamos ya con la Federación?

Ni el General ni Venancio contestaron; pero aquellas palabras siguieron golpeando en sus rudos cerebros como un martillo sobre el yunque.

Ascendían la cuesta, al tranco largo de sus mulas, pensativos y cabizbajos. Anastasio, inquieto y terco, fue con la misma observación a otros grupos de soldados, que reían de su candidez. Porque si uno trae un fusil en las manos y las cartucheras llenas de tiros, seguramente que es para pelear. ¿Contra quién? ¿En favor de quiénes? ¡Eso nunca le ha importado a nadie!

La polvareda ondulosa e interminable se prolongaba por las opuestas direcciones de la vereda, en un hormiguero de sombreros de palma, viejos kakis mugrientos, frazadas musgas y el negrear movedizo de las caballerías.

La gente ardía de sed. Ni un charco, ni un pozo, ni un arroyo

¡Este . . . hacer! That tenderfoot certainly knew how to manage things!

con agua por todo el camino. Un vaho de fuego se alzaba de los blancos eriales de una cañada, palpitaba sobre las crespas cabezas de los huizaches y las glaucas pencas de los nopales. Y como una mofa, las flores de los cactos se abrían frescas, carnosas y encendidas las unas, aceradas y diáfanas las otras. 5

Tropezaron al mediodía con una choza prendida a los riscos de la sierra; luego, con tres casucas regadas sobre las márgenes de un río de arena calcinada; pero todo estaba silencioso y abandonado. A la proximidad de la tropa, las gentes se escurrían a ocultarse en las barrancas. 10

Demetrio se indignó:

—A cuantos descubran escondidos o huyendo, cójanlos y me los traen —ordenó a sus soldados con voz desafinada.

—¡Cómo!... ¿Qué dice? —exclamó Valderrama sorprendido—. ¿A los serranos? ¿A esos valerosos que no han imitado a 15 las gallinas que ahora anidan en Zacatecas y Aguascalientes? ¿A los hermanos nuestros que desafían las tempestades adheridos a sus rocas como la madrepeña? ¡Protesto!... ¡Protesto!...

Hincó las espuelas en los ijares de su mísero rocín y fue a alcanzar al general. 20

—Los serranos —le dijo con énfasis y solemnidad —son carne de nuestra carne y huesos de nuestros huesos... "Os ex ossibus meis et caro de carne mea"... Los serranos están hechos de nuestra madera... De esta madera firme con la que se fabrican los héroes... 25

Y con una confianza tan intempestiva como valiente, dio un golpe con su puño cerrado sobre el pecho del general, que sonrió con benevolencia.

¿Valderrama, vagabundo, loco y un poco poeta, sabía lo que decía? 30

Cuando los soldados llegaron a una ranchería y se arremolinaron con desesperación en torno de casas y jacales vacíos, sin encontrar una tortilla dura, ni un chile podrido, ni unos granos de sal para ponerle a la tan aborrecida carne fresca de res, ellos, los hermanos pacíficos, desde sus escondites, impasibles los unos con la impasi- 35 bilidad pétrea de los ídolos aztecas, más humanos los otros, con una sórdida sonrisa en sus labios untados y ayunos de barba, veían cómo aquellos hombres feroces que un mes antes hicieran retemblar de espanto sus míseros y apartados solares, ahora salían de sus chozas, donde las hornillas estaban apagadas y las tinajas secas, abatidos, con la cabeza caída y humillados como perros a quienes se arroja de su propia casa a puntapiés.

Pero el general no dio contraorden y unos soldados le llevaron cuatro fugitivos bien trincados.

II

—¿Por qué se esconden ustedes? —interrogó Demetrio a los prisioneros.

—No nos escondemos, mi jefe; seguimos nuestra vereda.

—¿Adónde?

—A nuestra tierra... Nombre de Dios, Durango.

—¿Es éste el camino de Durango?

—Por los caminos no puede transitar gente pacífica ahora. Usted lo sabe, mi jefe.

—Ustedes no son pacíficos; ustedes son desertores. ¿De dónde vienen? —prosiguió Demetrio observándolos con ojo penetrante.

Los prisioneros se turbaron, mirándose perplejos sin encontrar pronta respuesta.

—¡Son carranclanes! —notó uno de los soldados.

Aquello devolvió instantáneamente la entereza a los prisioneros. No existía más para ellos el terrible enigma que desde el principio se les había formulado con aquella tropa desconocida.

—¿Carrancistas nosotros? —contestó uno de ellos con altivez—. ¡Mejor puercos!...

—La verdad, sí, somos desertores —dijo otro—; nos le cortamos a mi general Villa de este lado de Celaya, después de la cuereada que nos dieron.

—¿Derrotado el general Villa?... ¡Ja!, ¡ja!, ¡ja!...

Los soldados rieron a carcajadas. Pero a Demetrio se le contrajo la frente como si algo muy negro hubiera pasado por sus ojos.

—¡No nace todavía el hijo de la... que tenga que derrotar a mi general Villa!° —clamó con insolencia un veterano de cara cobriza con una cicatriz de la frente a la barba.

Sin inmutarse, uno de los desertores se quedó mirándolo fijamente, y dijo:

—Yo lo conozco a usted. Cuando tomamos Torreón, usted andaba con mi general Urbina. En Zacatecas venía ya con Natera y allí se juntó con los de Jalisco... ¿Miento?

El efecto fue brusco y definitivo. Los prisioneros pudieron entonces dar una detallada relación de la tremenda derrota de Villa en Celaya.

Se les escuchó en un silencio de estupefacción.

Antes de reanudar la marcha se encendieron lumbres donde asar carne de toro. Anastasio Montañés, que buscaba leños entre los huizaches, descubrió a lo lejos y entre las rocas la cabeza tusada del caballuco de Valderrama.

—¡Vente ya, loco, que al fin no hubo pozole!... —comenzó a gritar.

Porque Valderrama, poeta romántico, siempre que de fusilar se hablaba, sabía perderse lejos y durante todo un día.

Valderrama oyó la voz de Anastasio y debió haberse convencido de que los prisioneros habían quedado en libertad, porque momentos después estaba cerca de Venancio y de Demetrio.

—¿Ya sabe usted las nuevas? —le dijo Venancio con mucha gravedad.

—No sé nada.

—¡Muy serias! ¡Un desastre! Villa derrotado en Celaya por Obregón. Carranza triunfando por todas partes. ¡Nosotros arruinados!

El gesto de Valderrama fue desdeñoso y solemne como gesto de emperador:

—¿Villa?... ¿Obregón?... ¿Carranza?... ¡X... Y... Z...!

¡No... Villa! The son of a — who can beat General Villa hasn't been born yet!

¿Qué se me da a mí? ... ¡Amo la Revolución como amo al volcán que irrumpe! ¡Al volcán porque es volcán; a la Revolución porque es Revolución! ... Pero las piedras que quedan arriba o abajo, después del cataclismo, ¿qué me importan a mí? ...

5 Y como al brillo del sol de mediodía reluciera sobre su frente el reflejo de una blanca botella de tequila, volvió grupas y con el alma henchida de regocijo se lanzó hacia el portador de tamaña maravilla.

—Le tengo voluntá a este loco —dijo Demetrio sonriendo—, 10 porque a veces dice unas cosas que lo pone a uno a pensar.

Se reanudó la marcha, y la desazón se tradujo en un silencio lúgubre. La otra catástrofe venía realizándose callada, pero indefectiblemente. Villa derrotado era un dios caído. Y los dioses caídos, ni son dioses ni son nada.

15 Cuando la Codorniz habló, sus palabras fueron fiel trasunto del sentir común:

—¡Pos hora sí, muchachos... cada araña por su hebra!° ...

III

Aquel pueblecillo, a igual que congregaciones, haciendas y rancherías, se había vaciado en Zacatecas y Aguascalientes.

20 Por tanto, el hallazgo de un barril de tequila por uno de los oficiales fue acontecimiento de la magnitud del milagro. Se guardó profunda reserva, se hizo mucho misterio para que la tropa saliera otro día, a la madrugada, al mando de Anastasio Montañés y de Venancio; y cuando Demetrio despertó al son de la música, su 25 Estado Mayor, ahora integrado en su mayor parte por jóvenes ex federales, le dio la noticia del descubrimiento, y la Codorniz, interpretando los pensamientos de sus colegas, dijo axiomáticamente:

—Los tiempos son malos y hay que aprovechar, porque "si hay 30 días que nada el pato, hay días que ni agua bebe".

La música de cuerda tocó todo el día y se le hicieron honores solemnes al barril; pero Demetrio estuvo muy triste, "sin saber

cada ... hebra every spider's got to spin his own web

por qué, ni por qué sé yo", repitiendo entre dientes y a cada instante su estribillo.

Por la tarde hubo peleas de gallos. Demetrio y sus principales jefes se sentaron bajo el cobertizo del portalillo municipal, frente a una plazuela inmensa, poblada de yerbas, un quiosco vetusto y podrido y las casas de adobe solitarias.

—¡Valderrama!—llamó Demetrio, apartando con fastidio los ojos de la pista—. Venga a cantarme *El enterrador.*

Pero Valderrama no le oyó, porque en vez de atender a la pelea, monologaba extravagante, mirando ponerse el sol tras de los cerros, diciendo con voz enfática y solemne gesto:

—"¡Señor, Señor, bueno es que nos estemos aquí! ... Levantaré tres tiendas, una para ti, otra para Moisés y otra para Elías".

—¡Valderrama! —volvió a gritar Demetrio—. Cántame *El enterrador.*

—Loco, te habla mi general —lo llamó más cerca uno de los oficiales.

Y Valderrama, con su eterna sonrisa de complacencia en los labios, acudió entonces y pidió a los músicos una guitarra.

—¡Silencio! —gritaron los jugadores. Valderrama dejó de afinar. La Codorniz y el Meco soltaban ya en la arena un par de gallos armados de largas y afiladísimas navajas. Uno era retinto, con hermosos reflejos de obsidiana; el otro, giro, de plumas como escamas de cobre irisado a fuego.

La lucha fue brevísima y de una ferocidad casi humana. Como movidos por un resorte, los gallos se lanzaron al encuentro. Sus cuellos crespos y encorvados, los ojos como corales, erectas las crestas, crispadas las patas, un instante se mantuvieron sin tocar el suelo siquiera, confundidos sus plumajes, picos y garras en uno solo; el retinto se desprendió y fue lanzado patas arriba más allá de la raya. Sus ojos de cinabrio se apagaron, cerráronse lentamente sus párpados coriáceos, y sus plumas esponjadas se estremecieron convulsas en un charco de sangre.

Valderrama, que no había reprimido un gesto de violenta indignación, comenzó a templar. Con los primeros acentos graves se disipó su cólera. Brillaron sus ojos como esos ojos donde resplandece el brillo de la locura. Vagando su mirada por la plazoleta, por el ruinoso quiosco, por el viejo caserío, con la sierra al fondo y el cielo incendiado como techo, comenzó a cantar.

5 Supo darle tanta alma a su voz y tanta expresión a las cuerdas de su vihuela, que, al terminar, Demetrio había vuelto la cara para que no le vieran los ojos.

Pero Valderrama se echó en sus brazos, lo estrechó fuertemente y, con aquella confianza súbita que a todo el mundo sabía tener 10 en un momento dado, le dijo al oído:

—¡Cómaselas!... ¡Esas lágrimas son muy bellas!

Demetrio pidió la botella y se la tendió a Valderrama.

Valderrama apuró con avidez la mitad, casi de un sorbo; luego se volvió a los concurrentes y, tomando una actitud dramática y su 15 entonación declamatoria, exclamó con los ojos rasos:

—¡Y he ahí cómo los grandes placeres de la Revolución se resolvían en una lágrima!...

Después siguió hablando loco, pero loco del todo, con las yerbas empolvadas, con el quiosco podrido, con las casas grises, con el 20 cerro altivo y con el cielo inconmensurable.

IV

Asomó Juchipila a lo lejos, blanca y bañada de sol, en medio del frondaje, al pie de un cerro elevado y soberbio, plegado como turbante.

Algunos soldados, mirando las torrecillas de Juchipila, suspira- 25 ron con tristeza. Su marcha por los cañones era ahora la marcha de un ciego sin lazarillo; se sentía ya la amargura del éxodo.

—¿Ese pueblo es Juchipila? —preguntó Valderrama.

Valderrama, en el primer período de la primera borrachera del día, había venido contando las cruces diseminadas por caminos y 30 veredas, en las escarpaduras de las rocas, en los vericuetos de los arroyos, en las márgenes del río. Cruces de madera negra recién barnizada, cruces forjadas con dos leños, cruces de piedras en montón, cruces pintadas con cal en las paredes derruidas, humildísimas cruces trazadas con carbón sobre el canto de las peñas. El rastro de sangre de los primeros revolucionarios de 1910, asesinados por el Gobierno. Ya a la vista de Juchipila, Valderrama echa pie a tierra, se inclina, dobla la rodilla y gravemente besa el suelo. Los soldados pasan sin detenerse. Unos ríen del loco y otros le dicen alguna cuchufleta.

Valderrama, sin oír a nadie, reza su oración solemnemente:

—¡Juchipila, cuna de la Revolución de 1910, tierra bendita, tierra regada con sangre de mártires, con sangre de soñadores... de los únicos buenos!...

—Porque no tuvieron tiempo de ser malos —completa la frase brutalmente un oficial ex federal que va pasando.

Valderrama se interrumpe, reflexiona, frunce el ceño, lanza una sonora carcajada que resuena por las peñas, monta y corre tras el oficial a pedirle un trago de tequila.

Soldados mancos, cojos, reumáticos y tosigosos dicen mal de Demetrio. Advenedizos de banqueta causan alta con barras de latón en el sombrero, antes de saber siquiera cómo se coge un fusil, mientras que el veterano fogueado en cien combates, inútil ya para el trabajo, el veterano que comenzó de soldado raso, soldado raso es todavía.

Y los pocos jefes que quedan, camaradas viejos de Macías, se indignan también porque se cubren las bajas del Estado Mayor con señoritines de capital, perfumados y peripuestos.

—Pero lo peor de todo —dice Venancio— es que nos estamos llenando de ex federales.

El mismo Anastasio, que de ordinario encuentra muy bien hecho todo lo que su compadre Demetrio hace, ahora, en causa común con los descontentos, exclama:

—Miren, compañeros, yo soy muy claridoso..., y yo le digo a mi compadre que si vamos a tener aquí a los federales siempre, malamente andamos... ¡De veras! ¿A que no me lo creen?... Pero yo no tengo pelos en la lengua,° y por vida de la madre que me parió, que se lo digo a mi compadre Demetrio.

Y se lo dijo. Demetrio lo escuchó con mucha benevolencia, y luego que acabó de hablar, le contestó:

Pero... lengua But I'm not afraid to speak my mind

—Compadre, es cierto lo que usted dice. Malamente andamos: los soldados hablan mal de las clases, las clases de los oficiales y los oficiales de nosotros... Y nosotros estamos ya pa despachar a Villa y a Carranza a la... a que se diviertan solos... Pero se me
5 figura que nos está sucediendo lo que a aquel peón de Tepatitlán. ¿Se acuerda, compadre? No paraba de rezongar de su patrón, pero no paraba de trabajar tampoco. Y así estamos nosotros: a reniega y reniega y a mátenos y mátenos° ... Pero eso no hay que decirlo, compadre...

10 —¿Por qué, compadre Demetrio? ...

—Pos yo no sé... Porque no..., ¿ya me entiende? Lo que ha de hacer es dármele ánimo a la gente. He recibido órdenes de regresar a detener una partida que viene por Cuquío. Dentro de muy poquitos días tenemos que darnos un encontronazo con los
15 carranclanes, y es bueno pegarles ahora hasta por debajo de la lengua.°

Valderrama, el vagabundo de los caminos reales, que se incorporó a la tropa un día, sin que nadie supiera a punto fijo cuándo ni en dónde, pescó algo de las palabras de Demetrio, y como no
20 hay loco que coma lumbre,° ese mismo día desapareció como había llegado.

V

Entraron a las calles de Juchipila cuando las campanas de la iglesia repicaban alegres, ruidosas, y con aquel su timbre peculiar que hacía palpitar de emoción a toda la gente de los Cañones.

25 —Se me figura, compadre, que estamos allá en aquellos tiempos cuando apenas iba comenzando la revolución, cuando llegábamos a un pueblito y nos repicaban mucho, y salía la gente a encontrarnos con músicas, con banderas, y nos echaban muchos vivas y hasta cohetes nos tiraban —dijo Anastasio Montañés.

30 —Ahora ya no nos quieren —repuso Demetrio.

a reniega ... mátenos we keep grumbling and grumbling but we still fight and fight

es ... lengua it will be great to give them a sound thrashing

coma lumbre can stand up under fire

—¡Sí, como vamos ya de "rota batida"!° —observó la Codorniz.

—No es por eso... A los otros tampoco los pueden ver ni en estampa.°

—Pero ¿cómo nos han de querer, compadre?

Y no dijeron más.

Desembocaban en una plaza, frente a la iglesia octogonal, burda y maciza, reminiscencia de tiempos coloniales.

La plaza debía haber sido jardín, a juzgar por sus naranjos escuetos y roñosos, entreverados entre restos de bancas de hierro y madera.

Volvió a escucharse el sonoro y regocijante repique. Luego, con melancólica solemnidad se escaparon del interior del templo las voces melifluas de un coro femenino. A los acordes de un guitarrón, las doncellas del pueblo cantaban los "Misterios".

—¿Qué fiesta tienen ahora, señora? —preguntó Venancio a una vejarruca que a todo correr se encaminaba hacia la iglesia.

—¡Sagrado Corazón de Jesús!—repuso la beata medio ahogándose.

Se acordaron de que hacía un año ya de la toma de Zacatecas. Y todos se pusieron más tristes todavía.

Igual a los otros pueblos que venían recorriendo desde Tepic, pasando por Jalisco, Aguascalientes y Zacatecas, Juchipila era una ruina. La huella negra de los incendios se veía en las casas destechadas, en los pretiles ardidos. Casas cerradas, y una que otra tienda que permanecía abierta era como por sarcasmo, para mostrar sus desnudos armazones, que recordaban los blancos esqueletos de los caballos diseminados por todos los caminos. La mueca pavorosa del hambre estaba ya en las caras terrosas de la gente, en la llama luminosa de sus ojos, que, cuando se detenían sobre un soldado, quemaban con el fuego de la maldición.

Los soldados recorren en vano las calles en busca de comida y se muerden la lengua ardiendo de rabia. Un solo fonducho está

como . . . batida because we are now a beaten army
A . . . estampa. They can't stand the sight of the other side either.

abierto y en seguida se aprieta. No hay frijoles, no hay tortillas: puro chile picado y sal corriente. En vano los jefes muestran sus bolsillos reventando de billetes o quieren ponerse amenazadores.

—¡Papeles, sí! ... ¡Eso nos han traído ustedes! ... ¡Pos eso coman! ...—dice la fondera, una viejota insolente, con una enorme cicatriz en la cara, quien cuenta que "ya durmió en el petate del muerto para no morirse de un susto".°

Y en la tristeza y desolación del pueblo, mientras cantan las mujeres en el templo, los pajarillos no cesan de piar en las arboledas, ni el canto de las currucas deja de oírse en las ramas secas de los naranjos.

VI

La mujer de Demetrio Macías, loca de alegría, salió a encontrarlo por la vereda de la sierra, llevando de la mano al niño.

¡Casi dos años de ausencia!

Se abrazaron y permanecieron mudos; ella embargada por los sollozos y las lágrimas.

Demetrio, pasmado, veía a su mujer envejecida, como si diez o veinte años hubieran transcurrido ya. Luego miró al niño, que clavaba en él sus ojos con azoro. Y su corazón dio un vuelco cuando reparó en la reproducción de las mismas líneas de acero de su rostro y en el brillo flamante de sus ojos. Y quiso atraerlo y abrazarlo; pero el chiquillo, muy asustado, se refugió en el regazo de la madre.

—¡Es tu padre, hijo! ... ¡Es tu padre! ...

El muchacho metía la cabeza entre los pliegues de la falda y se mantenía huraño.

Demetrio, que había dado su caballo al asistente, caminaba a pie y poco a poco con su mujer y su hijo por la abrupta vereda de la sierra.

—¡Hora sí, bendito sea Dios que ya veniste! ... ¡Ya nunca nos dejarás! ¿Verdad? ¿Verdad que ya te vas a quedar con nosotros? ...

"ya ... susto" she was so close to death that nothing can ever frighten her again

La faz de Demetrio se ensombreció.

Y los dos estuvieron silenciosos, angustiados.

Una nube negra se levantaba tras la sierra, y se oyó un trueno sordo. Demetrio ahogó un suspiro. Los recuerdos afluían a su memoria como una colmena.

La lluvia comenzó a caer en gruesas gotas y tuvieron que refugiarse en una rocallosa covacha.

El aguacero se desató con estruendo y sacudió las blancas flores de San Juan, manojos de estrellas prendidos en los árboles, en las peñas, entre la maleza, en los pitahayos y en toda la serranía.

Abajo, en el fondo del cañón y a través de la gasa de la lluvia, se miraban las palmas rectas y cimbradoras; lentamente se mecían sus cabezas angulosas y al soplo del viento se desplegaban en abanicos. Y todo era serranía: ondulaciones de cerros que suceden a cerros, más cerros circundados de montañas y éstas encerradas en una muralla de sierra de cumbres tan altas que su azul se perdía en el zafir.

—¡Demetrio, por Dios!... ¡Ya no te vayas!... ¡El corazón me avisa que ahora te va a suceder algo!...

Y se deja sacudir de nuevo por el llanto.

El niño, asustado, llora a gritos, y ella tiene que refrenar su tremenda pena para contentarlo.

La lluvia va cesando; una golondrina de plateado vientre y alas angulosas cruza oblicuamente los hilos de cristal, de repente iluminados por el sol vespertino.

—¿Por qué pelean ya, Demetrio?

Demetrio, las cejas muy juntas, toma distraído una piedrecita y la arroja al fondo del cañón. Se mantiene pensativo viendo el desfiladero, y dice:

—Mira esa piedra cómo ya no se para...

VII

Fue una verdadera mañana de nupcias. Había llovido la víspera toda la noche y el cielo amanecía entoldado de blancas nubes. Por la cima de la sierra trotaban potrillos brutos de crines alzadas y colas tensas, gallardos con la gallardía de los picachos que levantan su cabeza hasta besar las nubes.

Los soldados caminan por el abrupto peñascal contagiados de la alegría de la mañana. Nadie piensa en la artera bala que puede 5 estarlo esperando más adelante. La gran alegría de la partida estriba cabalmente en lo imprevisto. Y por eso los soldados cantan, ríen y charlan locamente. En su alma rebulle el alma de las viejas tribus nómadas. Nada importa saber adónde van y de dónde vienen; lo necesario es caminar, caminar siempre, no estacionarse 10 jamás; ser dueños del valle, de las planicies, de la sierra y de todo lo que la vista abarca.

Arboles, cactus y helechos, todo aparece acabado de lavar. Las rocas, que muestran su ocre como el orín las viejas armaduras, vierten gruesas gotas de agua transparente.

15 Los hombres de Macías hacen silencio un momento. Parece que han escuchado un ruido conocido: el estallar lejano de un cohete; pero pasan algunos minutos y nada se vuelve a oír.

—En esta misma sierra —dice Demetrio—, yo, sólo con veinte hombres, les hice más de quinientas bajas a los federales... 20 acuerda, compadre Anastasio?

Y cuando Demetrio comienza a referir aquel famoso hecho de armas, la gente se da cuenta del grave peligro que va corriendo. ¿Conque si el enemigo, en vez de estar a dos días de camino todavía, les fuera resultando escondido entre las malezas de aquel 25 formidable barranco, por cuyo fondo se han aventurado? Pero ¿quién sería capaz de revelar su miedo? ¿Cuándo los hombres de Demetrio Macías dijeron: "Por aquí no caminamos?"

Y cuando comienza un tiroteo lejano, donde va la vanguardia, ni siquiera se sorprenden ya. Los reclutas vuelven grupas en des-30 enfrenada fuga buscando la salida del cañón.

Una maldición se escapa de la garganta seca de Demetrio:

—¡Fuego!... ¡Fuego sobre los que corran!...

—¡A quitarles las alturas!° —ruge después como una fiera.

Pero el enemigo, escondido a millaradas, desgrana sus ametra-

¡A... alturas! Drive them from the hills!

lladoras, y los hombres de Demetrio caen como espigas cortadas por la hoz.

Demetrio derrama lágrimas de rabia y de dolor cuando Anastasio resbala lentamente de su caballo, sin exhalar una queja, y se queda tendido, inmóvil. Venancio cae a su lado, con el pecho horriblemente abierto por la ametralladora, y el Meco se desbarranca y rueda al fondo del abismo. De repente Demetrio se encuentra solo. Las balas zumban en sus oídos como una granizada. Desmonta, arrástrase por las rocas hasta encontrar un parapeto, coloca una piedra que le defienda la cabeza y, pecho a tierra, comienza a disparar.

El enemigo se disemina, persiguiendo a los raros fugitivos que quedan ocultos entre los chaparros.

Demetrio apunta y no yerra un solo tiro... ¡Paf!... ¡Paf!... ¡Paf!...

Su puntería famosa lo llena de regocijo; donde pone el ojo pone la bala. Se acaba un cargador y mete otro nuevo. Y apunta...

El humo de la fusilería no acaba de extinguirse. Las cigarras entonan su canto imperturbable y misterioso; las palomas cantan con dulzura en las rinconadas de las rocas; ramonean apaciblemente las vacas.

La sierra está de gala; sobre sus cúspides inaccesibles cae la niebla albísima como un crespón de nieve sobre la cabeza de una novia.

Y al pie de una resquebrajadura enorme y suntuosa como pórtico de vieja catedral, Demetrio Macías, con los ojos fijos para siempre sigue apuntando con el cañón de su fusil...

VOCABULARY

If the gender of nouns does not appear, those nouns ending in **-o** and **-ón** are masculine and those nouns ending in **-a, -ión, -dad, -ez, -tad, -tud,** and **-umbre** are feminine. A dash (—) means the repetition of the key word. The few abbreviations used in the vocabulary are self-explanatory with the possible exception of *pej.* for pejorative suffixes. Words not generally used in the Spanish of Spain are marked either (*Mex.*) if they are Mexican forms or (*Amer.*) if they are used elsewhere in Spanish America as well. No attempt has been made to distinguish Central American usage from that of South America. The popular forms used in the text appear with their corresponding accepted forms. In the case of verbs, the vowel changes of radical-changing verbs and, frequently, prepositional usage are given in parentheses.

Unless used in a peculiar sense or requiring explanation, the following words have been omitted: the vocabulary contained in the passages translated at the foot of the pages of the text; names of persons; easily recognizable cognates; regular past participles; verbal nouns when the infinitive is given; adverbs in **-mente** when the adjectives on which they are formed appear already; and adjectives in **-ísimo** unless irregular.

A

a to, toward, at, in, into, in order to, on, with, by, by means of, from, about; *not translatable before a personal direct object or proper noun;* **— lo que parece** according to the way it seems; **— los tres días** after three days; **¿— qué . . . ?** why? for what purpose (reason)? **de — cuatro dólares** at four dollars a pair

abajito (de) (*dim. of* **abajo**) just beyond

abajo (de) below, under, down, on the ground, underneath; **más —** farther down; **los de —** those farther down, *as title* The Underdogs; **pa(ra) —** down; **¡—, pelón!** Down you go, baldy!

abandonar to abandon, give up, let go of

abanico fan; **en —s** like fans, fanlike

abarcar to include

abatido dejected, discouraged

abeja bee

abierto (*p. p. of* **abrir**) open, opened, pierced, wide-open, spread

abismo abyss

abnegación self-denial, sacrifice

abocar to aim

abonado fertilized

aborrecido hated, despised

abotagado bruised, swollen

abrazados with their arms around each other

abrazar (se) to embrace

abrigo refuge, shelter, protection

abrir to open, flap (*wings*), whet; **—se lugar** to make a place for oneself; **—se paso** to make one's way; **en un — y cerrar de ojos** in a moment

abrupto steep

absorber to absorb (*attention*), take up

absorto lost in thought

abstraído lost in thought

absurdo: la lógica del — absurd logic

abuelito (*dim. of* **abuelo**) grandpa

abundar to be abundant, be plentiful

aburrir to bore; **—se** to get bored

acá here; **por —** around here, in this section; **dije — pa mí** I said to myself
acabado clever, smart
acabar (de) to finish, finish off, kill; **—se** to finish, be used up, be gone; **— de** + *inf.* to have just (*in pres. and imperf. tenses*); **— por** + *inf.* to end by ...-ing, to finally ...; **acabado de lavar** newly washed
acalenturado feverish
acampar to camp, encamp
acanterado stone
aceitunado olive-colored, olive
acémila pack-mule
acento accent, tone, strain
acera sidewalk
acerado waxen, waxlike
acercar(se) to reach for, bring near, approach, go
acero steel
acertado correct, wise
aclararse to become clear (light, bright)
acoger to accept, receive, welcome
acompañamiento retinue, followers
acompañante *m.* friend, companion
acompañar to accompany, go with
acompasado rhythmical
acontecimiento event, incident, happening
acordarse (ue) (de) to remember, recall
acorde *m.* strain
acostado lying down, reclining
acreedor *m.* recipient; **— a la confianza** recipient of the confidence
acribillado riddled
actitud attitude, act
acuchillar to stab, knife
acudir to answer, heed, turn to, resort to, rush up
acuñar to coin
acurrucarse to huddle up
achinarse to quiver
adelantar to go on, spur; **—se** to go on ahead, go (come) forward
adelante ahead, in the lead; **más —** farther on
Adelita, La *a popular song of the Revolution that was sung especially by the troops of Pancho Villa*
adentro within; **— de** = **dentro de; para sus —s** inwardly
aderezado arranged
adherido clinging
adiós good-by
adivinar to guess
admirable wonderful, admirable
adobe *m.* adobe, sun-baked brick
adonde where, wherever
adormilado sleepy, drowsy
adusto stern, hard, sullen
advenedizo newcomer; **— de banqueta** young upstart
advertir (ie, i) to warn, notice, note
afectuoso affectionate
afigurarse = **figurarse** to imagine; **se me afigura** I reckon
afilado sharpened
afilarse to grow thin, become gaunt, lengthen
afinar to tune
aflojar to loosen
afluir to swarm
africano negroid
afuera outside
agarrar (*Amer.*) to catch, get, take; to press, grab, squeeze
agilidad agility
agitar agitate, wave
aglomerarse to be grouped
agotamiento exhaustion
agotar to spend; **—se** to be exhausted, be worn out, run low
agradecer to thank, be grateful
agradecimiento gratitude
agregar to add
agrupado grouped (joined) together
agua water, spring, watering place
aguacero cloudburst
aguantar(se) to put up with, stand
aguardentoso alcoholic
aguardiente *m.* whisky, brandy, alcohol
Aguascalientes *the capital city of the state of Aguascalientes in central Mexico and the scene of the National Convention (November 10, 1914) dominated by Villa*
agudo piercing, sharp
agüerado (*Mex.*) fair, light-complexioned

águila eagle
aguilita (*dim. of* **águila**) general's eagle (insignia)
aguilucho (*dim. of* **águila**), eagle, eaglet
agujerear to make a hole in, puncture
agujerito (*dim. of* **agujero**) small hole
agujero hole
ahí there
ahogar to stifle, smother, suppress; **—se** to be drowned out; **ahogándose en sollozos** sobbing bitterly; **medio ahogándose** panting
ahora now; **— sí** well; **— bien** now then, as a result
ahorcado hanged, a hanged man
ahorcar to hang
ahorros *m. pl.* savings
ahuecado hollowed out
ai = **ahí** there, here; *sometimes not translatable*
airado angered, angrily
aire *m.* air, wind, attitude; **al — libre** in the open air
airoplano = **aeroplano** airplane
airosamente haughtily
aistá = **ahí está**
ajeno unrelated, apart, foreign
ajo: **¡Mal — pa . . . !** The devil take . . . !
al (=**a**+**el**) *with expressions of time* after; **—** + *inf.* after, upon (on) . . . -ing
ala wing, flap, brim
alacrán *m.* scorpion; **volverse un —** to become furious with rage
alagartado lying, stretched out, reclining
alargar to stick out, thrust forward, hand, give
alarido shout, whoop
alba dawn
albazo surprise attack at dawn
albear to whiten, bloom
albergue *m.* home, dwelling place
albísimo very white
albor *m.* ray
alborotado matted, tousled
alborozo joy
albur *m.* draw (*in cards*)
alcanzar to reach, catch up with, overtake; **— a** + *inf.* to succeed in . . . -ing; **a mí no se me alcanza** I don't understand (get)
alegre happy, happily, gaily
alegría joy
alejarse to go away, move away
aletargar to cause to faint
alfombra rug
algarabía racket, noise
algo (de) something, anything; **— asi** something like (that)
alguien somebody, someone, anybody, anyone
algún, alguno some, someone, somebody; **algunos** a few, any; **en parte —a** anywhere, nowhere
alhaja jewel
alhajita *dim. of* **alhaja** jewel
alharaca din, hubbub
alimentarse (de) to live (on)
alineado in a row
aliviado better, cured
alma soul; **mal —** cruel-hearted, harsh; **mi —** darling, honey
almidonar to starch; **sin —** unstarched
almorzar (ue) (*Amer.*) to eat breakfast; to serve breakfast, give breakfast to
almuerzo breakfast
alojamiento lodging
alojar to lodge, quarter
alquería palatial residence
alta halt; **causar —** to enlist, enter the ranks; **dado de —** enlisted
alterarse to become disturbed (agitated)
altercado quarrel
altiplanicie *f.* plateau, high plain
altito (*dim. of* **alto**) small attic room
altivez pride, arrogance, haughtiness
altivo proud, haughty
alto tall, high; **lo —** top, crest; **lo más —** top; **en —** in the air
altura height
alumbrarse to be lighted
alumno student
alzar to raise (high), lift, send up, shrug (*shoulders*); **—se** to rise; **—se de hombros** to shrug one's shoulders
allá there; **— voy** just a minute, wait a minute, I'm coming (to that); **los**

de — those over there; **más —** farther on; **más — de** beyond
allí there
amabilidad kindness
amable kind, amiable, friendly
amanecer to awaken, appear; *impers.* to dawn; **amanecí en el cuartel** in the morning I was in the barracks; **Dios amanece** dawn; **¿Cómo amanecieron?** How did you feel this morning? **— crudo** to wake up with a hangover; **amanecieron algunos muertos** in the morning there were a few dead
amansar to tame, break in
amante *m. or f.* lover, loved one
amargar to embitter
amargosamente bitterly
amargura bitterness
amarillento yellowish
amarillo yellow
ambicionar to long for, want
ambiente *m.* atmosphere, air
amenaza threat
amenazador threatening
ameno pleasant, amusing
ametralladora machine gun
amigo friend, my friend
aminorar to lessen
amistad friendship; **gastar con —es** to spend on one's friends; **hicieron muchas —es** they made lots of friends
amistosamente amicably, in a friendly manner (way)
amo owner, master
amodorrado drowsy
amontonado piled, heaped
amontonamiento pile, heap
amor *m.* love, lover, darling, "honey"; **mi mero —** my man
amoralidad amorality, lack of moral sense
amorosamente amorously
amoscado uneasy, disturbed, annoyed
amparar(se) to protect, help; to seek shelter (protection)
amplio wide, broad
amueblado furnished
anaranjado orange
anca side, hindquarters, haunch; **—s** crupper, haunches; **se lo puso en —s** put him up behind him
ancho wide, broad
andar to go, walk, be; **¡Ande! ¡Anda!** Go on! Why! **¡Ándale! ¡Ándele!** Come along! Come on! **— +** *pres. part.* (*ger.*) to go about . . . -ing
andrajo rag, ragged clothing
angosto narrow
anguloso angular
angustiado grieved, sorrowful
angustioso sorrowful, nervous
anidar to roost
anillo ring
animado animated, excited
animar to excite, animate; **—se** to get up sufficient courage, become excited
ánimo spirit; **con —** spiritedly
aniquilar to annihilate, wipe out
anoche last night
anochecer to grow dark, to go to bed; **anochecí a doce leguas de mi pueblo** at night I was twelve leagues from my town
anquilosado gnarled
ansia anxiety; **comer —** to be anxious
ansiedad eagerness
ansioso anxious, eager, anxiously, impatiently
ante before, in the presence of
anteayer the day before yesterday
antes before; **— de (que)** before
anticipo advance payment
antojo whim; **cumplir el —** to get what one wants
antorcha torch
anudar to tie; **—se** to form a lump (*in the throat*)
anunciar to announce
añadir to add
añico fragment; **hacerse —s** to be crushed and torn (broken)
año year
apaciblemente peacefully
apagar to put out, muffle; **—se** to grow dim, fade
aparador *m.* cupboard
aparato article
aparecer(se) to appear, exist

apartado lonely, isolated
apartar to push aside, take away; **—se (de)** to separate (from), leave
apaste *m.* (*Mex.*) tub, bucket, pail
apastito (*Mex.*) (*dim. of* **apaste**) bowl, pitcher
apear to cut, to help dismount; **—se** to dismount, get down
apenado troubled
apenas scarcely, hardly; **— pa comer** scarcely enough to eat
apero implement
aplicar to apply
apolillado moth-eaten
aporreado beaten up
apostar (ue) to place, post, bet
aprebe = apruebe (*from* **aprobar**)
apreciar to appreciate, respect; **su amigo que lo aprecia** your affectionate friend
aprender to learn, be able
apresurado in haste
apresurarse to hasten
apretar (ie) to close, stuff, fill completely, clasp, tighten, hold; **—se** to hold
aprobar (ue) to approve, try, taste
aprontarse to hasten
aprovechar to take, seize, take advantage; **—se de** to profit by, take advantage of
aproximar to bring closer
apuesta bet, wager
apuntar to aim, take aim
apuñalar to stab
apuración trouble, difficulty, mess
apurar to drink down; **—se** to be troubled, be worried, be in need
aquel, aquella that; **aquellos, -as** those; **aquél,** *etc.* that one, the former, that fellow (man); **aquello** that
aquí here; **por —** here; **Luisito por — y Luisito por allí** Louie this and Louie that
arado plow
araña spider
árbol *m.* tree
arboleda grove
arbusto bush
arder to burn; **— de sed** to die of thirst
ardilla squirrel
aridez aridity, dryness
arista edge
arma rifle, gun, arm, weapon
armadura armor
armamento arms
armar to arm; **—se** to start, begin
armazón shelf
armita *dim. of* **arma** gun
arrabal *m.* district; **— de gente alegre** red-light district
arracada pendant earring
arrancar(se) to pull off, rip off, cut off, pull out
arrastrar to drag; **—se** to crawl, creep, drag oneself along, flow along slowly
arrebatado snatched up, surrounded
arreglar(se) to arrange, fix up
arremolinarse to crowd
arrendar (ie) (a) to deign to
arrepentirse (ie, i) to repent, change one's mind
arriba (de) above, top, up, on top; **¡—!** up and at 'em! **los de —** the upper-crust, the ones on top; **más — de** beyond, above; **patas —** on its back
arribeño (*Mex.*) highlander, *an inhabitant of the central* **meseta** *or plateau of Mexico*
arriero muleteer; *adj.* persevering, determined, tenacious
arriesgar to risk
arrimar to bring up, fetch, carry, put (be) near (close), cling to; **—se** to approach, come near
arriscar to curl, fold, twist back
arrodillarse to kneel
arrojar to throw, hurl, send forth, shed; **—se sobre** to fall upon, rush upon
arroyo stream, brook, dry bed of a stream
arroyuelo (*dim. of* **arroyo**) small stream, brook
arruga wrinkle
arruinado ruined, done for
arrullado lulled to sleep, made drowsy
artero treacherous
asaltante *m.* attacker
asalto attack
asar to roast

ascendiente *m.* power, renown, influence
ascenso ascent, climbing, promotion
asco nausea; **tener —** to hate, despise
ascua coal, ember
asegurar to assure, state, claim
asentimiento assent
asentir (ie, i) to assent, agree, confess
asesinar to kill, murder, assassinate
asesino assassin, murderer; **el —** *epithet given to Huerta for the murder of Madero*
asiento seat, place, chair
asilenciarse to become quiet
asir to seize
así thus, in this way, so, then; **—es que** so
asistente *m.* orderly
asociarse to join together, form a partnership
asolar (ue) to ruin, lay waste
asomar(se) to appear, come out, show oneself, approach, come near
asombrado astonished
asombro surprise, astonishment
aspereza impatience, harshness
áspero rough
aspirante *m.* cadet; **escuela de —s** military school
asqueroso filthy, loathsome
astillado splintered, battered, broken
astro sun
asustado frightened
atacar to attack
atardecer to draw toward evening; **cuando atardeció** as the sun set; *m.* evening; **al —** in the evening
ataviarse to dress especially, fix up
atejonado lying, reclining
atención duty
atender (ie) to heed, pay attention to
atenerse (ie) to heed, pay attention
atento attentive, polite
aterciopelado soft, velvety
atizar to feed (*a fire*)
atónito astonished, amazed
atraer to attract, pull close, draw near; **— el sueño** to go to sleep
atrapar to catch
atrás back, backward; **de días —** for days
atravesar (ie) to cross, get through
atreverse to dare, venture
atrio paved terrace
atronar *m.* din, roar
atropellar to trample down, run down, bump into
aturdir to dull, daze, frighten
augurar to forecast, expect
aullar to howl, shriek, growl; **aúlla que aúlla** growling
aullido roar, howl, whoop
aun even; **aún** still, yet
aunque although, even though
aurora dawn
ausencia absence; **en —** behind their backs
auxiliar *m.* helper, assistant
auxilio aid, assistance, help
avance *m.* advance; (*Mex.*) loot, booty, "swag," "haul"
avanzar to advance; (*Mex.*) to loot, get as booty, "bag"
ave *f.* bird; **— de rapiña** bird of prey
aventurar to venture
avería disease, venereal disease
avezada accustomed, trained
avidez eagerness; **con —** greedily
avido eager, avid
avinagrado sour, peevish
avíos *m. pl.* equipment, tools
avisar to advise, warn, tell
aviso news, information
avivar to increase, intensify
axiomáticamente sententiously, laconically, tersely
¡ay! oh!
ayer yesterday
ayuda aid, help, assistance
ayudante *m.* helper, assistant, adjutant
ayudar to help
ayuno de barba beardless
azabache *m.* jet
azadón (*aug. of* **azada**) hoe
azorado amazed, frightened
azoro fear, terror
azotar to beat; **azotando las aceras** making the sidewalks resound with hoof beats
azotea roof, housetop
azul blue, bluish
azuzar to urge on, spur

B

bache *m.* mudhole
bagazo pulp
baile *m.* dance
baja casualty
bajar(se) to descend, go down, lower, get down
bajo low, under, after, on, in a low voice
bajorrelieve *m.* bas-relief
bala bullet
balancearse to sway
balazo bullet wound, shot; **tirar el —** to shoot
balbucir to babble, mutter
bambilete *m.* (*Mex.*) windlass; *a crude device used in Mexico for drawing water from wells*
bambolearse to waver, sway
banal trivial
banca bench, seat
bandera flag, banner
bandido bandit; **— providencia** bandit-savior
banqueta (*Mex.*) sidewalk
bañada shower (*of lead*)
bañar to bathe
baraja cards
baranda railing
barba chin, beard; **—s** beard, face
barbado bearded
barbaridad cruelty; **¡Qué —!** How terrible! What a mess! **ser una —** to be terrible
barbarie *f.* barbarity
bárbaro barbarian, fool
barbecho furrow
barda wall
barnizado varnished
barra bar
barranca deep canyon, gorge, precipice
barranco ravine, gully
barrer to sweep, sweep away
barretón (*aug. of* **barreta**) crowbar
barriga stomach, belly; **de — al sol** face up
barril *m.* barrel
barrio district; **— de las muchachas** red-light district
barro clay, earthenware
barullo babble, noise, din
barzón yoke-strap
bastante quite, very
bastar to suffice, be enough
basuras *f. pl.* refuse
basurero garbage heap, refuse heap
batea tray
batir to fight, beat
bayeta flannel
bazofia refuse
beata pious woman
beber to drink; **— a borbotones** to gulp down
belleza beauty
bellísimo excellent, exceptional
bello beautiful
bendecir to bless
bendición blessing
beneficiar to benefit
bendito blessed, holy
bermejo red, ruddy
berrear to bellow
berrinche *m.* fit of anger, anger
besar to kiss, touch, reach
bestia beast, horse
bibelot *m.* figurine
bien well; **— a —** closely; **más —** better, rather; **— muerto** stone-dead
bigote *m.* mustache; **— borgoñonés** large mustache
bilimbique *m.* bill
billete *m.* bill, banknote
blanco target; *adj.* white, fair
blandir to brandish, swing
blanquecino whitish, white
Blanquet, Aureliano *a Federal general under the Díaz, Madero, and Huerta governments. He took part in the treacherous coup d'état and murders committed in the military revolt against Madero.*
blanquillo (*Mex.*) **egg**
blusa blouse
boa reptile, boa constrictor
boba fool
boca mouth, opening, entrance, threshold; **— arriba** on his (her, their) back(s); **— de palo** tongue-tied, speechless
bocacalle *f.* street corner, street crossing

bocanada mouthful
bocaza mouthful; **un ruido de —s y grandes tragantadas** a noise of chewing and of swallowing
bocina trumpet, horn; **en —** like a trumpet
bofe *m.* lung; **echar los —s** to blow one's lungs out
bofetada blow, punch
bola ball, thing
bolita (*dim. of* **bola**) marble
bolsillo pocket
bonito pretty, dainty, nice(ly), fine, excellent
boquiabierto open-mouthed
borbotar to bubble forth
borbotón gulp, rising smoke cloud; **a borbotones** in gulps, in spurts
bordado display
bordear to fringe, tint
borgoñonés Burgundian; **bigote —** large mustache
borrachera drunk, drunkenness; **ponerse una —** to get drunk
borrachito *dim. of* **borracho** drunk
borracho drunk, drunkard; *adj.* drunken, drunk; **de —** drunk
borrarse (de) to disappear, leave
borrico burro
bostezar to yawn
bote *m.* tin, tin can
botecito (*dim. of* **bote**) small tin
botella bottle
botón bud
botonadura set of buttons
bramar to roar
brasa live coal
bravo brave; **toro —** wild steer, angry bull
brazo arm, branch
breña crags, rough ground
breve: en — soon, shortly; **—s segundos** a few seconds
bribón scoundrel, rascal
brida bridle, reins
brillante *m.* diamond; *adj.* shining
brillar to shine, gleam
brillo shine, brilliance, gleam, glare
brilloso shiny
brindar to toast, make a toast
brindis *m.* toast
brío spirit, liveliness
brioso lively, noble-spirited
bromear to joke, make fun of
bromista joking
bronce *m.* bronze
broncíneo bronze
bronco rude, severe, rough
brusco sudden, quick
bruto brute, stupid fool; *adj.* wild
búcaro pot
buen(o) good; **¡—!** all right, "O.K.," that's right, of course; **de —as a primeras** all of a sudden, right away
buey *m.* ox
Bufa, La *a mountain near the city of Zacatecas*
bufanda muffler
bufar to snort
buir=bullir ¡No te buigas! Don't move!
bulto form; **comprar a —** to buy the whole lot
bulla hubbub
bullirse to move
burbuja bubble
burdo rough, coarse
burro burro; stupid, dumb(bell)
busca search
buscar to seek, search, look for

C

cabal exact; **¡—!** that's right! **—mente** precisely
cabalgadura mount, horse
cabalgar to ride
caballería mount, cavalry
caballeriza stable, mount, horse
caballero gentleman
caballo horse; **a —** on horseback; **uno de a —** a man on horseback
caballuco (*pej. of* **caballo**) horse, nag
cabecera head (*of a bed*), upper end, pillow
cabecilla *m.* leader, bandit-leader
cabellera hair
cabello hair; **—s** hair
caber to go into, be contained in; **lo que les puede —** what they will hold

cabestro halter, halter-rope
cabeza head, horn (*of a saddle*)
cabizbajo with lowered head, crestfallen
cabo corporal, end; **al — de** after; **al —** after all
cabra goat; **es de —** it's goat's milk
cabriola: hacer —s to prance
cacarizo (*Mex.*) pock-marked
cacique *m.* political boss
caciquismo political bossism
cacto cactus
cachetada slap in the face
cada each, every; **— vez más** more and more
cadáver *m.* corpse, dead body
cadera hip; **—s** hip, thigh
caer to fall, penetrate, attack; **— en** to come out at; **—se de risa** to be convulsed with laughter; **si usted le cae bien a Villa** if Villa takes a liking to you; **caída la cabeza** their heads lying on the ground
cai = cae
caída fall
caja box, case
cajita (*dim. of* **caja**) small box
cajón (*aug. of* **caja**) drawer
cal *f.* lime, whitewash; **a piedra y —** airtight
calabaza pumpkin, squash, head; **en la pura —** right in the head
calce *m.* (*Amer.*) bottom
calcinado calcinated, powdered, crumbling
caldear to become warm (heated)
caldillo (*dim. of* **caldo**) soup, light broth
calentar (ie) to warm up
calentura fever
calenturón (*aug. of* **calentura**) bad fever
cálido warm
caliente warm
calina mist
calor *m.* warmth, heat, fever
calosfrío chill
caluroso heated, warm, heartfelt
calvo barren
calzado shoes, footwear
calzón trousers; **calzones** trousers
calladamente quietly
callado tight-lipped, unexpressive, quiet
callar(se) to be quiet, "shut up"; **¡Calla!** Well, well!
calle *f.* street
callejero street; **perros —s** stray dogs
callejón alley
callejoncito *dim. of* **callejón** alley
calloso calloused
cama bed
camarada *m.* comrade, companion
cambiar to change; **— de chaqueta** to become a turncoat; **— de opinión** to change one's mind
cambio change; **en —** on the other hand; **meter en un —** to give as change
camilla stretcher
caminar to travel, walk
camino road, way, journey; **— real** highway
camisa shirt
camiseta undershirt
camisón chemise
campamento camp, encampment
campanario belfry
campanilla gullet, insides
campaña campaign
campo field
camposanto cemetery
cana gray hair; **blanco de —s** white-haired
canalla cur; **—s** rabble
canana cartridge belt
canasta basket
canción song
candidez candor, innocence
candil *m.* lamp
cansarse to tire, become tired
cantar to sing, crow, confess, "squeal"
cantáridas *f. pl.* Spanish fly, *an aphrodisiac*
cántaro pitcher
cantina saloon, bar
cantinero bartender
canto song, hum, noise, surface
caña reed, sugar cane
cañada ravine
cañón canyon, barrel; **la gente de los cañones** people of the Juchipila district
capa cape; **— dragona** officer's cape

capaz capable
capilla church, chapel
capital *m.* capital (*money*), profit
capitán *m.* captain; **— primero** captain of the first grade
capitancillo (*dim. of* **capitán**) dandified captain
capitancito (*dim. of* **capitán**) fine little captain
capote *m.* army cape
cara face
carabina rifle
caracol *m.* spiral staircase
caracolear to move back and forth
carácter *m.* character, social prestige
¡caramba! gosh! gee-whiz! golly!
carátula face
carbón coal, ember, charcoal
carcajada loud laughter, guffaw; **a —s** uproariously; **lanzar una —** to laugh loudly (uproariously)
cárcel *f.* jail
carcomido eroded
carga charge, weight, burden
cargador *m.* round of bullets
cargar (*Amer.*) to carry, possess, have; **— con** to carry off, to take care of; **me cargan** they make me carry
cariñoso affectionate(ly)
carita *dim. of* **cara** face; **billete de dos —s** double-faced bill
carmín *m.* carmine, red dust (powder), rouge
carne *f.* flesh, meat; **—s** flesh
carnero sheep
carnicería butchery
carnoso meaty, fleshy, solid
carranclán *m.* (*Mex.*) Carrancista; *a derogatory name given to the followers of Carranza*
Carranza, Venustiano (*1859–1920*) *a senator under Porfirio Díaz who supported Madero and later led the revolt against Huerta. His subsequent break with his ally, Villa, forms an important part of the background of "Los de abajo." President of Mexico 1917–1920*
Carranzo *error for* **Carranza.** *Pancracio, who makes this mistake, shows in doing so his ignorance of the revolt in which he is taking part.*
carrera career, race, gallop; **hacer — to** study for a profession; **a toda —** rapidly, quickly
Carrera Torres, Francisco S. *a general in the Constitutionalist or anti-Huerta army who fought principally in San Luis Potosí*
carretera highway
carretón *aug. of* **carreta** wagon
carrillo cheek
carro cart, wagon; (*Mex.*) railroad car, carload
carruaje *m.* carriage
carta letter
carterita (*dim. of* **cartera**) wallet
cartilla primer; **enseñarnos la —** to show us what to do
cartuchera cartridge belt
cartucho cartridge, bullet, glass
casa house, home
cascada waterfall
cáscara peel, skin
caserío group (row) of houses, houses
caserón (*aug. of* **casa**) large house
casi almost
casita (*dim. of* **casa**) small house
casona (*aug. of* **casa**) large house
castigar to punish
casuca (*pej. of* **casa**) hut
cataclismo cataclysm
cataplasma poultice
cateo (*Mex.*) thorough search
catorce fourteen
catrín *m.* (*Mex.*) dandified aristocrat, rich person, dude
cáusticos *m. pl.* caustics, *a medicinal application that burns diseased tissue, leaving a scar.*
cazuela earthenware bowl
cebolla onion
cecina: carne hecha — jerked meat
ceja eyebrow; **—s** brow; **las —s muy juntas** frowning
Celaya *a town in the state of Guanajuato, the scene of a crushing defeat of Villa by Obregón on April 15, 1915*
celuloide *m.:* **billetes de —s** "rubber" dollars

cenar to eat; **echar de —** to feed the horses; **algo de —** something to eat
ceniciento ashen, pale
centavo cent
centésimo hundredth
centenar *m.* hundred
centinela *m.* sentry, guard; **estar de —** to be on guard
centro center, center of the room
ceñidor *m.* sash, rag belt
ceñir (i) to buckle on
ceño frown; **fruncir (plegar) el —** to frown
cera wax
cerca near; **— de** near, near by, nearly, almost; *f.* fence
cercanías *f. pl.* vicinity
cercano near by; **más —** nearest
cerdo pig, pork
cerebro brain
cerquita (*dim. of* **cerca**) very near
cerradura lock; keyhole
cerrar (ie) to close, heal, bring up
cerrito (*dim. of* **cerro**) hill, small mountain
cerro mountain
cerrojo bolt, lock
cervatillo (*dim. of* **cervato**) young deer
cerveza beer
cesar (de) to stop, cease
cesto basket
cicatriz *f.* scar
cicatrizado healed
ciego blind man
cielo(s) heaven(s), sky
cien a hundred
ciencia knowledge; **a — cierta** exactly
cierto certain, true; to be sure; **— que** of course
cigarra locust
cigarro (*Amer.*) cigarette; **— de hoja** corn-husk cigarette
cima hill, hilltop, top, summit
cimbrador swaying
cinabrio: de — vermilion
cincuenta fifty
cinta strip, ribbon, stripe
cintareada beating, drubbing
cintilar to glimmer
cintura waist
cinturón belt
circo circus
circundado (de) surrounded (by), hemmed in (by)
circunvecino surrounding
cirujano surgeon
ciudad city
Ciudad Juárez *a border city of the state of Chihuahua opposite El Paso, Texas, the scene of several battles between opposing factions in the early years of the Revolution*
Ciudadela, La *the arsenal or citadel in Mexico City where the military uprising against Madero began on February 9, 1913*
clamar to exclaim, cry, cry out, cry out for
clarear to make clear, clarify; **comenzaba a — el alba** at dawn; **clareó el día** dawn broke
claridad clearness, light
claridoso (*Mex.*) frank, straightforward
clarín *m.* bugle
clarito (*dim. of* **claro**) very clearly
claro clear, glassy; **¡— está!** of course! naturally! **sacar en —** to understand
clase *f.* kind, noncommissioned officer, "noncom"
clavar to nail, fasten, fix
cobertizo roof, straw roof
cobrar to collect
cobre *m.* copper
cobrizo copper-colored
cocer (ue) to cook
cocido cooked, boiled
cocimiento potion, remedy
cocina kitchen
codicia greed
codiciosamente enviously
codo elbow; **— a — con** beside, alongside of; **charlatán hasta por los —s** extremely talkative
codorniz *f.* partridge; **La Codorniz** *a nickname in "Los de abajo"*
Cofradía *A religious organization, usually for women, comparable to a* sodality *among U.S. Roman Catholics.*
coger to take, snatch, take up, pick up, catch, get, clutch, hold, handle

cohete *m.* signal rocket, skyrocket; **—s** fireworks
cojear to limp
cojitranco lame, limping
cojo crippled
cola tail
colación: traer a — to bring up, recall
colecta collection
colega *m.* colleague
cólera anger
colgar (ue) to hang
cólico colic, cramps
colina hill
colmar (de) to heap, overload, pile high
colmena hive, beehive; como una — like bees in a hive
colmillo tooth, fang; **tener el — duro** to be experienced, be an "old hand" (*at something*)
colorado: ponerse — to blush
coloso giant
columna troop
comadre *f.* gossip, village woman
comandante *m.* chief
combatiente *m.* soldier, combatant
comedor *m.* dining room
comentarse to be told, be commented on
comentario comment
comenzar (ie) to begin
comer to eat, believe, fall for; **¡Cómaselos!** Drink them! **—se uno a corajes** to go to pieces from anger; **ya no hay de —** there's nothing left to eat any more; **— ansia** to be anxious
comestibles *m. pl.* food
comevacas *m.* cattle-rustlers
comida food, dinner, meal
comisario police chief
comisión commission, carrying out of commands, collection, special duty (assignment)
comistrajos *m. pl.* messy edibles
¿cómo? how? what? **¿A — . . . ?** For how much . . . ? **¿— que no?** Why not? What do you mean 'you're not'? **¡—!** What? **¡Como que . . . !** Why, . . . !
como as like, since, about, approximately, somewhat; **— que** since; **— de** as though by
comodidad comfort; **—es** comfort
compa *m.* (*abbreviation of* **compadre)** pal, friend, buddy
compadecido big-hearted, generous
compadre *m.* partner, pal
compañero companion, comrade
compañía company
compartir to share
compás *m.* rhythm, time
compasivo kindly, tender-hearted
complacencia complacency
complacer to please; *impers.* to like
comprender to understand, appreciate
compuesto composed
común common
comunicar(se) (con) to tell, communicate with, connect with
con with; **— que** and so, then, so then, so, if, whether; **— que** + *subj.* as long as; **— tal de que** provided that; **— ser** even though; **— todo y cabalgaduras** horses and all; **¡— un . . . !** What in the name of . . . ? **¡Pero, — una . . . !** By Heaven!, What the hell!
cóncavo turned up
conceder to grant, concede
concluir (por) to end in (with)
concurrente *m.* spectator
concurrir *m.* attendance
concha pearl
condenado wretch; **—s** confounded people, scoundrels; *adj.* cursed, damned
condescendiente condescending, polite
conducir to carry, take, lead; **se hace —** he has them take him
confesar (ie) to hear confession; **—se** to confess
confianza familiarity
confidencia confession
confidente *m.* settee
confundirse to fuse
confuso confused
congeniar to be congenial
congregación small community
cónico conical

conmigo with me, to me
conmover (ue) to move, awaken pity, stir, agitate
conocer to know, be (get) acquainted with, meet
conocido known, well known; *m.* acquaintance
conocimiento knowledge; **—s** knowledge; **poner en el superior —** to inform
¿conque? so? **¿— si . . . ?** What if . . .?
conseguir (i) to attain, obtain, get, succeed in; **—le el ser admitido** to get you admitted
consejero adviser, counselor
consejo advice, counsel; **tomar — de** to consult with
consentimiento permission
conservar to keep, retain
consideración reflection; **sin más consideraciones** without further delay
considerar to consider; **no saben —** they have no consideration for others
consolar (ue) to console, comfort
constituir to constitute, make up
consuelo comfort, consolation; **sentir —** to feel better; **no tenía más — en esta vida** I was her only joy in life
contagiado infected, buoyed up
contar (ue) to count, relate, tell, say, talk, have; **— con** to count on, have; **no tengo qué —** I have nothing to tell
contemplar to look at
contener (ie) to contain, hold; **—se** to restrain oneself
contenido contents
contentar to calm; **—se** to content oneself
contento happy, contented; *m.* satisfaction, contentment; **es más —** it's better fun
contestar to answer, reply
continente *m.* mien, manner
continuar to continue, remain
contorno form, shape, outline
contraer(se) to contract, wrinkle, change
contraorden *f.* counterorder
contrario: al — on the contrary
contraseña countersign, password
convencer to convince
Convención, La the Convention; *the constitutional convention held at Aguascalientes November 10, 1914, and dominated by Villa*
conveniente desirable, good, good idea
convenir to agree (upon)
convertir(se) (ie, i) to convert, change into
convulso convulsed in rage, convulsively
copa mug, goblet, drink, top (*of a hat*)
copete *m.* crownwork
copeteado (*Mex.*) chuck-full
copita (*dim. of* **copa**) little drink
coraje *m.* anger
corajudo quick-tempered, prone to anger
corazón heart
corcel *m.* charger, steed
cordel *m.* rope, cord
cordillera mountain range, cordillera
coriáceo coriaceous, leatherlike
coro choir
coronel *m.* colonel
correligionario coreligionist, sympathizer
correoso leathery
correr to run, chase, go, run away; **— el cerrojo** to draw back the lock (bolt); **— la sierra** to run around the sierra; **— la baraja** to deal the cards; **a todo —** as fast as possible; *m.* race, dash
correría scurrying
corresponsal *m.* correspondent
corrido continuous, complete
corriente current, ordinary, plain; **enero del —** January of this year
corro group
cortar to cut (off); **—se** to desert
corteza rind
cortina curtain, drape
corva calf (*of the leg*), leg
cosa thing, matter; **¡— de morirse uno de risa!** that's a good one!
cosechar to harvest
coser to sew; **máquina de —** sewing machine

costado side
costal *m.* sack, bag
costar (ue) to cost; **cueste lo que cueste** no matter what the cost may be, at all costs, at any cost
costilla rib
costo cost; **al** — at cost
costroso crusty, crusted
costumbre custom, habit; **como de** — as usual
cotense *m.* (*Mex.*) coarse cloth
cotona (*Mex.*) jacket
cotorra parrot
covacha cave, grotto
coyote *m.* (*Mex.*) coyote, prairie wolf
cráneo skull, head
creer to believe, think
creiba = **creía**
crepitar to crackle
crepuscular of the sunset (twilight)
crespo curly, feathered
crespón veil
cresta comb, crest
cresteria slope, summit
crestón (*aug. of* **cresta**) mound, rise, rock, summit
criatura child
crin *f.* mane
crispado clasped, clenched, taut, tense
cristal crystal, glass
cristalería glassware
cristalino crystalline, transparent
cristiano human being
Cristo Christ; **un Santo** — a crucifix; — **Crucificado** Christ Our Lord upon the Cross
croar *m.* croaking
crucificar to crucify
crudo untanned, raw, bare; **amanecer** — to wake up with a hangover
crujir to click
cruz *f.* cross, withers; **la Santa Cruz** the True Cross
cruzar to exchange, cross, sling
cuaco (*Mex.*) horse
cuadrar (*Mex.*) to please; **me cuadra** I like
cuadril *m.* hip; — **a** — **con** side by side with
cuajado studded
cuajarón clot
cual as
¿cuál? what? which?
cualquer = **cualquier**
cualquier(a) any; **¡Es — cosa!** It's nothing at all!
cuan largo era at full length
cuando when; — **menos** at least
¿cuándo? when?
cuanto as many, all the, all that; **unos** —s a few; **¡Cuánta vieja encuerada!** Just look at all the naked women!
¿cuánto? how much? **¿—s?** how many?
cuarenta forty
cuartel *m.* barracks
cuartelazo coup d'état, barracks revolt
cuartito (*dim. of* **cuarto**) small room
cuarto room
cuatro four
cubierta cover, top
cubierto covered
cubo bucket, pail
cubrir to cover; **—se** to replace; **—se de rubor** to blush
cuclillas: en — squatting, crouching; **ponerse en** — to squat, crouch
cuchufleta jest, joke, "wise crack"
cuchilla large knife
cuchillo knife
cuello neck, throat, line of the collar; **al** — around(at) his(her) neck
cuenta account, report; **a — y —** counting and counting; **darse — de** to realize, notice; **venir a —s** to occur (*to one*), cause to realize
cuento story, tall tale; **¡Y se acabó el —!** That's all there is to it!
cuerda rope, cord, string; **—s** stringed instruments
cuereada beating, licking
cuerno horn
cuero leather, hide, skin; **en —s** naked
cuerpo body, detachment; **de — entero** full length
cuesta slope; **a —s** on his(their) back(s)
cuico (*Mex.*) policeman, "cop," "bull" (*The Mexican term is derogatory.*)
cuidado care; — **con** take care with . . . ,

be careful with . . . ; **no hay —** don't worry
cuidar to care for, look after
cuita troubles, sorrows
culata butt (*of a rifle*)
culatazo blow with the rifle butt
culebra snake
culpa fault, blame
cumbre summit, top, peak
cumplir to fulfill, get; **— el antojo** to get what one wants
cuna cradle
Cuquío *a town in Jalisco*
cura *m.* priest
curación recovery, cure, curing
cural priest's, pertaining to a priest
curar to cure, look after, take care of
curiosear to pry into another's affairs, nose about
curiosidad curiosity, carefulness
curro (*Mex.*) tenderfoot, dude; *a derogatory term applied to members of the upper classes. Its meaning is the same as that of* **señorito** *in Spain.*
curruca linnet
cúspide *f.* summit
cuyo (**-a,** *etc.*) whose

CH

chacal *m.* jackal
chacotear to look for a fight, fool around
chaleco vest
chalupa (*Mex.*) raft
chamaco (*Mex.*) small child
chamaquita (*Mex.*) (*dim. of* **chamaca**) nice little girl
chamarra (*Mex.*) jacket, *of lambskin or brushed felt adorned with braid and other decorations*
champaña *m.* champagne
champurrao = **champurrado** (*Mex.*) *a drink made of chocolate and* **atole** (*semiliquid cornmeal*)
chapa (*Amer.*) lock, fastener; (*Mex.*) head; **en la mera —** right in his head
chaparral *m.* dwarf-oak grove, dwarf oaks
chaparro dwarf oak, brush
chapeado gold-plated
chapete *m.* (*Mex.*) rosy cheek
chaqueta coat; **cambiar de —** to become a turncoat, change sides
charamusquero (*Mex.*) candy-maker
charco pond, pool
charlar to chat
charlatán talkative; **— hasta por los codos** extremely talkative
charretera epaulet
charro (*Mex.*) cowboy
chasco disappointment
chasquear la lengua to make a clicking noise with the tongue
chata (*Amer.*) darling, honey
chatita (*Amer.*) *dim. of* **chata** darling, honey
chato stubby, short and thick
chico child, small boy, "kid"
chicotear (*Mex.*) to wipe out, kill
chicoteo (*Mex.*) spatter, crackling, rattle (*of musketry*)
chicharra insect, cicada, locust
chicharrón (*aug. of* **chicharra**) crackling
Chihuahua *the capital city of the state of Chihuahua in north-central Mexico*
chile *m.* chile, chile pepper
chillón (**-ona**) shrill
chiquilla (*dim. of* **chica**) a young girl
chiquito (*dim. of* **chico**) very small
chirriar to creak, squeak
chisme *m.* story; **—s** gossip, tales, filth, lies
chismorrear to gossip
¡chist! hush! quiet!
chistar to mutter, mumble; **no —** to be dumfounded, not open one's mouth
chiva female goat; **— parida** goat and her kid
chivarras *f. pl.* (*Mex.*) chaps
chivo male goat, goat
chocar to displease, "gripe"; **— el vaso con** to drink with; **— con** to meet; **¡Chóquela!** Shake!
chomite *m.* (*Mex.*) homespun
choque *m.* clinking together, quarrel, run-in
chorizo sausage
chorrear to drip, bleed

chorro stream of water
choza hut
chupar to puff

D

daca (da + acá) give me, hand me
daga knife, dagger
dama woman
daño harm, evil; **hacer —** to hurt, harm
dao = dado
dar to give, produce, make, yield, cause, offer, sell; **— alaridos (gritos)** to shout, yell; **— carcajadas** to laugh loudly (uproariously); **— con** to meet, come upon, run into, find, hit, lay; **— coraje** to make angry, enrage; **— de comer** to give something to eat, feed; **— de palos** to beat, whip, drub; **— empellones** to shake; **— en tierra** to fall; **— gracias** to thank; **— la espalda** to turn one's back (to, on); **— la mano** to give a hand, help out; **— licencia** to permit, allow; **— parte** to inform, advise; **— pasos** to take steps; **— salto(s)** to jump, leap; **— sorbos** to swallow in gulps, gulp down; **— un paso** to take a step; **— una vuelta** to take a turn (walk) about; **— vergüenza** to shame, make ashamed; **— voces** to shout, yell; **— vueltas** to walk back and forth; **—se** to surrender, give oneself up; **¡Están dados!** They give themselves up!; **—se coraje** to become (get) angry; **—se cuenta de** to realize, notice; **—se prisa** to hurry; **—se un encontrazo** to have a run-in with, have to meet up with; **¡Pos, a— le!** Well, let's go to it! **¿Qué se me da a mí?** What's the difference to me? **a la Pintada, nada se le dio** it made no difference to La Pintada; **¿A cómo los da?** How much do you want for them? **dio con sus huesos quebrantados** he rested his weary bones; **me dieron fríos** I had chills and fever; **hoy nos está dando de cara** today it is shining in our faces; **ir a — a** to end up in, "land" in; **no —se por entendido** to pretend not to notice; **da tanta gana de**+*inf.* you want so much to . . .
dardear to filter, pierce
dato detail
de of, from, for, with, by, as (a); in, between, on; **— . . . en . . .** from . . . to . . . ; **— cuatro en cuatro** by fours; **— veras** real(ly); truly, **— quererlo** as far as loving him goes; **— que** if, when
debajo (de) under, beneath
deber to owe; +*inf.* must; **ésas deben haber sido** it must have been that
debido proper, due; **a su — tiempo** at the right time
débil weak, dull, dim
decente well-dressed, tidy, neat, decent, well-behaved
decir to say, tell, speak, mean; **di que no** say "no"; **es —** that is to say
declinar to decline, approach the end; **al — la tarde** at dusk
dedicarse (a) to devote oneself (to)
dedo finger, toe
definitivo definite
deglución swallowing
dejar to permit, allow, let, leave, infuse, instill; **— caer** to drop, let fall; **— de** +*inf.* to stop . . . -ing, fail to, help being; **— libre** to free; **—se caer** to fall down, drop to the ground; **—se traicionar** to betray oneself, give oneself away; **cuando me deje bueno** when you get me well; **hasta no — uno** until not a single one is left alive
delantal *m.* apron
delante ahead, forward
delantito (*dim. of* **delante**): **los de —** those up ahead
delicia delight, joy
delirio frenzied rapture
Delmónico Delmonico's restaurant (*in Chihuahua City*)
demacrado gaunt, wasted away, pale
demandar to demand, require
demás other; **los —** the rest, the others; **por lo —** besides, furthermore

demasiado too much
demolido torn up, demolished
demudarse to change in expression
dende = **desde**
dentadura teeth
dentro (de) in, inside of, within
depósito storehouse, shed
depreciarse to depreciate
deque (*Amer.*) give me
derecho right; **a la derecha** on the right
derramar to shed
derribar to topple over, crush, destroy, storm, pull (tear) down (off, from), knock over (down)
derrocar to overthrow
derrota rout, defeat
derrotar to rout, defeat
derruido destroyed, crumbled
desabrimiento rudeness
desafiar to challenge
desafinado loud, harsh
desahogar to unburden oneself, have one's say
desairar to slight, ignore, disregard, rebuff, treat with disrespect
desamparar to abandon
desangrarse to bleed
desaparecer to disappear
desaprobación disapproval, dissatisfaction
desarmar to disarm
desastre *m.* disaster
desatar to untie, break loose
desazón *f.* uneasiness, uncertainty, anxiety
desazonado gloomy, moody, uneasy, disturbed
desbarrancarse to topple over the edge of a cliff
desbocado riderless; **a caballo —** at breakneck speed
descalzo barefooted
descansar to rest, lie, pick on, cool off, feel better
descanso rest; **sin —** continuously
descarga volley, discharge
descargar (sobre) to strike, hit
descender (ie) to descend, go down, droop
descerrajar to break the (a) lock off
descolgar (ue) to take down
descolorido colorless, pale
descomponer(se) to refract
descompuesto broken
desconcertar (ie) to throw into confusion, confuse, rouse
desconcierto confusion
desconchado cracked, slashed
desconocido stranger; *adj.* strange
desconocer to refuse to recognize
desconsolado disappointed, sad
descontento grumbler
describir to describe
descubierto bare, uncovered
descubrimiento discovery
descubrir to uncover, see, sight, find; **al —** without aiming
desde from, since; **— que** since; **— hoy (mañana,** *etc.*) beginning today (tomorrow, *etc.*); **— luego** immediately
desdeñoso disdainful
desear to desire, want
desembocar to enter
desencanto disillusionment
desenfrenado mad, reckless
desensartar to take out (down), draw forth
desensillar to unsaddle
desesperado desperate, despairing
desfiladero steep slope, cliff
desgarrado ragged, tattered and torn
desgranar to shell, empty, remove kernels (from)
desgreñado tousled, disheveled
deshacer to muss, undo; **—se** to break up, disappear; **—se de** to get rid of
desheredado unfortunate, downtrodden, underdog
desigualdad inequality
deslavado grimy
deslizar to unravel
deslumbrado astonished, dazzled
deslumbrante dazzling
desmayado fainted
desmayo swoon, faint; **sufrir un —** to faint
desmenuzado crushed, crumpled
desmesuradamente unusually, extremely
desmolado toothless
desmontar to dismount

desmorecido seized
desnudar to strip
desnudo bare, naked
desorbitados bulging, popping
despabilar to trim (*the wick of a lamp*)
despachar to send (off); **— a . . .** to chase away, send packing, "shake"; **y nosotros estamos ya pa — a Villa y a Carranza a la . . .** and we are sure ready to shake both Villa and Carranza
desparpajo pertness, boldness, impudence
desparramarse to overflow, scatter, spread
despatarrado stretched out
despavorido terrified
despectivo scornful(ly)
despedirse (i) to say good-by, take leave
despegar to remove, take away; **se me despegó** I am rid of
despeñadero slope, rocky slope
desperdigarse to scatter
despertar (ie) to awaken
desplegar (ie) to part, open; **—se** to open, spread
desplomarse to collapse, topple over
despojar to despoil, rob, take
despojos *m. pl.* spoils
despreciativo scornful
desprenderse to fall, break away
desprendido honest, generous, disinterested
desprestigiar to harm, hurt
desprevenido unprepared, off guard
después afterward, later, then; **— de** after
desquitar to earn
destacar(se) to stand out, emerge
destechado roofless
desteñido discolored, faded
desternillarse de risa to split one's sides with laughter
destino destiny, fate
destrozar to shatter, maim, mangle
desvanecido fainted, in a faint
desventurado unfortunate
desviar to turn aside
detallar to tell in detail
detener to stop, detain; **— el paso** to bar the way; **—se** to stop; **—se sobre** to meet, stop in front of
detenidamente carefully
detentador *m.* oppressor
determinar to cause, determine
detrás (de) behind
devolver(se) (ue) to return, give back, go back
deyecciones *f. pl.* excrement
día *m.* day; **de —s atrás** for days; **fue de —** day broke; **ocho —s** week; **quince —s** two weeks
diablo devil; **¿Qué —s . . . ?** What the devil . . . ?
diablura trick; **—s** mess
diario daily, daily newspaper, per day; **a —** daily
diafanidad clarity, clearness
diáfano clear, transparent
Díaz, Félix *the nephew of Porfirio Díaz and a general in his army. He retained his post under Madero, Díaz's successor. He led an unsuccessful revolt against Madero, who magnanimously spared his life. Later he played a prominent part in the Huertista overthrow of the Madero government and in the subsequent murder of Madero.*
dibujo design
díceres *m. pl.* (*Amer.*) gossip
diciembre *m.* December
dicharachero making vulgar remarks
dicharacho remark (*usually vulgar*)
dicho (*p. p. of* **decir**) aforementioned
diente *m.* tooth
diestra right hand
diestro right
diez ten
difuntito *dim. of* **difunto** dead man
difuso blurred, diffuse
digno worthy
dije *m.* trinket
dilatado wide
dilatar to delay; **— en** + *inf.* to be long before; **—se** to extend, stretch
diminuto small, tiny, dwarflike
dinero money
Dios God; **por —** for Heaven's sake;

— del cielo God in His Heaven; **por mi —** I swear by God
dipsómano dipsomaniac, addicted to drink
dirigir(se) to direct, turn
discernir (ie) to make out, discern
discurso speech; **hora va de —** now comes the speechmaking
diseminarse to scatter, spread
disimulo pretense; **con —** pretending to be unconcerned
disiparse to disappear
disparar to shoot, spur
disparo shot
dispensar to excuse
dispersarse to scatter
dispersión: en — scattering, rushing
disperso scattered
disponerse to get ready, prepare, be about to
dispuesto determined, ready, prepared
distancia distance, difference; **a —** aside
distar to be distant
distinguirse to be unique, stand out
distinto distinct
distraído absent-minded, distrait
divertido amused, amusing, gay
divertirse (ie, i) to have a good time, amuse oneself; **a que se diviertan solos** so they can amuse themselves all alone
dizque = dicen (dijeron) que *or* **dice que**
doblar to bend, bow, go around, double, fold; **— el cuello** to nod; **— la rodilla** to kneel
doce twelve
docena dozen
dócil obliging
dolencia pain
doler (ue) to pain, hurt, ache
dolor *m.* pain, suffering
dolorido pitiful
dominar to dominate, overlook, rise above
don *title;* **un — nadie** a nobody, a person of no importance
doncella maiden, young girl
donde where, in order to, where they (he, *etc.*) could; **¿dónde?** where? **¿en —?** *or* **¿a —?** where?
dondequiera: por — everywhere
dorado golden, gold-colored
dormido asleep; **muy —s** sound asleep
dormir (ue, u) to sleep; **—se** to go to sleep
dorso back
dos two; **en — por tres** in a jiffy
doscientos two hundred
dotor *m.* **= doctor**
dragona: capa — officer's cape
dueño owner, master
dulce sweet, gentle
dulzón *aug. of* **dulce** mild, gentle, sweet
dulzura sweetness
Durango *a state in north-central Mexico*
durante during
durar to last
duro hard

E

e (= **y** *before* **i-** *or* **hi-**) and
ebrio drunkard; *adj.* drunk, intoxicated
ebullir to effervesce, bubble
echao = echado
echar to throw, cast, give, reach, blow out, emit, pull; **— de cenar** to feed the horses; **— de ver** to note, notice, see; **— fuera** to free, liberate; **— mentiras** to lie, tell lies; **— pestes** to complain bitterly; **— pie a tierra** to dismount; **— un trago** to have a drink; **— una bendición** to give a blessing; **— vivas** to cheer; **reír a — las tripas** to laugh until one's sides split; **—se** to throw oneself, lie down, put on, put around; **—se de la casa** to rush out; **—se encima** to set upon; **—se los máuseres a la cara** to take aim; **se los echó** he beat them; **para que me eche encima a la federación** to get the whole government after me; **los caballos echados** the horses stretched out
edificio building
efecto effect; **en —** in fact
egoísmo selfishness
ejecutar to carry out, execute

ejemplar *m.* example, copy, edition
ejemplo example
ejercer to exert
ejército army, troops
el la, lo, los, las the; *with parts of the body, articles of clothing, etc.* my, his, her, their, its, *etc.;* **el,** *etc.* **de** that of, those of, the one of, the ones from, the one with, *etc.;* **el,** *etc.* **que** the one that
él he, him, it
El Paso *a city in Texas located directly opposite Ciudad Juárez, Chihuahua. Many political refugees from turbulent Mexico have escaped to this city.*
elegir (i) to elect
elevado high
Elías Elijah
elogios *m. pl.* praise
elote *m.* (*Mex.*) ear of corn
ella she, her, it
ello it; **— tan claro así** it was all so clear
ellos they, them
emanación vapor, fume
embadurnar to grease, smear, rub
embalsamado fragrant, perfumed
embargado speechless
embebecido amazed
embelesado fascinated, delighted, charmed
embeleso: con — fascinated, adoringly
embellecer to embellish
emborracharse to get drunk
embrutecer to become an animal
emisión issue
empapado soaked, dripping, wet
empellón shake, shove, push, bump; **dar empellones** to shake
empenachado plumed
emperador *m.* emperor
empinadísimo very steep
empinar to drink
empiojado lice-ridden, lousy
empolvado dusty, dust-covered
emprender to take up, begin, undertake, enter
emprestar = **prestar**
empujar to push
empuñar to clasp, grip
en in, on, into, at, with
enaguas *f. pl.* skirt
enamorado in love
enano dwarf; **los —s** the dwarf dance
enarcado arched
encabritarse to rise on the hind feet, rear (up)
encaje *m.* lace; **—s** lacework
encallecido calloused
encaminarse to set out, walk; **— hacia** to go toward
encanijado wasted away, thin
encantado charmed, enchanted
encapillar (*Mex.*) to lock up
encarado: mal — with an ugly face
encaramado perched
encaramarse to climb
encargarse (de) to undertake
encariñarse (con) to take a liking to
encarnar to heal
encender (ie) to light; **—se** to become flushed; **—se como un madroño** to become as red as a beet
encendido burning, glowing, flaming, flushed
encerrar (ie) (se) to lock up, enclose
encima on, upon; **echarse —** to set upon; **venirse —** to run down
encoger to lower; **—se** to curl up
encogido drawn up, contracted
encolerizado angry
encontrar(se) (ue) to find, meet
encontronazo: darse un — to have a run-in with, meet up with
encorvado curved, arched
encuadrado framed
encuentro meeting, engagement; **al — de** to meet; **a su —** toward her
encuerado half naked, naked
enchilada (*Mex.*) enchilada, *a Mexican dish consisting of a highly-seasoned* **tortilla** (*corn cake*) *with cheese sauce and onions;* **hojas —s de tamales** corn-husk covers from tamales
enchomitado (*Mex.*) dressed in home-spun
enderezarse to stand up, straighten up
enemigo enemy; **el — malo** the devil
energías *f. pl.* strength
enero January
enfático emphatic(ally)

enfatuado conceited
enfelizada unhappy woman
enfrentar to bring close; **—se** to look at, face
enfrente in front
enfurecido furious
engañar to deceive
engrandecimiento betterment
enhuevada pregnant
enigma *m.* question, doubt
enjuto thin, skinny, bony
enladrillado brick floor, pavement
enmarañado tangled, tousled, matted
enmohecido rusty
enmudecer to become silent
ennegrecerse to be black, become black
enojarse to become angry, get sore
enojo anger, rage; **—s** suffering, trouble
enriquecerse to get rich
enrojecido flushed
ensanchar(se) to extend, open wide, expand
enseñar to show, teach, train; **—nos la cartilla** to show us what to do
ensillar to saddle
ensombrecerse to become gloomy (clouded)
ensordecer to deafen; **a —** loudly, deafeningly
ensotanado dressed in a cassock
entender (ie) to understand
enteramente entirely
entereza presence of mind
enternecimiento tenderness
Enterrador, El The Gravedigger
enterrar (ie) to bury
entoldado covered by a canopy
entonación tone
entonar to sing, chant
entonces then
entrada entrance, way to get in
entrado: hasta ya muy entrada la noche until very late at night
entraña heart; **¡ . . . tan mala —!** his heart's rotten to the core!
entrar to enter
entre between, among, through, in
entreabierto half-opened
entrecerrar (ie) to half close
entrecortado interrupted, broken
entregado (a) given over to, busy with
entregar to give up, hand over, betray; **—se** to surrender
entretanto meanwhile
entreverar to mix, intermingle
entrometido: por — because he didn't mind his own business
entumecido benumbed
entusiasmado enthusiastic
envalentonar to encourage
envanecido conceited, vain
envejecido aged
envenenar to poison
enviar to send
envidia envy
envolver (ue) to envelop
envuelto (*p. p. of* **envolver**) involved
¡epa! (*Mex.*) hey! listen! **¡—, pior!** hey, stop it!
epíteto name
equilibrio balance
equipaje *m.* luggage; **—s** belongings
equivocación mistake
equivocarse to be wrong, be mistaken
erguir (i) to thrust forward; **—se** to straighten up
erial *m.* uncultivated land
erizado protrudent, projecting, bristling
errar (ie) to miss the mark, go astray
eructar to belch (up), eructate
esbelto slender
esbozarse to be outlined, begin to take form (stand out)
escalar to climb, scale, reach
escalera stairway
escalón (*aug. of* **escala**) step
escalpelo scalpel, surgeon's knife
escama scale
escarlata crimson, scarlet
escarpa cliff
escarpadura escarpment, steep side
esclavo slave
escoba broom
escoger to pick out, choose
escolta troops
escombros *m. pl.* debris, ruins
esconder(se) to hide
escondite *m.* hiding place
escondrijo hiding place, corner
escopeta shotgun

escribir to write
escritorio writing desk
escrofuloso scrofulous, consumptive, afflicted with tumors
escuchar to listen, hear
escudito *dim. of* **escudo** insignia
escudo scutcheon, insignia
escudriñar to scrutinize, search, look at
escuela school; **— de aspirantes** military academy
escuelante *m.* (*Amer.*) school kid
escueto lean, thin
esculcar to search
escupida: una — en las barbas I spit in his face
escupir to spit (up), vomit (up)
escurrirse to scurry away
ese, -a, *etc.* that; **ésa será usté** that's what you'd do; **en ésas** meanwhile; *after a noun with contempt or scorn, e. g.* **el viejo ese** that horrible man
esfera sphere, environment
esfuerzo attempt, effort
esfumarse to be lost in the haze, disappear, appear hazily
esgrimir to brandish
eso that; **en —** with that; **— de que** that custom of, the fact that; **— es** that's right
espadas *f. pl.* spades
espalda shoulder, back; **—s** back; **de —s** on his back; **a —s de** behind, back of
espantar to frighten (away), terrify
espanto fear
especie *f.* rumor, sort, type, species, piece of news
espectro ghost, specter
espejo mirror
esperanza hope
esperar(se) to hope, wait (for), expect, await
espeso thick, heavy, bushy
espesura thickness, density
espía *m.* spy
espiga wheat stalk
espinazo back
espíritu *m.* mind, spirit
espolear to spur
espolvoreado sprinkled
esponjar to ruffle
esposa wife
espuela spur
espulgar to remove fleas from (*an object*)
espuma foam
esqueleto skeleton
esquina corner
esquivo sly, evasive
estaca stake, brace, hook
estacionarse to stop
estado state; **— mayor** staff
Estados Unidos United States
estallar to explode
estallido detonation, explosion
estampa print, engraving, picture
estampida (*Amer.*) stampede; **de —** stampeding
estampido: dar el — to get away, escape
estar to be; **— de pie** to be up (awake); **— pa(ra)** to be on the point of, be about to; **¡Están dados!** They give themselves up!
estatuilla statuette
éste, -a, *etc.* this one, the latter, he, she; **en éstas** at this moment
este, -a, *etc.* this
estentóreo stentorian, clear and loud
estercolero manure heap
estiércol *m.* manure
estimación esteem; **tener —** to esteem highly
estimado esteemed; **Muy — Venancio** My dear Venancio
estímulo stimulus, inspiration
estirado wide
estirar to draw tight, crease, stretch
estómago stomach, sides
estorbar to bother, disturb
estragado tired, worn out
estrechamente closely, tightly
estrechar to grasp, clasp, press, shake hands with, embrace; **— la mano** to shake hands
estrella star; **— de mar** starfish
estrellado starry, star-lit
estrellar(se) to smash into bits, break
estrellita (*dim. of* **estrella**) little star, *a military insignia showing officer's rank*
estremecerse to shudder, shake, quiver
estrépito noise; **con —** noisily

estrepitoso noisy, loud
estriado streaked, stained
estribar (en) to lie in, rest on, be based on
estribillo refrain
estridente shrill, piercing, strident
estrofa stanza
estruendo shattering din
estruendoso loud
estudio study
estupefacción stupor
estúpido stupid; **¡—!** you stupid fool!
eterno eternal
evitar to prevent; **¿No sería conveniente —les esto?** Wouldn't it be a good idea to make them stop this?
exaltado excited, angry
excitación excitement
exhalar to utter, exhale
eximirse to avoid
éxito success
éxodo emigration, exodus
experencia=**experiencia**
explanada clearing, clear place
explicación explanation
explicar to explain
exponer to explain
exprimir to press, squeeze; **— sus ojos rasos** to hold back the tears in her eyes
extinguirse to be lost, be drowned out, die out, disappear
extraer to extract, pull out, take, steal
extrañamiento wonderment
extrañar to surprise, miss
extraño stranger; *adj.* strange
extraviado wild
extremo end, corner

F

fábrica factory
fabricar to make, manufacture
faceto (*Mex.*) tiresome fool; *adj.* affected, smart
fácil easy; **creo —** I think it will be easy
facilidad ease; **tiene tal —** it's so easy
faena task, labor
faja streak (of light)
fajo bunch, wad, roll
falda side, brim, skirt
falsete falsetto, high-pitched voice
falso false; **en —** false
falta lack; **a — de** lacking, having exhausted
faltar to be lacking (missing); **lo que falta** what remains to be done; **— al respeto** to insult, harm
fama reputation
famélico starved, hungry
fandango dance
fanega acre (*the* **fanega** *is in reality 1.6 acres*); bushel (*1.6 bushels*)
fardo bundle
fastidiar to annoy
fastidio boredom; **matar el —** to kill time
fatiga exhaustion; **con —** exhausted
fatigado exhausted, tired
fatigoso tired
favor *m.* favor; **por —** please; **¿en — de quiénes?** for whom?
favorecer to favor, help, aid
faz *f.* face
fe *f.* faith
fecha date, time
federación federation, federals, *the government of Huerta*
federal *m.* federal soldier, government soldier, federal
felicitación congratulations
felicitar to congratulate
feo ugly, improper, indecent, sad
feroz ferocious
ferrocarriles *m. pl.* railroad
festejar to entertain
festivo festive, gay, light-hearted
fiebre *f.* fever
fiel faithful, clear
fieltro felt hat
fiera wild beast
figurarse to imagine; **se me figura** I imagine (guess)
figurita *dim. of* **figura** figure
fijamente fixedly
fijar to fix; **—(se) en** to note carefully; **fijaba sus pupilas** stared
fila rank, row; **a —s** in the ranks; **en segunda —** behind
filigrana filigree
filo ridge
filtrarse to seep in

fin *m.* end; **al —** finally; **por —** finally
final *m.* end
finca farm
fineza compliment
fingir to pretend
fino refined, excellent, fine, sharp
fisgonear to spy, pry
fisonomía features, physiognomy
fláccido dislocated, limp
flaco thin, skinny, frail, weak
flamante crisp, fiery, flashing
flameante flaming, flashing
flanco flank, side
flojera: con mucha — lazily
flor *f.* flower; **— de San Juan** (*Macrosiphonia sp.*) dogbane
florido blooming, flowery
foco lamp, light bulb
fogón fire, hearth
fogueado trained
foguear to fire on
follaje *m.* foliage
fonda hotel, inn, restaurant
fondera lunchroom owner
fondo bottom, seat; **—s** funds; **al —** in the background; **en —** abreast; **del —** in the back of the room
fonducho (*pej.*) dirty lunch stand
forcejear to struggle
forjar to forge, create, make
forrado lined, covered
fortificar to fortify
fortuna luck, good fortune, opportunity; **la — es que** it's lucky that
forzado forced
fosfatina phosphate; **— Falliéres** Fallieres Phosphatine, *a patent medicine*
fracaso failure
fragmento piece
fragor *m.* din, crash
franquear to go through, pass through, cross
frasco flask
frase *f.* statement, sentence, phrase
frazada blanket
fregar (ie) to bother
freír (i) to fry
frenesí *m.* frenzy; **con —** enthusiastically
frente *m.* front, face; **al — de** in front of; **a la del —** to the other across the street; **— a** facing; *f.* forehead, face
fresco fresh, ruddy; **al — de la tarde** in the cool of the afternoon
Fresnillo *a city in Zacatecas*
fresno ash tree
fresquecito (*dim. of* **fresco**) nice and cool
frijol *m.* bean(s)
frío cold; **—s** (*Amer.*) fever, chills and fever
fritura fried food
frondaje *m.* foliage
frontero opposite
frotar to rub
fruncir to contract; **— el ceño (las cejas)** to frown
fruto fruit
¡fuche! go on! I don't believe it! bosh! baloney! phooey! ugh!
¡fuchi!=**¡fuche!**
fuego fire, flame, firing
fuente *f.* fountain, spring
fuera outside; **de —** outside; **— de** out of, outside of; **— de sí** beside herself (himself) with grief (anger, rage); **echar —** to free, liberate
fuero right, charter, legality; **religión y —s** religion and legality, *the motto of a conservative faction in the War of the Reform (1858–1861)*
fuerte strong, vigorous, hard, loud, heavy; **peso —** peso coin
fuertemente tightly, firmly, warmly
fuerza force, strength; **—s** strength, troops, forces; **a — de** by dint of
fuga flight
fugaz fleeting
fulgor *m.* brilliant ray
fulminar to fulminate (against), hurl epithets at
fumador *m.* smoker
funda holster
fundirse to fuse
furgón box car
furibundo furious
fusil *m.* rifle
fusilar to shoot, kill
fusilería rifle shots, gunfire
futura future wife

G

gala gay (festive) attire; **de —** in gala colors, in festive costume; **estar de —** to be clad in gay attire (gala colors); **hacer — de** to glory in, make a display of
galantear to court, pay compliments to
galería hangings, rod; **con todo y —** rod and all
galón galloon, braid, chevron
galoneado embroidered, gallooned, trimmed with braid
gallardía pride, haughtiness
gallardo proud, haughty
gallina chicken, hen
gallinita *dim. of* **gallina** chicken
gallo rooster, fighting cock, "bird"
gamuza chamois, suede
gana desire; **tener —** to feel like, want to; **de muy buena —** very willingly (gladly); **adonde le (te) dé su (la) gana** wherever you please; **si le da su mucha —** if he jolly well fells like it
ganar(se) to earn, gain, win, beat
garabato scrawl, mark
garganta throat; **exclamar con la —** to croak
garra claw; (*Mex.*) strip, piece; **— de jorongo** poncho; **—s de camisa y chaleco** tattered shirt and vest
gasa gauze
gastar to spend
gatillo trigger
gato cat
gaznate *m.* neck
gemido groan, moan
gendarme *m.* (*Mex.*) policeman
genio disposition, nature
gente *f.* people, person
gentío crowd, rabble
gesto gesture
gigantesco gigantic
giro (*Amer.*) yellowish, sand-colored
glauco greenish-gray
gloria glory
gobierno government
golondrina swallow
golpe *m.* blow, stamp(ing)
golpeado threateningly, menacingly
golpear to beat, strike
golpecito (*dim. of* **golpe**) small (slight) pain
golpiza beating, whipping
gorda (*Mex.*) tortilla (corn cake)
gordinflón flabby, fat
gordo fat
gorrita *dim. of* **gorra** cap
gorrudos *m. pl.* (*Mex.*) big-hats, *nickname given to the rebels because of their sombreros*
gota drop
goteante dripping with sweat
gotear to drip with sweat
gozar (de) to enjoy
grabado engraving
gracia boon, request; **—s** thanks
grado rank; **de buen —** willingly
gran, grande large, huge, great, bad, serious, severe
granada (hand) grenade
granado select, choice; **lo más —** the finest (best)
granitificarse to turn to granite, solidify
granizada hailstorm, hail, shower, volley
grano grain, kernel
grato pleasant, kind; **su grata de enero** your letter of last January
gratificación tip
grave serious, grave, melancholy
gravedad seriousness
Grillo, El *a mountain near the city of Zacatecas*
gringo (*Mex.*) American
gris gray
gritar to shout
grito shout, cry, scream
grueso large, heavy, thick, swollen
gruñido groan, growl
gruñir to grunt, growl, mutter
gruñón growling
grupa crupper; **poner a —s** to hoist up behind (on a horse); **volver —s** to turn one's horse about, wheel about, turn tail
Guadalajara *the capital city of the state of Jalisco;* **— chiquita** Little Guadala-

jara, *a name for Tepatitlán, Jalisco*
Guadalupe *a suburb of Mexico City and the site of the famous church of* **Nuestra Señora de Guadalupe,** *a shrine which commemorates the miraculous appearance of the Virgin to the Indian, Juan Diego, in 1531. The Virgin of Guadalupe is the patron saint of Mexico.*
guaje *m.* (*Mex.*) silly fool
guajolote *m.* (*Mex.*) wild turkey
guarache *m.* (*Mex.*) sandal
guardar to keep, preserve, protect, guard, put, help
guardia lair, hiding-place
guarniciones *f. pl.* harness, saddle-trappings
güelvan = vuelvan
güeno = bueno; —s días le dé Dios hello, good day
güerito (*Mex.*) *dim. of* **güero** "Whitey," "Blondie"
güero (*Mex.*) blond, "Whitey"; **el —** "Blondie," "Whitey"
guerra war
guerrero warrior
güevo = huevo
guía *m.* guide; **hombre —** guide
guija pebble, stone
guiñar to wink
guiño wink
guisado prepared, cooked
guiso stew
guitarra guitar
guitarrón (*aug. of* **guitarra**) guitar, large guitar
gustar to like, please
gusto pleasure, desire; **a —** pleasurable, pleasant; **¡Mucho —!** Delighted to meet you! **tener —** to be pleased
gustoso joyfully, with pleasure
gutural guttural, deep

H

haber (*auxiliary*) to have; **— de** + *inf.* to have to, be bound (likely) to, be going to, must, shall, should, will; **he de** I am to; (*impersonal*) to be; **hubo (había)** there was (were); **hubo quien** there was somebody; **hay que** + *inf.* it is necessary to, one (you) must; **habiendo quien cabalgara** some of whom rode; **no hay como** there's nothing like; **no hay que** you mustn't, don't; **¡Que ha que se metió el sol!** It's after sundown now! **lo que haiga con él hay conmigo** whatever concerns him concerns me; **con eso ha habido para que ...** that was enough for him to ...; **he aquí (ahí)** behold; **habérselas con** to oppose, have to deal with, pit oneself against
haberes *m. pl.* wages, pay, money
habilidad skill
habla speech; **hasta el — me niegas** you won't even talk to me
hablar to speak, talk
hacer to make, prepare, have, do, commit; **—** + *inf.* to cause to, have, order to, make; **— blanco** to make a direct hit; **— caso de** to pay attention to; **— crac** to go crack, make a cracking noise; **— daño** to hurt, harm; **— de cuenta** to imagine; **— el sordo** to pretend not to hear; **— falta** to be needed, be lacking; **— frente** to stand up against, oppose; **— fuego** to fire; **— la lucha** to get along; **— las once** to have a small lunch at about noon; **— por** + *inf.* to make a move to ...; **— presente** to offer; **— que** + *inf.* to cause to, have, *e. g.:* **hizo que lo llevaran** had them take him; **— ruedo** to form a circle, encircle; **— silencio** to become silent; **—se** to become, form, cast; **—se** + *inf.* to have oneself + *p. p.;* **—se a** to get used to; *impersonally in expressions of time* for, since, ago, *e.g.:* **hace un mes** a month ago; **hacía tres meses (días)** three months (days) before (ago); **desde hacía diez años** for ten years; **¿Cuántas horas se hacen ...?** How many hours does it take to go ...? **eso no le hace,** that doesn't matter; **está haciendo sereno** it's getting damp, it's a damp night; **haciendo oír el choque de**

los pesos duros permitting the clinking together of the coins to be heard; **se me hace** it seems to me; **si se me hace el milagro** if the miracle happens
hacia toward, in the direction of; **— atrás** backward
hacienda hacienda, estate, ranch
hacinamiento heap, cluster; **una multitud de —** a crowding multitude
haiga = **haya**
hallar(se) to find
hallazgo discovery, finding
hambre *f.* hunger, famine
hambriento hungry
haraposo ragged, dressed in rags
hartar to disgust, bore, make sick
harto much, a great deal, plenty, satisfied; **me tiene —** I've had enough of her
hasta until, even, to; **— a cincuenta centavos máquina** as low as fifty cents apiece; **— entonces** only then; **— que** until, even
hatajo small herd
haz *m.* bundle, bunch
hazaña deed, feat, undertaking
hebra thread, web; froth, drooling
hebroso fibrous, stringy
hecho fact, circumstance, deed, feat; *p. p.* of **hacer**; **—s uno** welded together, as if forming a single being; **quedó — añicos** remained smashed to bits; **tres jornadas muy bien hechas** three long days' marches; **—s pedazos** broken to bits
helecho fern
hembra woman
henchido filled, swelled
hendidura crack
herbazal *m.* tall grass
herida wound
herido wounded man
hermana sister
herramienta tools
hervido boiled
hervir (ie, i) to boil (up)
hidalgo (*Mex.*) hidalgo, *gold ten-peso coin*
hiel *f.* bitterness, gall
hielo ice
hierba grass
hierro iron
hija daughter
hijo son, child
hila rag
hilacha thread; **—s** (*Mex.*) rags
hilo thread
hincar to press, thrust
hinchar to swell
hirsuto hirsute; **de pelo —** with (of) thick (coarse) hair
hoja leaf, blade, knife; **—s enchiladas de tamales** corn-husk covers from tamales
hojita (*dim. of* **hoja**) leaf, small leaf
hojarasca swirling leaves
hombre man; **¡—!** man alive!
hombrecillo (*dim. of* **hombre**) short man
hombro shoulder
hondonada hollow
honrarse (en) to have the honor to
hora = **ahora**; **Pos — sí, muchachos ...** Well, boys ...
hora hour, time; **a estas —s** at this time; **a muy buena —** very early
horcar = **ahorcar**
horchata sirup; **usté no tiene la sangre de —** you have red blood in your veins
horita [*dim. of* **hora (ahora)**] just now, right now
horizonte *m.* horizon
hormiga ant
hormiguero swarm, cluster
hornilla oven
hosco sullen(ly)
Hostotipaquillo *a village in Jalisco*
hoy today
hoyanco hole
hoz *f.* sickle
hueco cranny, nook, place, hollow
huella trace, trail
huérfano orphan
Huerta, Victoriano (*1852–1916*) *a general in the army under Porfirio Díaz and leader of the military revolt against Madero, who succeeded Díaz; dictator of Mexico from February 18, 1913, to July 15, 1914; known as* **El**

Asesino (*the Assassin*) *because of his part in the treacherous murder of Madero and his aides*
huerto orchard, graden
hueso bone; **dio con sus —s quebrantados** he rested his weary bones
huesudo bony
huevo egg
huir to flee
huizachal *m.* (*Mex.*) grove of huizache trees
huizache *m.* (*Mex.*) huizache, *a spiny tree found in Mexico* (*Acacia sp.*)
humareda cloud of smoke
humilde poor, humble
humeante smoking
humedad dampness, tears, moisture
húmedo damp, soaked, saturated, moist
humillado humbled, humiliated
humo smoke
hundir to sink, bury, insert; **—se** to sink down, fall
huracán *m.* hurricane
huraño shy, unsociable
¡huy! gosh! golly!

I

icir = decir
iglesia church
igual the same; **a — que** the same as, as; **— de** just as, equally as; **— a** like, just like
ijar *m.* flank
iluminarse to be lighted up
iluso deluded person
imagen *f.* image, picture
impasibilidad impassivity
impasible impassive, expressionless
impedimenta impedimenta, supply division (*of an army*)
imperioso commanding, imperious
impertinencia: con — impertinently
ímpetu *m.* force, spirit; **con —** spiritedly, impetuously
impetuosidad: con — impetuously
implacable unyielding, unrelenting
importar to matter
imprecación curse, oath
imprescindible inevitable, unavoidable, unescapable
impreso printed sheet, broadside
imprevisto unforeseen, unexpected
improvisado makeshift
improviso: de — suddenly
impulso speed
inadvertido unnoticed
inagotable inexhaustible
inaudito unheard of
incalificable: ¡Eso es —! That's the lowest thing imaginable!
incansable untiring, tireless
incendiado burning, fiery, glowing
incendio fire, burning
incesante ceaseless
incisivo cutting, direct, incisive
inclinar(se) to stoop, bend down, bow down, nod
incoloro drab, colorless
incomensurable immeasurable, measureless
incomodado disturbed, annoyed
incorporarse to sit up; **— a** to join
increpar to rebuke, scold
incrustado inlaid, set
incrustar(se) (en) to bury itself in
indecencia oath, curse, insult
indeciso hesitating
indefectiblemente without fail, relentlessly
indicar to indicate, point out, show, say
indígena *m.* Indian
indignarse to become indignant
indispensable essential, necessary
individuo fellow
indolencia indolence, laziness, idleness; **con —** lazily
indomable indomitable, untamable, unconquerable
infamia: ¡Una —! It's downright shameful!
infantería infantry
infantil childish
infeliz unfortunate, unhappy, unlucky, scoundrel
infierno hell; **federales del —** accursed federals
inflamar(se) to become inflamed (red)

infligir to inflict
informar to inform; **—se (de)** to find out (about)
ingenuidad innocence, candor
ingenuo innocent, candid
ingrato ungrateful, unkind
iniciar to begin
injuria insult
injuriar to insult
inmediaciones *f. pl.* vicinity
inmediato neighbor, neighboring, near by, immediate, companion
inmensidad immense expanse
in mente (*Lat.*) mentally
inmóvil motionless
inmovilizarse to lie motionless
inmutable expressionless
inmutabilidad immutability, lack of expression
inmutarse to change one's expression
inquerir (ie, i) to ask, inquire
inquieto disturbed, embarrassed, restless
inquietud confusion, embarrassment
insignificancia insignificant thing
insinuante insinuatingly, suggestively
insiñar = enseñar
insistencia insistence, persistence
insolencia insolent remark, oath, insult
insolentarse to become insolent
instantáneo momentary, passing, sudden
instante *m.*: **por —s** at times; **por el —** at the moment
insulso dull, futile
intacto unhurt, unharmed
integrado (por) made up (of), composed (of)
integrar to make up
intempestivo sudden, inopportune, tempestuous
intentar to try
interés *m.* interest
interesar to interest; **—se a** to be interested in
interminablemente endlessly
internarse (en) to reach
interpelado the person addressed (spoken to)
interrogador questioning
interrogar to question, ask
interrumpir to interrupt; **—se** to stop
intimar to become intimate (with)
intruso intruder
inútil useless
invicto unconquerable
inyectado bloodshot
ir to go, be; **—se** to go away, leave; **— +** *ger.* (*pres. part.*) (*to express progressive idea*) to go (keep) on, do something gradually, become more and more; **¿Cómo va . . . ?** How is . . . ?; **hora va de discurso** now comes the speechmaking; **¡Hora voy yo!** Now it's my turn! **iban y venían** moved back and forth; **que allá voy yo** for I'm coming; **vamos a +** *inf.* let's . . . ; **vámonos** let's go; **y ¡vamos!** well, well; **vamos, muchachos** come on, boys
Irapuato *a city in the state of Guanajuato*
irisado rainbow-hued; **cobre — a fuego** fiery-tinted copper
irredento unredeemed, lost
irritado angry, angered
irrumpir to erupt
izque = dizque
izquierdo left

J

ja, ja, ja ha! ha!
jacal *m.* (*Mex.*) hut
jacalito (*Mex.*) (*dim. of* **jacal**) **hut,** small hut
jacalucho (*Mex.*) (*pej. of* **jacal**) **ugly hut**
jácara squabbling, quarreling
jaiga = haya
Jalisco *a state in central Mexico*
Jalpa *a town in Zacatecas, the site of a shrine dedicated to the Virgin. The Virgin of Jalpa is revered by the country folk of the area.*
jallé = hallé
jallo = hallo
jamás never, ever
jamelgo nag
jaqueca headache
jaral *m.* reed, clump of reeds
jarro jug

jefe *m.* chief, leader, officer
jervir (ie, i) = **hervir** to boil; **sin —** unboiled
jícara (*Mex.*) cup, bowl (*made of the lower half of a gourd or of earthenware*)
jierre=**yerre** (*inf.* **errar**)
jijo=**hijo**
jitomate *m.* (*Mex.*) tomato
jornada day's march
jornalero day laborer
jorongo poncho; **garra de —** poncho
José Joseph
joven young
jovencita young girl
joya jewel
Juan John; **los —es** the "Johnnies" (*federal soldiers*)
jubiloso joyful(ly)
júbilo joy
Juchipila *a small town in Zacatecas, the scene of the first bloodshed in the revolt against Porfirio Díaz.*
judío errante, El "The Wandering Jew," *a very popular 19th-century French novel by Eugène Sue (1801–1857)*
jue=**fue**
juego gambling, game, child's play
juera = **fuera; va por —** is applied externally; **voy pa —** I dash (run) outside
juerga spree
juerte = **fuerte**
juerza = **fuerza**
jugador *m.* gamester, gambler
jugar to play, gamble
juntar(se) to join, collect; **— las cejas** to scowl
junto(s) together
jurar to swear, promise
justo just, sound, right; **su — precio** what's what
juzgar to judge

L

la the, it, her, you
labio lip
labor *f.* cultivated soil, tillage, land
labranza farming
lacio straight
ladera hillside, side
laderita *dim. of* **ladera** side
lado side; **al — de** with, beside; **de un —** on one side; **por mi —** as far as I am concerned
ladrar to bark
ladrillo brick
ladrón thief; **ladrones nixtamaleros** corn-thieves
lago lake
Lagos *a city in Jalisco*
lágrima tear
lamentar to regret, be sorry about, lament
lamento moan, wail
lamido carefully combed
lámina blade; print, illustration, picture
lampiño beardless
lana wool; **de —** woolen
lanceolado lanceolate, lance-shaped
languidez languor, languidness
lanza lance; a shrewd person
lanzar to utter, give forth, emit, spit; **—se** to hurry; **—se al encuentro** to fly at each other; **—se sobre** to leap at; **— una carcajada** to laugh uproariously
largar to give, get rid of, chase away; **—se** to go away, "beat it"; **me parece bien que ya te largues mucho a la . . .** I think it's a good idea for you to get the devil out of here
largo long; **a lo — de** along; **caer de —** to fall flat
las the, them, you
lascivo sensual
lástima pity, shame; **¡—!** It's a shame! **¡— de . . . !** too bad about; **¡— de sangre!** Vain bloodshed! **— que** it's a pity that . . .
lata tin; **hoja de —** tin; **¡Qué —!** What a "pill"!
latigazo blow with a whip
latón brass, brass instrument
latrofaccioso thieving rebel
lavar(se) to wash, clean
lavativa enema

laxitud laxity, laxness, limpness
lazar to lasso, rope
lazarillo guide
le him, you
leche *f.* milk
leer to read
legua league (*4.6 miles*)
lejanía distance
lejano distant
lejos far (away, off)
lengua tongue
lentamente slowly, gently
lentitud slowness; **con —** slowly
leña firewood
leño timber, log, wood
leopoldina watch chain
lepra sore
les you, them
lesionado wounded, injured
letrero sign
leva draft; **de —** drafted (men)
levantar to raise, pick up, tuck up; **—se (en armas)** to rise (up), rebel
leyenda legend
liado wrapped, tied
librar to free, protect
libre free, clear
libro book
licencia permission, leave; **dar —** to permit
liebre *f.* rabbit, hare
lienzo cloth
ligadura bandage(s)
ligeramente slightly
ligereza swiftness, speed
Limón *a ranch near Juchipila, Zacatecas*
limosna alms, something for nothing
limpiar(se) to clean (off, out), wipe
límpido clear, limpid
línea line, facial line
listo ready, prepared
liviano light, soft, skilled
lívido pale, livid
lo the, it, you, him; **—** + *adj.* what is, the ... thing, the ... part; **— más** + *adj.* the ...est, what is most ...; **de — que** than; **— que** what, that which, + *sbj.* whatever; **— que es** as far as, *e. g.*: **— que es yo** as far as I am concerned; **— que es pa mí** in my opinion; **— que es de este hecho** as far as this little deed goes; **— que es ahora** as far as the present goes; **¡— que es eso de ...!** What a wonderful thing it is ...!; — + *p. p.* what, *e. g.*: **lo sucedido** what has (had) happened
loco mad, crazy; madman; crazily, like a madman; **loca** fool, crazy woman
locura madness
lograr to succeed in, be able
loma hill
lomerío group of hills
los the, them, you
losa flat stone
lotecito *dim. of* **lote** lot
l'otro = el otro
lúbrico sensual
lucir to display, wear; **—se** to shine, do well (splendidly)
lucha struggle; **hacer la —** to get along
luchar to fight, struggle; **— por** to strive to, try to
luego then, immediately; **— que** as soon as, when, after; **luego luego** right away
lugar *m.* place, town
lúgubre mournful, sad
Luisito (*dim. of* **Luis**) Louie, Lou
lujoso fine, luxurious
lumbre fire
luminoso shiny, luminous
luna moon
lupanar *m.* house of prostitution, whorehouse, brothel
luz *f.* light; **luces** light(s), reflections

LL

llama flame
llamado called, so-called; *m.* call
llamar to call, knock; **—se** to be named (called)
llamarada burst of flame, flame; **en —s** amid flaming rays
llanto grief
llave *f.* key; **debajo de siete —s** under lock and key, well locked up
llegar to arrive, reach, go, approach;

llegaban a las manos they would come to blows; **— a general** to be a general
llenar to fill, get full; **— el ojo** to please; **—se de** to get overcrowded with
lleno full, filled
llevar to wear, carry, bring, bear, have, raise, lead, take; **— a rastras** to drag; **—se** to carry (take) off, raise, take away (along)
llorar to cry, weep; **— a gritos** to scream
lloriqueo whimpering, whining
llover (ue) to shower (upon)
lluvia shower

M

macizo solid, sturdy
machito (*dim. of* **macho**) he-man
madera wood, timber, stuff; **usté es de otra —** you're different from us
maderista *m.* maderista, *follower of Madero*
Madero, Francisco (*1873–1913*), *the leader of the revolt against Porfirio Díaz and President of Mexico (October 1, 1911, to February 18, 1913). Madero was deposed by the Huerta reaction and assassinated in Mexico City on February 23, 1913.*
madre mother; **¡— mía de Jalpa!** Holy Virgin of Jalpa! **¡— santísima de Guadalupe!** Holy Virgin of Guadalupe!
madrepeña moss
madroño bearberry (*Arbutus sp.*); **encenderse como un —** to become as red as a beet
madrugada dawn, early morning
magullado bruised
maicito (*dim. of* **maíz**) corn, little bit of corn
maíz *m.* corn, maize
majestad majesty; **su Divina —** the Lord, God
mal *m.* sickness; *adv.* poorly, badly
malamente andamos we're in a bad way
malcriado shameless
maldecir to swear
maldición curse, hatred
maldito cursed
maleta suitcase
maleza brush, brambles
malhora (*Mex.*) trouble, misfortune, catastrophe
malhumorado in a bad humor
maligno cruel, perverse
malo bad, cruel, sick
malvado wicked, fiendish; **¡Hombres —s!** You swine!
mamá mother, mama
mampostería masonry, stonework
mancebo lad, young man
mancera plow
manco maimed, minus an arm or hand
mancuernilla cufflink
mancha stain, spot, blotch
manchado stained
manchón (*aug. of* **mancha**) patch
mandar to command
mandato command
mando command; **al — de** under the orders of
manejar to manipulate, handle, manage
manera manner; **a — de mentira** impossible
manga sleeve
mango handle; mango, *a Mexican fruit* (*Mangifera indica*)
manifestar (ie) to show
manifiesto obvious
maniobra maneuvering
mano (*Mex.*) = **hermano** brother, pal, friend, buddy
mano *f.* hand, stone base; **a la — on** hand
manojo bunch, cluster
manotada sweep of the hand
mansedumbre gentleness, kindness
manta blanket; (*Mex.*) cotton
manteca lard; **El —** "Greasy"
mantener to support, keep, hold; **—se** to remain, keep
maña fault
mañana tomorrow; *m.* tomorrow, future; *f.* morning; **hacer la —** to pay an early morning visit

máquina machine; **— de coser** sewing machine; **— de escribir** typewriter
maquinaria piece of machinery
mar *m.* sea
maravilla marvel, marvelous gift
marcar to mark, accompany; **su paso marcó un compás grotesco** his walk had a grotesque rhythm; **— su paso a balazos** marking his progress with shots
marco frame
marchar to march, walk, go
marchito withered
marfil *m.* ivory
margen *f.* margin, edge, bank
María Mary; **— Santísima** Holy Mary
marido husband
marihuana (*Mex.*) marihuana, *a Mexican narcotic* (*Cannabis sativa*)
mariposita (*dim. of* **mariposa**) small butterfly
maroma somersault, tumble
martillo hammer
mártir *m.* martyr
marrazo (*Mex.*) bayonet, machete
más more, most, still more, most of all; **— allá (de)** beyond; **— de** more than, over; **— que** except, more than; **no —** (*Amer.*) only, just, *e. g.*: **¿Qué te parece no —?** Just what do you think of it? **no — que** only, except; **hasta de —** even in good measure; **por — que** no matter how much; **los —** most of them, the majority of people; **¡qué —!** what's more, even more
mas but
masa mass
mascada (*Mex.*) silk handkerchief
matado scrawny, saddle-bruised
matadura gall, sore; **— de la cruz a la cola** galled from neck to tail
matar to kill
mate dull
materia matter
material *m.* material; **—es** equipment
materialmente literally
matiz *m.* shade, color
máuser *m.* Mauser rifle, rifle
mayor *m.* major; *adj.* major, larger; **misa —** High Mass
mayordomo boss, foreman
mayoría majority
mazorca ear of corn
me me, (to, for) me, myself
mecer(se) to sway, rock
Meco (*Mex.*) *shortened form of* **chichimeco,** *a term applied to a person of pure Indian blood*
mecha wick, candle; **— de sebo** tallow candle
mechón (*aug. of* **mecha**) lock of hair
media stocking
medianía middle
médico doctor, physician
Medina, Julián *a general in the revolutionary army and a supporter of Villa in Jalisco*
medio half; **a — vivir** to live a hand-to-mouth existence; **a medias** half; **media noche** midnight; *m.* middle, center; **en — de** in the middle of, amidst, amid; half real *or about* 3 cents *in U.S. money at time of Mexican Revolution;* **a —a plaza** in the middle of the bullring
mediodía *m.* noon
meditabundo thoughtful
meditar to think (about), plan, meditate
mejilla cheek
mejor better, best, rather
melancólico melancholy
melifluo mellifluous, honeyed
melindres *m. pl.* coyness
memoria: hacer — to recall, remember
menear to shake
menguante *f.:* **en —** declining, decreasing
menos less; **es lo de —** that doesn't matter at all
mentar (ie) to mention
mentao = mentado
mentir (ie, i) to lie; **¿Miento?** Am I right?
mentira lie; **— que** it's not true that; **parece —** it seems impossible; **No, —s, . . .** No, I was only fooling, . . .
mentiroso liar, fibber
menudamente with great detail

menudear to become frequent
menudo stew, *composed of beef entrails*
mercar to buy
mercé = **merced** *f.* grace; **su —** you
merecido well-deserved
merito: en la —a frente right in my forehead
mero mere; (*Amer.*) himself, myself, themselves, right, just, *e.g.:* **allí —** right there; **en la mera chapa** right in his head; **la mera espalda** right at the back; **la mera verdá** the plain truth; **a mí — me lo dijo** he told me himself; **eso es mi — gusto** that's just what I like to do; **mi — amor** my man; **lo — bueno** the best part
mes *m.* month
mesero waiter
meseta plateau, mesa
mesmo = **mismo**
mesón (*aug. of* **mesa**) hotel, tavern, inn
metate *m.* (*Mex.*) metate, *a stone used to grind corn*
meter to put (in), plunge; **—se** to get (in), enter; **—se con** to bother; **— una trompada** to punch, hit, strike, "sock"; **— un navajazo** to stab; **ya se metió el sol** the sun has already set
metido hidden
metro meter (39.37 inches)
México Mexico; Mexico City, *capital of Mexico located in the Federal District* (*D. F.*)
mezcal *m.* (*Mex.*) mescal, *an alcoholic drink distilled from the maguey* (*Agave sp.*) *plant;* **se bebió muy buen —** a great quantity of mescal was drunk
mezquite *m.* (*Mex.*) mesquite (*Prosopis sp.*)
mí me
mi my; *do not translate before* **sargento, teniente, general,** *etc.*
mi = **mira**
miedo fear; **tener —** to be afraid
miembro member, leg, limb
miente *f.* mind; **—s** mind; **parar —s** to pay attention
mientras while, until; **— que** while
mil thousand
milagro miracle
milagroso miraculous
militar to fight; *adj.* military
milpa (*Mex.*) corn field, maize field, cornstalk(s)
millarada: a —s by thousands
millón million
mimbres *m. pl.* wicker, cane
miniatura: de — miniature, toy
ministro minister
minucia detail
mío, -a, *etc.* my, of mine, mine
mirada look, glance
mirar(se) to look (at), see, regard; **se miraban entre sí** they looked around at themselves; **mire, mira,** *etc.* see here, look here
miríada myriad, swarm
misa Mass; **— mayor** High Mass
miseria(s) misery, wretchedness
misericordia mercy
mísero miserable, wretched
mismo same, very, own, himself, yourself, *etc.;* **en las mismas aguas** right in the water; **los —s que tengo de andar aquí** that's the length of time that I have been here
Misterios, Los The Mysteries (*of the recitation of the rosary*)
mitad half; **a la —** halfway through
mochito (*Mex.*) (*dim. of* **mocho**) federal, tory, fine little soldier
mocho (*Mex.*) tory, federal soldier, *a derogatory term given to federal soldiers by the revolutionaries*
modal *m.* way, manner
modo manner, way(s); **a — de** as a; **¿De — (es) que . . . ?** So . . . ?
mofa jest, mockery
Moisés Moses
mojado soaked, covered
mojicón blow, punch
molde *m.* mold, form
molestar to bother, molest
molesto bothersome
molienda grinding
momentáneo momentary
momento moment; **por el —** at present,

right now; **de un — a otro** any moment now
moneda coin
monito (*dim. of* **mono**) picture
mono monkey
monocorde monotonous
monologar to soliloquize
monorrítmico monotonous
monótono monotonous
monstruo monster
montado mounted, rider
montadura setting
montaña mountain, peak
montar to mount, ride; to put up on (*a horse*)
montón heap, pile; **en —** in a heap, piled up
montura saddle
moñito (*dim* of **moño**) adornment, figure, design
moo = modo
morador *m.* dweller, inhabitant
morder (ue) to bite; **—se la lengua** to bite one's lips
morenita dark-skinned girl
moreno swarthy
morir (ue, u) to die; **—se** to die; **¡Mueran . . . !** Death to . . . !
mortal deadly, mortal
moro black, dark mulberry-colored
morragia = hemorragia; las —s de sangre hemorrhages
mosco hornet, mosquito
mostrador *m.* counter
mostrar (ue) to show, display
motivo motive, inspiration, opportunity, occasion
movedizo moving
moverse (ue) to move
movimiento move, movement
Moyahua *a small town in Zacatecas*
moza girl; **¡— de mi vida!** Sweet lady!
mozalbete *m.* young man
mozo young man, waiter
mozuela (*dim. of* **moza**) little girl
muchacha girl
muchachilla (*dim. of* **muchacha**) little girl
muchacho boy, young man; **¡Mire, y tan —!** Oh, how young he is!
mucho much, a great deal (of), very much, a long time; **—s** many
mudo mute, silent
mueble *m.* piece of furniture
mueca mask, expression, grimace
muela tooth
muelle *m.* spring
muerte *f.* death, murder
muerto dead man, ghost; *adj.* dead; **¡—s de hambre!** Starved dogs!
mugre *f.* dirt, filth, grime
mugriento dirty, grimy
mujer woman, wife
mula mule
múltiple complex
muncho = mucho
mundo world; **todo el —** everybody
muñeca wrist
muñeco doll
muralla wall
muro wall
murria boredom, "blues"; **una —** a sort of "blues"
musgo moss; *adj.* dark brown
música band, music
músico musician
muslo thigh
mustio sad, gloomy
mutuo mutual
muy very

N

naa = nada
nacer to be born, spring
nada nothing; *f.* nothingness; **¡—!** Nothing happened!
nadar to swim, float
naderías *f. pl.* nothing at all
nadie nobody, anybody
naditita (*double dim. of* **nada**) absolutely nothing; **. . . pero — que me jallo por acá . . .** absolutely nothing strikes me right around here
naiden = nadie
naipe *m.* (playing) card
naranja orange
naranjo orange tree
nariz *f.* nose, nostril

Natera, Pánfilo *a general in the revolutionary army and a supporter of Villa in Durango*
navaja knife, blade, spur; **— sin filo** dull knife
navajazo knife thrust; **meter un —** to stab
necesidá = necesidad
necesidad need; **no tengo —** I am not poor; **tener — de** + *inf.* to have to
necesitar to need, have to, must; **—se** to be needed (necessary)
negar (ie) to deny
negocio business, line of business; **hacer un — muy bonito** to do a fine business
negrear to blacken, darken, appear black (*against a lighter background*); **el — de los capotes** the dark color of the army capes; **el — movedizo** the moving blackness
negro black, bitter; **ponerse —** to become furious
negruzco blackish
nervio nerve, "guts"
nervudo powerful, sinewy
netamente typically
ni nor, or, not even, even; **— siquiera** not even; **— ganas del metate** I don't feel like working
nicho niche, case
niebla fog
nieve *f.* snow, white
niño, -a small child, infant, baby; **niña sola** spinster; **— Dios** the Christ Child
niquelado nickel plating
nixtamal *m.* (*Mex.*) nixtamal, *corn meal prepared in a special way for tortillas*
no not, no
nobilísimo very noble
noche *f.* night; **media —** midnight
nómada nomadic
nomás (*Amer.*) just, simply, only
nombrar to name
nombre *m.* name
Nombre de Dios *a town in southern Durango*
nopal *m.* (*Mex.*) nopal, *a Mexican cactus* (*Opuntia sp.*)
noria noria, well. *The noria is a well equipped with a water wheel having buckets on its rim and operated by a mule or horse.*
norte *m.* north; **División del —** Northern Division, *name given to Villa's soldiers*
norteño from the north
nos us, to us, ourselves
nosotros we
notar to note; **hacer —** to call attention to
noticia news
notificar to notify, tell
novedad originality; **—es** news
novia sweetheart, bride
nube *f.* cloud; **con una — en un ojo** nearly blind in one eye
nublarse to become clouded
nuca nape of the neck
núcleo center, core, stone
nudo knot
nuestro our
nuevas *f. pl.* news
nuevecito (*dim. of* **nuevo**) brand-new, very young
nuevo new, fresh, another; **de —** again, once more; **un —** + *noun* another . . .
número number
nunca never
nupcias *f. pl.* wedding; **mañana de —** beautiful morning
nutrido heavy, abundant

Ñ

ña = señora
ñervo = nervio

O

o or
obedecer to obey
oblicuo slanting, oblique
obligar (a) to force
obnubilarse to become cloudy
obra work; **— de** a matter of; **¡— de Dios!** God's will be done!

Obregón, Álvaro (*1880–1928*) *an able general in the revolt against Huerta. In the subsequent revolt against Carranza he supported the latter against Villa; in 1920 he led the revolt against Carranza. He was President of Mexico 1920–1924.*
obrero builder
obscuridad darkness
obscuro dark, swarthy
obsesionante obsessing
obsidiana obsidian, *a glossy, black volcanic rock*
obstante: no — notwithstanding, in spite of
obstinación obstinacy, stubbornness
obtener to obtain, get
ocasión chance
ocre *m.* ochre, yellow coloring
ocultar to hide
oculto hidden
ocupar to occupy; **pué que hasta te ocupen** maybe they'll even give you a job
ocurrido; lo — what had happened
ocurrir to happen, occur, take place; **—sele a una persona** to occur to one; **¿A quién se le ocurre . . . ?** Who would ever think of . . . ?
ochenta eighty
ocho eight; **— días** a week
odio hatred
ofender to offend, hurt
oficial *m.* officer; *adj.* official
oficio job, dispatch
ofrecer to offer; **—se como** to appear (as)
ofrenda offering
oídas: de — hearsay
oído ear
oír to hear, listen to; **—se** to be heard
ojazo large eye
ojeroso having rings under the eyes
ojo eye; **a — cerrado** blindly
olfatear to sniff, smell
olor *m.* odor
olvidar(se) (de) to forget
olla jar, pitcher, bowl
ombligo stomach, navel
once eleven; **hacer las —** to have a small lunch at about noon
onda ripple
ondulación wave
ondular to waver
onduloso waving, wavering
opinar to opine, state, say
opresión pressure, tightness
oprimir to press, squeeze, oppress; **— sus pechos** to torture them
opuesto opposite, opposing
ora . . . ora now . . . now
oración prayer
orden *m.* order; *f.* order; **a la —** at your service
ordenar to order
orearse to be exposed
oreja ear
organillo (*dim. of* **órgano**) hurdy-gurdy
orgulloso proud, "stuck-up"
orilla bank; **—s** outskirts; **a —s de** on the bank of, at the edge of
orín *m.* rust
oro gold; **de —** golden, gold
Orozco, Pascual (*1881–1915*) *a general who supported Madero but later rose against him. This revolt was crushed by Huerta, at that time still loyal to Madero, on July 3, 1912, at Bachimba. Later he led a counterrevolutionary band against Villa.*
orozquista orozquista, *follower of Orozco*
os ex ossibus meis et caro de carne mea (*Lat.*) bone of my bones and flesh of my flesh (*Gen. 2: 23*)
osar to dare
oscuridad darkness
oscuro dark, swarthy
ostensible visible, apparent
ostentación show; **hacer —** to show off
ostentar to display, wear
otate *m.* (*Mex.*) goad, reed sheath, hook
otro, -a other, another, more; *with* **día** *or* **noche** next; **—s tantos** as many
ovoide oval

P

pa = **para**
pacer to graze
pacífico noncombatant; *adj.* peaceful
padre father, priest; **—s** parents
padrecito (*dim. of* **padre**) dear father
¡paf! bang!
pagado pleased, delighted
pagador *m.* paymaster
pagar to pay (for), reward, repay; **me la pagó** got it
país *m.* country; **El —** *a conservative newspaper published in Mexico City*
paisaje *m.* landscape, countryside
paisano peasant, farmer
paja straw
pajarillo (*dim. of* **pájaro**) bird, small bird
pájaro bird
pal = **para el**
pala shovel
palabra word, **¡—!** Word of honor!; That's the truth!
palanca lever; **haciendo — con el mango** pushing the handle down; **hacer —** to trip (up)
palidecer to become pale
pálido pale
palma straw
palmear to pat
palmotear to clap one's hands
palo stick, wood; **boca de —** tongue-tied, speechless
palomar *m.* dovecote
palomo pigeon, dove; *the name of Demetrio's dog*
palpitar to beat, heave, palpitate, sway, hang
pan *m.* bread
panal *m.* nest
pantalón trouser leg, trousers; **pantalones** trousers, pants
pantano swamp
paño cloth; (*Mex.*) handkerchief
pañuelo (*dim. of* **paño**) kerchief, bandanna
papalina drunkenness; **ponerse una —** to get very drunk
papel *m.* paper, paper money, bill, part, role
par: de — en — wide
para for, in order to, to, as for; **— acá** this way; **— mí** as for me, in my opinion; **— que** so that, in order that
parado standing, on foot
parar(se) to stop, put up at; **— de** + *inf.* to stop, quit, leave off; **y pare usté de contar** and that's all there was to it; **ya no se para** it keeps on going; **no le paraba la boca de contenta** she didn't stop talking, she was so happy
pardear to stand out in drab colors
parecer to seem, appear; **¿Qué te parece . . . ?** What do you think . . . ? *m.* opinion
pared *f.* wall, side
pariente *m. or f.* relative
parir to bear
parlanchín *m.* chatterer
parpadear to twinkle, blink
parpadeo glow
párpado eyelid
parque *m.* ammunition
Parral *a city in the state of Chihuahua*
parroquia parish church
parte *m.* report; *f.* part, share; **¿De — de quién . . . ?** On whose side . . . ?; **en — alguna** anywhere; **por otra —** on the other hand, furthermore; **por todas —s** everywhere
participar (de) to take part in
partida departure, band, troop of men, game
partir to come forth, divide
parvedá = **parvedad**
parvedad small gift (offering)
pasado last
pasar(se) to pass, spend (*time*), happen, grind; **me paso a su brigada** I'll join your brigade; **¡Que pase buena noche!** Sleep well!
pasear to pass, run; **— los ojos** to glance
pasmado astonished, surprised
pasmo wonder, astonishment
paso step, gait, way, pace; **al —** with the gait, slowly; **a su —** on (along) their way; **abrirse —** to force one's

way; **dar —s** to take steps; **— a —** slowly, deliberately; **a sus —s** at the sound of his steps

pata leg; **— rajada** hillbilly, hick, country bumpkin

patalear to kick

patear to kick, stomp back and forth

patio patio, inner courtyard

pato duck

patria fatherland, country

patrón boss

paulatinamente very slowly, little by little

pavimento tile floor

pavor *m.* fear, terror

pavoroso terrible, terrifying

payasada clownish trick; **hacer —s** to act like a clown

paz *f.* peace

pecado sin

pecoso blotchy, pock-marked, freckled

pecho chest, breast; **— y espaldas desnudos** stripped to the waist; **guardó en el —** he put in his shirt

pedazo piece, bit

pedir (i) to request, ask (for)

pedregal *m.* stony ground

pedregoso stony

pegar to hit, strike; **— fuego** to set fire; **— un tiro** to shoot, put a bullet

pelado (*Mex.*) peon

pelar to peel; **— gallo** (*Mex.*) to die, cash in one's checks; **—se** to clear out, make a getaway

pelea fight

pelear to fight

peliar = pelear

peligro danger

peligroso dangerous

pelo hair; **— de barba** beard

pelón (*Mex.*) (*aug. of* **pelo**) baldy, *derogatory term applied to federal soldiers*

peluche *f.* plush

pellejo skin, hide

pellizcar to pinch

pena grief, sorrow

penar to suffer

penca leaf

penco unfortunate

pender to hang

pendiente hanging, dangling; *m.* earring; **—s de** awaiting

penetrar to enter

penitenciaría penitentiary, pen; **— de Escobedo** *a famous penitentiary located in Guadalajara, Jalisco*

pensamiento thought(s)

pensar (ie) to think (about), imagine; **— en** to think about

pensativo thoughtful, pensive

penumbra shadow(s)

peña rock

peñascal *m.* rocky mountainside

peñasco rock

peor worse

pepenar (*Mex.*) to seize, grab

pequeño small

percibir to perceive, see, make out

perder (ie) to lose; **—se** to get lost, be lost; **se le perdían** disappeared

perdón pardon, forgiveness

perfil *m.* profile

perfilarse to file, go in single file

perilla (*dim. of* **pera**) bedstead ornament (*ball-shaped*)

periódico newspaper

periodista *m.* journalist

peripecia incident

peripuesto very neatly dressed

perito expert

perjudicar to harm

perla pearl, pearly-gray; **diga que le fue de —s** consider yourself lucky

perlar to form beads; **— el sudor** to cause beads of sweat to form

permanecer to remain

perniabierto riding astride

pernoctar to spend the night

pero (que) but; **¡—, con una . . . !** By Heaven!

perorar to declaim

perplejo disturbed, nonplused, perplexed

perro dog; **— del mal** mad dog; *adj.* wretched; **este — y maldito oficio** this cursed dog's job

perseguir (i) to pursue, chase, hunt, have (*ideals*)

persistir to remain

pertenecer to belong

pesadilla nightmare, wild dream
pesado heavy
pesar to be heavy, weigh
pesaroso grieved, sad, sorrowful
pescado fish
pescar to catch, get, understand
pescuezo neck
peseta (*Mex.*) peseta (*25 centavos, or the fourth part of a peso*)
peso (*Mex.*) peso (*Mexican monetary unit worth about 50 cents U.S. cy. at time of Mexican Revolution. A* peso *has* 8 reales, 16 medios, or 100 centavos); — **duro** silver peso coin
pestañear to blink
peste *f.* pestilence, plague; **—s** offensive words; **echar —s** to complain bitterly
pestillo lock
petaca (*Amer.*) suitcase
pétalo petal
petaquilla (*Mex.*) *dim. of* **petaca** trunk
petate *m.* (*Amer.*) sleeping mat, straw
pétreo stony, stonelike
pezuña hoof
piar to warble, sing
pica pick
picacho crag, peak
picado ground, chopped up
picar to bite, prick, spur
pico beak; **— largo** talker
pichón young pigeon
pie *m.* foot; **a —** on foot; **de —** standing up
piedad piety
piedra stone, precious stone; **a — y cal** airtight
piedrecita (*dim. of* **piedra**) pebble
piel *f.* hide, skin
pierna leg; **lanzar carcajadas a — suelta** to double up with laughter
pieza piece
pila pile
pilón tip, gratuity; **dar de —** to throw in for good measure
piltrafa scrap, refuse, outcast; **— de pantalón** a ragged pair of pants
pinción *archaic form of* **pensión,** blues, melancholy; **¡Y aquella —!** Was I feeling blue? I was singing the blues!
pintado painted, rouged; **la Pintada** the Painted Lady, Rosy Cheeks
pintarrajeado heavily rouged
piojoso lousy, lice-ridden, mangy
pior = **peor; ¡—!** Worse yet! Stop it! Quit! **— que tú corriste** you were worse; you ran away
pisada footing
piso floor
pisoteado trampled, crushed
pista ring, cockfighting arena
pistola pistol, revolver
pitahayo pitahaya, *a Mexican cactus* (*Cereus variabilis or Carnegiea gigantea*)
pitayo = **pitahayo**
pizcador gleaning
placer *m.* pleasure, joy
plancha: tirar una — to draw a "lemon"
planchuela (*dim. of* **plancha**) strip
planicie f. plain
plano surface
planta foot, sole of the foot
plañidero plaintive
plata silver, money
plátano banana
plateado silvery
plática talk, discussion
platicar to talk, tell
platillo cymbal
plato plate, dish
plaza square, market; (*Mex.*) town, city; **que fue a dar a media —** which ran to the middle of the square
Plaza, Antonio (*1833–1882*) *a Mexican poet whose skeptical and bitter verses had a great popular appeal for his own generation as well as for the following generation*
plazoleta (*dim. of* **plaza**) small square
plazuela (*dim. of* **plaza**) square, small square
plegar (ie) to fold; **— el ceño** to scowl, frown; **— las cejas** to frown; **plegó sus líneas** wrinkled the lines of his face, frowned; **—se** to curl in a sneer
pleito fight; **Estaban de —** They were in great demand.
pliegue *m.* fold, slap, "sock"

plomazo (*Mex.*) bullet
plomo bullet, lead; **a —** sharply
pluma feather
plumaje *m.* plumage, feathers
población town
poblado covered, filled; *m.* town
poblar (ue) to people, populate
pobre poor (man)
pobrecito (*dim. of* **pobre**) poor, poor fellow; **¡— de ti!** Poor little boy!; **—a de ti!** Poor girl!
poco little; **—s** few; **un —** a little, somewhat; **— a —** little by little; **a —** shortly, soon; **¡A — son los mochos!** I'll bet it's the federals!
poder (ue) to be able; **puede ser** perhaps, maybe; **puede (pué) que** perhaps, maybe
poderoso powerful, mighty
podrido rotted, rotten
policía police: *m.* policeman
polvareda cloud of dust
polvo dust; **—s** powder
polvoriento dusty
ponderar to extol
poner to place, put, apply, set, lay, make (*a face*), to send (*a letter*); **—se** to become, set, be; **—se a**+*inf.* to begin to; to set about . . . ing; **—se en (de) pie** to stand up; **— cara** to react
popote *m.* (*Mex.*) thatch, straw
poquito (*dim. of* **poco**): **—s** very few
por for, on account of, by, for the sake of, through, along, about, over, up, among, to, with, in, at, after; **— cada uno** apiece; **— eso** as a result, consequently, however, all right; **— más que**+*subj.* in spite of the fact that; **¿— qué?** Why?
porcelana china
porque because, for, if, so that, in order that
portador *m.* bearer
portalillo (*dim. of* **portal**) portico
portentoso prodigious, marvelous
portillo: por mi lado no hay — as far as I'm concerned it's all right. *This is an elliptical expression. The complete expression is:* **Por mi lado no hay portillo; toda la cerca está caída.**
pos = pues; — cuando but, why; **— si** but, why, so
posada lodging; **nos dio —** took us in, put us up
posaderas *f. pl.* rump
poseedor *m.* possessor, owner
posesionarse (de) to take possession (of)
postrero last
potranca young mare, filly
potrillo (*dim. of* **potro**) colt
potro colt
pozo well
pozole *m.* (*Mex.*) pozole, *a stew made with red chile peppers, meat, and corn; by extension* blood, bloodshed
practicar to make
pradera meadow
precipitación: con — in all haste, hastily
precipitar(se) to hurry, hasten (away), rush
preciso necessary, exact, precise
precio price; **su justo —** what's what
preferir (ie, i) to prefer
pregonear to call out
pregunta question
preguntar to ask, inquire
prendido (a) clinging to; **— en** attached to
prensa press, newspapers
preocupado preoccupied
preparar(se) to get ready
presa prey, prize, booty
presenciar to witness, see
presentarse to present oneself (itself), appear; **— con** to offer one's services to
presente *m.* gift, present; **tener —** to remember
presentimiento presentiment, foreboding
preso prisoner; **el Divino —** *a picture of the Divine Prisoner, i. e. Christ*
prestar to lend, give; **—se** to lend each other
presuntuoso conceited
presuroso quick(ly)
pretencioso pretentious, showy
pretender to seek, try to, want
pretil *m.* railing, low stone wall, wall

prevenirse to get ready
priesa=**prisa**
prietilla (*dim. of* **prieta**) dark-skinned girl
prieto black
primer, primero first
principio beginning, first, principle
prisa haste; **a toda —** very quickly; **más que de —** as fast as possible
prisionero prisoner
privar to deprive
proceder *m.* procedure
procurar to try, attempt; **—se** to try to get
prodigalidad freedom
proeza deed, feat
proferir (ie, i) to say, speak, mutter
profundamente utterly, completely
prognato prognathous, having a projecting jaw
prójimo human being
prolongar to extend; **—se** to spread (out)
prometer to promise
prominencia rocky peak
prontitud: con — suddenly, hastily
pronto quick(ly), soon; **de —** suddenly; **¡Y que sea —!** Make it snappy! **por lo —** in the meantime
pronunciar to say, pronounce
propagar to spread
propicio favorable
propiedad property
propietario owner, proprietor
propinar to give, administer
propio own; **el — Anastasio** Anastasio himself; *m.* message
proponer to propose, suggest
proporcionar to give, provide
prorrumpir to break forth
proseguir (i) to continue, go on
protegido protected, sheltered
providencia precaution
provinciano provincial
proximidad approach
proyectil *m.* shot, bullet, shell
proyecto plan
¡pst! bah!
pué = **puede**
pueblecillo (*dim. of* **pueblo**) town, village
pueblito (*dim. of* **pueblo**) small town
pueblo town, village, people
puerco pig, hog
puerta door, doorway
puertecilla (*dim. of* **puerta**) small door
puerto port
pues well, then; **— bien** well; **— que...** Well, I'll be...
puesta del sol sunset
puesto placed, directed, set; **muy bien —** well set up; *m.* post, stand
pulmón lung
punta tip, corner, blade, point
puntapié *m.* kick; **arrojar a —s** to kick out
puntería marksmanship; **hacer —** to take aim
puntiagudo sharp-pointed
puntilla matador's sword, rapier
punto point; **— menos** worse yet, slightly less; **a — fijo** exactly
puñado handful
puñal *m.* dagger, knife
puño fist, closed hand, wrist, handful; **— cerrado** fist
pupila eye
puritito (*double dim. of* **puro**): **la puritita verdad** God's own truth
puro pure, sheer, only; **del — cañón** in the heart of the canyon; **el — reló** the watch alone; **los —s oficiales** the officers alone; **¡En la pura calabaza!** Right in the head! *m.* cigar
púrpura purple
purpúreo purple

Q

que *conj.* that, for, than, and, if; **¿A que no me lo crees?** I'll bet you don't believe it; **¿Que** + *question untranslatable*
que who, that, which
¿qué? what? so? well? why? **¿A —?** Why? **¿— tal?** How did you like that? What? **¿— tanto...?** How much...?

¡qué! what (a)! how! why! **¡— más!** what's more; **¡— sé yo!** I don't know; **¡— pliegue tan güeno . . . !** What a good slap . . . !
quebrantado weary, broken; **con voz quebrantada** brokenly
quebrarse (ie) to become fixed in a stare
quedar (se) to remain, stay, be, be left; **—se dormido** to fall asleep
quedo quietly
queja complaint
quejarse (de) to complain of
quejido moan
quemado burned, experienced
quemar to burn, shoot; **yo lo quemaba y ya** I'd just shoot him and be done with it
quén = quién
querer (ie) to wish, want to, love, like, expect, desire; *in pret.* to try to
querido dear
quero, queres, quere, queren = quiero, quieres, quiere, quieren
querubincito little angel
queso cheese
quesque = que dice que
quien who, whom, someone who; **¿Quién?** Who?
quieto composed, quiet
quince fifteen; **— días** two weeks
quinientos five hundred
quiosco kiosk, retail stall
quitar(se) to take away, remove, deprive, heal
quizá perhaps
quizque = que dice que

R

rabia anger, rage
ración ration
radioso radiant
ráfaga gust
rajado: pata —a hillbilly, hick, country bumpkin
rama branch
ramaje *m.* branches
ramazón *f.* branches
ramonear to browse
rana frog
rancio rancid, spoiled
ranchería ranch
ranchero farmer
ranchito (*dim. of* **rancho**) ranch, village
rancho ranch, farm, hamlet, village
rapado bald, stripped bare
rapidez rapidity
rapidísimo very rapid(ly)
raro rare; **—s** few
rascarse to scratch (oneself); scratch one's head
rasguño scratch
raso simple, plain, clear, tearful; **soldado —** private; **exprimir sus ojos —s** to hold back the tears in her eyes; *m.* satin
rastras: llevar a — to drag
rastro sign, trace, tracks, trail; **habían dejado ya su — vigoroso** had left strong evidences of occupancy
rastrojo stubble
rata rat
ratero thief, thieving
rato while
ratón mouse
raya line
rayo ray, lightning
raza race, blood, strain
razón *f.* reason, reasoning; **según —** according to what they say; **¡Con —!** No wonder!
real royal; **camino —** highway; real, *a Mexican coin worth about 6 cents U.S. cy. at the time of the Mexican Revolution*
realizar to realize, take form, carry out
reanudar to continue
reata rope, lariat
rebanar to slash, sever, cut
rebelde *m.* rebel
rebién very well
rebotar to ricochet
rebozo shawl
rebullir to stir
recámara bedroom

recepción graduation
recibir to receive, get; **—se** to graduate, be admitted to practice
recién recently, just; **— nacidos** newly sprouted
recio severe, fast
recitar to recite
recluta *m.* recruit
reclutado recruit
reclutar to recruit
recodo bend, angle, turn
recoger to gather, collect, retire
reconocer to examine, recognize
reconstituir to recall, conjure up
recordar (ue) to remember, recall
recortar to stand out, show, outline
recorrer to pass through
recostado reclining
recto straight, upright
recua mount, nag
recuerdo memory; **—s best wishes,** regards
recuperar to retrieve, round up, recover
rechazar to turn away, drive back
rechinar to grind, gnash
rechonchito (*dim. of* **rechoncho**) chubby
redacción wording
redención redemption, freedom
redoblar to redouble, renew
redoma glass, flask, bottle
redondo rounded, fat
reducirse (a) to turn out to be, be limited to
reducto stronghold
redundante superfluous
referir (ie, i) to describe, tell
reflejo reflection; **—s** sheen, glint
reflexión statement, observation, bit of reasoning
reflexionar to reflect, think
refrenar to control
refrescado refreshed
refuerzo(s) reinforcements
refugiarse to take (seek) refuge
refugio shelter, refuge
refulgente shining, brilliant
refulgir to shine
regado spread, scattered
regalar to present, give
regar (ie) to sprinkle, scatter, spatter, wash, steep
regazo skirts
Regional, El *a conservative newspaper published in Guadalajara, Jalisco*
registrar to search
regocijado joyful(ly)
regocijante joyous
regocijo joy
regordete, -a chubby, plump
regresar to return, retreat, go back
regüeno = rebueno very good
reguero scattering, collection, heap
reír (i) to laugh; **—(se) de** to laugh at; **— a echar las tripas** to laugh until one's sides split
reivindicación recovery
rejuvenecido rejuvenated
relación story, account
relamerse to lick one's lips
relámpago lightning, flash
relato story, tale, account
relinchar to neigh
relincho whinny, neigh
reló = reloj
reloj *m.* watch; **— de repetición** watch with chimes
relucir to shine
remangarse to be tucked up; **su falda se remangaba hasta la rodilla** her skirt was above her knees
remanso pool
rematar to finish off, end; **— en** to have at the end
remate *m.* end
remedar to imitate, mock
remendar (ie) to repair
remolino spiral, swirl (of dust)
remover(se) (ue) to stir (up, about in), move
remuda horse; relay (change) of horses
rendido worn-out, dead-tired
rendir (i) to take orders from, present, give; **al —** at the end of
renegar (ie) to curse, complain; **a reniega y reniega, pero a trabaja y trabaja** complain and complain but work hard
renegrido livid, blackish
renglón line; **a — seguido** immediately following

rentar (*Mex.*) to rent
reparar (en) to notice, heed, pay attention to
reparo (*Mex.*) rearing
repartir to divide
repasar to grind again, review, go over; **pasa y repasa su nixtamal** she grinds again and again her nixtamal
repelar (*Mex.*) to become furious (angry)
repente: de — suddenly
repentino sudden
repetición watch with chimes
repetido repeated; **—s** several; **repetidas veces** several times, repeatedly
repetir (i) to repeat
repicar to ring
repicolargo great talker
repique *m.* ringing
reponer to answer, reply, say
reposar to rest, lie
reposo rest, repose
representación realization
reprimido disguised, held back, repressed
repronto very soon
repuesto recovered
repulido glistening, shiny, radiant
requemado sunburnt
requero = requiero = quiero muchísimo
requiescat in pace (*Lat.*) "May he rest in peace"; finish, end
requisito: ¡Cuánto —! What unnecessary preliminaries! What a roundabout way!
res *f.* steer, cow, calf
resbalar to slide, slip
resaber to know very well
reseco very dry, parched
reserva reserve, spare, secrecy
resfrío cold
resolverse (ue) to resolve, decide, become, resolve into, turn into
resonar (ue) to echo, resound
resoplar to puff, breathe heavily
resorte *m.* spring; **los muelles y los —s** the spring locks
respaldo back
respetabilísimo very respectable
respiración breath
respirar to breathe in, inhale the odors of
resplandecer to shine (forth)
resplandor *m.* ornament
responder to answer, say, respond; **— de** to be responsible for, answer for
resquebrajadura crevice, fissure, crack
restablecer restore
restablecimiento recovery
resto rest; **—s** remains
restregarse to rub
resueltamente resolutely
resuelto resolved
resulta consequence
resultado result
resultar to turn up, show up, turn out to be
retaguardia rear
reteacabao = reteacabado very clever, smart
retemalo very bad
retemblar (ie) to tremble, quake
reticencias *f. pl.* reticence, reserve
retinto dark red (*almost black*)
retirar(se) to withdraw, take away, retire, go away
retorcer (ue) (se) to twist, curl
retozar to frisk about
retraído withdrawn, wrapped
retraimiento reticence, retiring nature
retrato portrait, picture
retroceder to retreat, retrace one's steps, go back
reunir to gather, get together; **—se con** to join
reventar(se) (ie) to burst, break, swell; **parecía —** seemed about to burst; **para que reviente el que quiera** enough to make a man burst
revés *m.* blow, slap
revivir to revive, come to life again
revolver (ue) to mix (in); **—se** to be mixed in with
revuelto confused, mixed up, tangled
rezandero singsong, monotonous, predicant
rezar to pray; **— entre dientes** to mutter a prayer
rezo prayer
rezongar to grumble, complain
rezongo grumbling

rial = **real**
rico rich (man)
riendas *f. pl.* bridle
rincón corner
rinconada cranny, nook
rinconera corner cupboard, whatnot, stand, bracket; **juguetes de —** figurines
río river
risa smile, laughter
risco crag, cliff
risotada burst of laughter
ríspido rough, harsh, gruff
risueño smiling
rizado curly, curled
robao = **robado**
robar(se) rob, steal
roble *m.* oak
Robles, Crispín *a leader of a revolutionary band opposed to Huerta*
robustez plumpness
rocalloso rocky
rocín *m.* horse
rodar (ue) to roll, tumble
rodear(se) to surround, encircle, form a circle
rodeos *m. pl.* reticence, circumlocutions
rodilla knee, foreleg
rodillazo blow with the knee
rojizo reddish
rojo red
romo flat
romper(se) to break, cut, burst, break out in
roncar to snore
ronco hoarse; **hablar — y golpeado** to speak in a loud and threatening voice
roña scabby (filthy) person
roñoso scabby
ropa(s) clothing
ropero wardrobe
rosa rose; **— de Castilla,** *a wild red rose* (*Lippia callicarpaefolia*); **— de San Juan** *a wild white rose* (*Bouvardia longiflora*)
rosado roseate, rose-colored, rosy
rostro face; **el Divino —** *a picture of Christ*
roto broken
rozar to graze
rubio blond, blondness
rubor *m.* blush; **cubrirse de —** to blush
ruborizar to cause to blush
rudo rude, dull, rough, hoarse, vigorous, sharp
rugir to roar
ruidazo (*aug. of* **ruido**) big noise
ruido noise, racket
ruidoso noisy
ruinoso crumbling, ruined
rumbo direction; **— a** toward, for
rumboso pompous
rumor *m.* noise, sound, murmur
rumorear to murmur

S

saber to know (how); to be able, learn; **—se** to know, understand; **¿Yo qué sé?** What do I know?
sabiduría knowledge, wisdom
sable *m.* sword, saber
sacar to take out, pull (drag) out, dispel, stick out, take, commandeer, steal; **saquen la cabeza** show your heads; **—le la verdad** to get the truth out of him; **— en claro** to understand; **— de su cuidado** to deliver the baby of
saciar to satisfy, satiate
saco bag
sacristán *m.* sexton
sacristía sacristy
sacudir(se) to shake, pelt; **se deja — de nuevo por el llanto** she sobs bitterly once more (again)
sagrado sacred; **— Corazón de Jesús** Feast of the Sacred Heart, *a movable holiday of the Easter cycle on the first Friday following the octave day of the Corpus Christi celebration. It usually is celebrated in the month of June.*
sal *f.* salt
sala living room
salario pay, wages
salida exit, departure, way to get out
salir(se) to leave, go out, come out

salón (*aug. of* **sala**) large room
saltar to jump (up, over), leap, drop off, come out, spring forth; **hacer —** to kick high in the air
saltito (*dim. of* **salto**) hop, little jump
salto jump
saltón protruding
salud *f.* health
saludar to greet
salvador saving, redeeming
salvar to save, get over, climb; **¡Sálvese el que pueda!** Run for your lives!
san saint
San Luis Potosí *the capital city of the State of San Luis Potosí in central Mexico*
sandía watermelon
sangre *f.* blood
sanguijuela leech
sanguinolento bloody
sano healthy, in good health
Santa Rosa *a ranch near Juchipila, Zacatecas*
santiamén *m.* jiffy
santo holy; **— y bueno** all well and good; **la Santa Cruz** the True Cross
sañudo furious, enraged
saquear to sack, pillage, loot
saqueo pillaging, sacking, loot, booty
sarape *m.* (*Mex.*) blanket
sarcasmo irony
sardina nag
sargento sergeant; **— segundo** sergeant
sastre *m.* tailor
sastrería tailor shop
satisfecho satisfied
sayón executioner
se himself, herself, themselves, itself; him, her, it, them; *with 3rd person of verb as substitute for passive* one, we, they, you; **se les escuchó** they listened to them; **se encendieron lumbres** fires were lighted (made)
sebo tallow; **mecha de —** tallow candle
seco dry, sharp
seda silk
segado mowed down, sacrificed, destroyed
seguido: muy — right away
seguir (i) to follow, continue, go on, be; **—** + *ger.* (*pres. part.*) to keep on, continue . . . ing; **sigue la bola** the ball (*i. e.* the revolution) keeps rolling
según according to
segundo second
seguro certain, safe, sure, trustworthy
seiscientos six hundred
semana week
semblante *m.* face, countenance
sembrar (ie) to sow, plant, cultivate
sementera fields
semidesnudo half-naked
semos = **somos**
sencillo simple
sendos, -as one each, one apiece; **haciendo blancos cruzaban sendas apuestas** each laid bets with the others on his marksmanship
seno bosom
sensación sensation; **de —** sensational
sentarse (ie) to sit down, sit
sentido sense(s)
sentir (ie, i) to hear, feel, regret, experience, **—se** to feel; **— en el alma** to regret deeply
señá = **señora**
señal *f.* signal, sign
señalar to point out, indicate
señor Mr., gentleman, lord; **¡—, — . . . !** Oh Lord, Lord . . . !; **— de la Villita** Our Lord of the Villita (*a miraculous image of Christ of a village church*)
señora madam
señoritín *m.* (*dim. of* **señorito**): **— de** capital city dude
señorito (*dim. of* **señor**) dandy, man about town
ser to be, happen, take place; **— de** to have; **es que** the fact is that, *sometimes untranslatable;* **¿No serían veinte?** Wasn't it twenty, perhaps?
serio serious
serrana mountaineer, mountain girl
serranía mountainside; **todo era —** everywhere mountains
serrano mountaineer
servidor *m. as a response to an introduction* Glad to know you, How do

you do? *or some similar English expression*
servir (i) to serve; **— de** to serve as, be used for; **sírvase** please
si if, why, whether
sí himself, herself, yourself, themselves, yourselves; **de por —** in his own right; **para —** to himself
sí yes, indeed, certainly; **¡Ahora —!** Now I understand!
siembra land, planting
siempre always; **— que** whenever
sierpe *f.* serpent, snake
siete seven
significado meaning, import
siguiente following
sigún = según; — razón according to what they say
Silao *a city in Guanajuato*
silbar to whistle, screech
silbido whistle
silencioso silent, quiet
silueta figure, outline, silhouette
silla chair, saddle
sillón (*aug. of* **silla**) armchair
simpático nice, likable, charming (fellow)
simpatizador *m.* sympathizer
simpatizar to please, like; **usted me ha simpatizado** I have liked you
sin (que) without
siniestro sinister
sino (que) but, but on the other hand, except; **no eran —** were nothing but
sinvergüenza *m.* rascal
siñor=señor
siquiera at least, at all, even; **¡—!** That's rich! That's nothing!
sitiar to besiege
sitio place; **abrir —** to make room for
situación location
so under, with
soberbio supreme, severe, superb, haughty, proud
sobra: de — to spare
sobrar to exceed, surpass, have to spare; **me sobra salud** I'm as fit as a fiddle
sobre on, upon, at, against
sobrecogido overcome, possessed
sobrepuesto one on the other
sobresaltado frightened, with a start
sobresalto fright
socarronamente slyly
sofocante suffocating
sofocar to suffocate, be suffocating
soga rope
sol *m.* sun, sunlight, heat of the sun; **al buen — hay que abrirle la ventana** make hay while the sun shines; **— de mayo** (*1868*) *a novel by Juan Antonio Mateos* (*1831–1913*), *a very popular novelist of prerevolutionary Mexico*
solapado cunning, crafty, artful, deceitful
solar *m.* home
soldadesca soldiery, soldiers
soldado soldier; **¡Yo, qué — ni qué nada había de ser!** I wasn't supposed to be a soldier or anything like it!
soldar (ue) to solder, weld
soledad solitude
soler (ue) to be accustomed to
solferino reddish purple
solicitar to beg
solicitud search, eagerness, deference, solicitude
solitario alone
sólo only; **— por eso que . . .** I merely wanted to tell you that . . . ; **— que** unless, except that, but
solo alone, unoccupied, single, by himself (herself, themselves *in pl.*)
soltar (ue) to free, let go (of), loosen, release; **— la lengua** to become communicative
sollozar to sob
sollozo sob
sombra shadow, darkness
sombrerazo (*pej. of* **sombrero**) wretched hat
sombrero hat
sombrío gloomy
somnolencia drowsiness; **gruñía el cerdo su —** the hog grunted drowsily
son *m.* sound, cry, shout
sonar (ue) to make a noise, jingle
sonoro loud, resounding, sonorous
sonreír (i) to smile; **—se** to smile
sonrisa smile

sonrosado rosy-cheeked

sonsonete *m.* singsong voice

soñador *m.* dreamer

soñar (ue) to dream

soplar to blow, fan (*a fire*), whisper

soplo force

soportar to carry, support

sorbo gulp

sordo dull, muffled, low

sorprendente surprising

sorprendido surprised

sorpresa surprise

sosegar (ie) to quiet

sospechar to suspect

sostener to support, hold up, bear

sota queen

sotana cassock, robes, vestments

soyate *m.* (*Mex.*) palm; **sombrero de —** *the wide-brimmed sombrero typical of Mexico*

su his, her, its, your, one's, their

suave smooth

suavemente gently

suavidad gentleness

subir to go up, climb; **se le sube el trago** the drinks go to his head

súbito sudden

substancias *f. pl.* remedy, medicine

subteniente *m.* second lieutenant

subyugado downtrodden, oppressed

suceder to happen; **—se** to follow one after another; **cerros que suceden a cerros** hills after hills

sucedido happening, what had happened

suceso event; **—s** doings

sucio dirty

sudadero saddle cloth, back cloth

sudado sweaty

sudar to sweat

sudor *m.* sweat, perspiration

sudoroso sweaty, sweating

sueldo wages

suelo ground, floor

suelto limp, lifeless, loose

sueño sleep, dream

suerte *f.* way, manner, luck, life, fate

sufrido patient, long-suffering

sufrir to suffer

suicidarse to commit suicide

sujeto fellow

suntuoso sumptuous

superior higher, superior; **con su —** has the curse

suplicar to beg

suplicatorio supplicant, in supplication

suponer(se) to suppose

surco furrow, fold

surgir to stand up

surtir to supply, provide

suspender(se) to stop

suspirar to sigh

suspiro sigh

sustancia = substancia

susto scare, shock, fright

susurrar to murmur

suyo his, hers, its, theirs, yours, of his, *etc.*, their, your, *etc.*; **el (la, *etc.*) —** his, his own, *etc.*

T

taco: en — folded, rolled up

tajo cut, slash, steep cliff

tal such, such a, certain; **el — Demetrio** that fellow Demetrio; **¿Qué —?** How did you like that? **Ni —es orozquistas, ni — combate** For there were neither any followers of Orozco nor even a decent fight

talego bag

talud *m.* ledge

tallado carved

talle *m.* form, figure

tamal *m.* (*Mex.*) tamale, *a food made of corn, meat, and chile, and wrapped in corn husks*

tamaño long, wide, such a; **echaban tamaña lengua** their tongues were hanging out

tambalearse to stagger, reel

también also, too

tampoco nor, neither, either

tan so; **si son — hombres** if you are real men

tantito (*dim. of* **tanto**) a bit, a short while, a little bit; **otro —** a little bit farther

tanto so much; **— como** as much . . . as; **por —** well, nevertheless, conse-

quently, as a result; **en — que** while; **¿Qué —s?** How many? *m.* **un — a** small amount, a bit, somewhat
tapar to cover
tapia wall
tapiz *m.* carpet
tararear to hum
tardar to delay; **— en** + *inf.* to be long before (in)
tarde *f.* afternoon; *adj.* late; *adv.* (too) late
tarea task
tarugo stupid
tasajo boob, stupid
taurino bullfight
techo ceiling, roof
te you, for you, yourself
tejano Texan
telaraña cobweb
telégrafo telegraph, telegraph pole
tema *m.* theme, subject
temblar (ie) to tremble
temer to fear
temerario daring
temeridad daring, temerity, rashness
temor *m.* fear
temperancia sobriety
tempestad storm
templar to draw up, play an instrument
templo church; **una verdad como un —** the gospel truth, a mouthful
temporada time, while
temprano early
tenate *m.* (*Mex.*) pouch
tendajonero shopkeeper
tender (ie) to stretch, hand, hold out, point (*a rifle*); **—se** to stretch out; **tendiendo una oreja** bringing his ear closer
tendido stretched out, outstretched, leaning, lying; *m.* deck (of cards)
tendinoso sinewy, muscular
tener to have, possess, keep; **no — a mal** to be willing, approve; **no — para** + *inf.* not to be able to; **— . . . años** to be . . . years old; **— asco** to hate, despise; **— cuidado** to be careful; **— ganas de** to feel like, want; **— gusto** to be pleased; **— hambre** to be hungry; **— miedo** to be afraid; **— presente** to remember; **— que** + *inf.* to have to; **— tristeza** to be sad; **¡Dios los tenga de su santa mano!** May God guide you! **No lo tengo malo** It's not so bad; **Ya lo tengo bien pensado** I've already made up my mind about that; **Tiene mucha sal** He's got a lot on the ball
teniente *m.* lieutenant
tenso tense, rigid
tentar (ie) (se) to feel, touch
teñir (i) to tint, dye, color
Tepatitlán *a town in Jalisco*
Tepic *the capital city of the state of Nayarit in western Mexico*
tequila (*Mex.*) tequila, *an alcoholic drink distilled from the maguey plant*
tercio bundle
terciopelo velvet
terco stubborn
terminar to finish, end
ternera calf
terroso earthen-colored, clay-colored
terso glossy, smooth
tersura smoothness
testa head
tetilla breast
tez skin, complexion
ti you, yourself
tibio warm
tibor *m.* large jar
tiempo time; **a —** in time
tienda store, saloon, tent, pavilion
tierno young, soft, tender
tierra land, country, ground, dirt
Tierra Blanca *a town in the state of Chihuahua*
tiesto flower pot
timbre *m.* tone
tinaja water jar
tinieblas *f. pl.* darkness
tinte *m.* color, tint, hue
tinto tinged, stained
tiñoso scabby
tío uncle, fellow, guy
tiranía tyranny
tirano tyrant
tirante: a pierna — stretched out
tirar to shoot, draw, throw (away), pour (out); **— de** to draw forth

(up), pull (up); — **el balazo** to shoot; — **una plancha** to draw a "lemon"; —**se** to lie down, stretch out
tiritar to shiver
tiro shot, bullet
tirón (*aug. of* **tiro**) pull, jerk, yank
tiroteo firing
titipuchal *m.* (Mex.) lot, great many; **son un —** there's a whole mob of them
título degree
tiznado sooty, begrimed
toa = toda
toavía: en — = todavía
tobillo ankle
tocar to play (*a musical instrument*), sound, touch, knock, **a usted le tocó la cajita** you got the little box; **le tocó la leva** the draft got him; **que le toca** that is yours
todavía yet, still
todo all; **del —** completely; **—es que uno haga por voltearse** all that's needed is for one of them to make a move to flee
toma taking, capture
tomar to take; **tomó la vertiente opuesta** he followed a path along the opposite slope **¡Toma!** There!
tonadilla (*dim. of* **tonada**) tune
tonadita (*dim. of* **tonada**) tone of voice
tonalidad coloring, tonality
tono tone, light
tontear to act foolishly, make stupid mistakes
tonto a stupid (silly) person
too = todo
topar to meet
toquilla de galón braided hatband
torbellino whirlwind
torcaz *f.* dove
torcer (ue) to turn
tordillo dappled gray
tordo thrush
torear to fight bulls in the ring; **en actitud de — a los federales** as though he were fighting the federals like bulls
tormentoso brutal, terrible, hard
tornar to return
torneo tourney, contest
torno: en — (de) around
toro bull, steer
torpeza awkwardness
Torreón *a city in southwestern Chihuahua captured by Villa October 1, 1913*
tortilla (*Mex.*) tortilla, *a thin corn-meal cake shaped like a pancake and used instead of bread*
torvo grim, sullen
torre *f.* tower
torrecilla (*dim. of* **torre**) small tower
tosco coarse, rough
tosigoso consumptive, with a severe cough
tovía = todavía
trabajar to work
trabajo work
trabajoso hard, difficult
traducirse to turn into, become
traer to bring, carry, have, wear; **— a colación** to recall, bring up; **— entre ojos** to take a liking to; **— miedo** to be afraid; **¿Qué trae?** What's new? **—se** to bring along
tragantada swallow
trago drink, swallow; **echar un —** to have a drink
trai, trais, train, traite = trae, traes, traen, tráete
traiba, traiban = traía, traían; ¡Cómo traiba oro el condenado! How much gold the wretch was wearing on his uniform!
traición treason, treachery
traicionar to betray
trair = traer
traje *m.* clothes, uniform, dress, gown
trampa trap
trance *m.* situation
tranco gait; **al — largo** at the slow gait
tranquilamente peaceably
tranquilizar to reassure
transcurrir to pass
transfigurado changed, transfigured
transitar to travel
trapo rag; **la lengua hecha —** her tongue cling(ing) to the roof of her mouth; **como si las piernas se le hu-**

biesen vuelto de trapo as if his legs had suddenly become so much cloth; **se me hace** — seems like cloth
tras after, behind
trasunto expression
tratar to treat; **—se de** to be a question of
través: a — de through
travieso prankish
traza sign
trazado drawn
trecho distance
treinta thirty; **— —** *m.* a thirty-thirty rifle
tremendo great
trémulo shaky, tremulous, quivering, trembling
tren *m.* train
trenza braided hair
trepado perched
trepar to climb
trer = traer
tres three; **en dos por —** in a jiffy
tribu *f.* tribe
trigueño dark, swarthy
trincado bound
trinchera line of trenches
tripa: reír a echar las —s to laugh until one's sides split
tripón (*aug. of* **tripa**) pot-bellied; **de tan tripones** because they were so pot-bellied
triques *m. pl.* (*Mex.*) odds and ends, rubbish
triste sad
tristeza sadness; **con —** sadly
triunfar to be victorious, win, triumph
triunfo victory, triumph
troje *f.* barn, shed
trompada punch, blow; **meter una —** to punch, strike, hit
tronar (ue) to shoot, kill
tropa(s) troops, soldiers
tropezar (ie) (con) to meet; **—se con** to stumble over
trotar to trot
trozo chunk, slice
trueno thunderbolt
tú you
tu your
tubo pipe, tubing
tuerto one-eyed
tumbar to spill, bring down; **—se** to lie down, stretch out
tumbos: dar — to stumble and fall down
tumultuosamente violently
tuna cactus fruit, prickly pear (*Opuntia sp.*)
turba mob
turbante *m.* turban
turbarse to become confused (disturbed)
turbio dark, muddy
turnarse to take turns
tusado (*Amer.*) close-cropped
tusero hole
tutear to use the familiar **tú** form of address, speak familiarly

U

ufano proud
¡újule! hey!
último last
ulular to howl, screech
umbral *m.* threshold
un(o) one, a, an; **— a —** one by one, single file; **una que otra** + *sing.* a few + *plu.;* **en —** together; **—s** some, a few, one of us; **—s tras otros** one after another; **—s cuantos** a few; **a una** together; **confundido . . . en — solo** fused together; **¡—s chapetes!** Such rosy cheeks!
uncir to yoke, hitch up
uncioso unctuous, oily-tongued, unduly suave
único only
unificarse to unite in agreement
untado adhering to, tightly closed
uña fingernail
Urbina, Tomás R. (*1877–1915*) *an officer in Villa's army and later Provisional President of San Luis Potosí*
urgencia: de — urgent
usado cast-off, used
usar to use; **—se** to be done
usté = usted

usted(es) you
utilidad profit

V

vaca cow
vaciar to empty; **—se en** to be abandoned for
vacilación hesitation
vacilante hesitant(ly)
vacilar to hesitate, waver
vacío empty
vadear to wade
vagabundo tramp
vagar to wander
vago vague, indistinct
vagoroso vague, indistinct, hazy
vaho vapor
vaivén *m.* movement
vale *m.* (*Mex.*) fellow, guy
valedura favor
valer to be worth
valeroso brave
valiente brave (man)
valor *m.* value, courage
valle *m.* valley
vanguardia advance guard
vano vain
vapor steam; **a todo —** at full steam, as fast as possible
vaporizar to evaporate, cool off
vaquero cowpuncher, ranchman
vaqueta leather, calfskin
vara vara, *a Spanish unit of linear measure almost the equivalent of a yard* (*2.8 ft.*)
varón man, male
varonil masculine, manly
vasija vessel
vaso glass
vecindad neighbor, proximity
vecindario neighborhood, village
vecino, -a neighbor, citizen
veinte twenty
veintena score
veinticinco twenty-five
veinticuatro twenty-four
veintiún twenty-one
vejarruca (*pej. of* **vieja**) wrinkled old woman
vela candle
velocidad speed
venado deer
vendar bandage
vendaval *m.* windstorm
vendedor *m.* vendor
vender to sell
venenoso poisonous
venia permission
venir to come, be; **—se** to come (along); **—** + *ger.* (*pres. part.*) to be . . .ing; **vengo escupiendo** I have been vomiting up; **—se a cuenta** to come out, turn out; **—se encima** to run down; **— a cuentas** to occur (*to one*), cause to realize
ventana window
ventanilla (*dim. of* **ventana**) small window
ver to see, look at, watch, stand, bear; **—se** to be, be seen; **a — si** we'll see if; **a —** let's see, see, all right; **a — la reata** let's have your rope; **así la verán** she's been just like that; **(si) viera** you ought to see, if you only knew
vera edge, side
veras: de — really, truly, real; **¡Ahora, va de —!** This times goes (really counts)!
verdá = **verdad**
verdad truth; **a la —** in truth, to be sure; **la —** in truth; **la — de la —** the whole truth; **la mera —** the plain truth; **una — como un templo** the gospel truth, a mouthful; **¿—?** Isn't it so? Isn't that the truth?
verdadero true
verde green
verdinegro dark green
verdugo executioner
vereda path, trail
vergüenza shame, pride; **sin —** shameless
vericueto cluster, rough (overgrown, pathless) area, maze (of paths)
verificarse to take place
vertebradura vertebrae, spinal column
verter (ie, i) to shed
vertiente *f.* drop, steep cliff, slope, side

vertiginoso dizzy, rapid
vértigo dizzy spell
vespertino late afternoon
vestido dress; **—s** clothes
vestir (i) to wear; **—se de** to dress as; **—se** to dress (oneself); *m.* sufficient clothing
veteado striped, streaked, cut
vetusto ancient
vez time; **a veces** at times; **a la —** at the same time; **de — en —** from time to time; **de una —** right away; **en — de** instead of; **otra —** again
vía way (up); **via crucis** (*Lat.*) way of the cross, the stations of the cross
víbora snake
viborita (*dim. of* **víbora**) snake; **esta — de cuero** this leather snake, *i.e. a money belt*
vida life; **en mi —** never in my life; **¡Güero de mi —!** My darling Blondie!
vidrio glass
vidrioso glassy
viejita (*dim. of* **vieja**) old woman
viejo old (man); **vieja** woman, old woman
viejota (*pej. of* **vieja**) old shrew, vixen, old hag
viento wind, breeze, wind instrument
vientre *m.* belly
viga beam
vigilancia watchful eye, vigilance
vigilante *m.* guard
vigoroso strong
vihuela guitar
vil vile
Villa, Francisco (Pancho) (*1877(?)–1923*) *the pseudonym of Doroteo Arango, who was the bandit leader of the Army of the North. In the revolution he supported Madero and Carranza but finally broke with the latter. Although ruthless in his methods, he has become the popular hero of the peons of northern Mexico.*
vino wine
virgen virgin; **la — de Jalpa** the Virgin of Jalpa
virtud virtue
víspera eve, night before
vista eyesight, sight; **a la — de** in sight of
visto seen
viuda widow
viudo widower
viva *m.* cheer
vivamente quickly, nervously
vivir to live; **¡Que viva...!** Long live...! Hurrah for...! **¿Quién vive?** Who goes there?
vivo bright, alive, sharp, lively
vocecita (*dim. of* **voz**) sweet little voice
vocerío tumult, hubbub, clamor
vociferar to shout
volar (ue) to fly
volcán *m.* volcano
volcar (ue) to pour forth; **—se** to overturn, tip over
voltear to spin round, turn over, plow; **—se** to turn tail, flee; **— de narices** to knock down (flat)
voluntá=**voluntad**
voluntad will, desire; **si le falta la —** if you don't like me; **tener —** to like; **cobrar —** to like; **tener mala —** to hate, not like
voluntario volunteer
voluptuosidad pleasure
volver(se) to turn into, become, transform, return, go back, turn; **— a** + *inf.* to do something again; **— grupas** to turn one's horse about, wheel about, turn tail; **sus ojos se vuelven de todos lados** her eyes peer all about; **volviéndolo por el vientre** turning it belly up; **volvió sobre sus pasos** he recanted, he took it back
voto vote
voz *f.* voice; **a una —** unanimously, to the last man; **en — alta** aloud
vuelco tumble, leap, jump
vuelta turn, return; **a la —** when we come back; **dar —** to whirl about
vuelto *p. p. of* **volver**
vulgar common

Y

y and; **¿Y qué . . . ?** And what if . . . ? **¿— . . . ?** And what about . . . ?

ya already, now, still, presently, quite, surely, indeed, perfectly, I assure you, of course, *sometimes untranslatable;* **me dices: —** you say "enough"; **— llegamos a** we're almost to; **es mi novia y —** she's my girl and that's all there is to it.

yacer to lie

yantar to eat

yegua mare

yerba grass, weed

yerbita (*dim. of* **yerba**) herb

yugo yoke

yo I, me

yunque *m.* forge, anvil

yunta pair, yoke (of oxen), oxen

Z

zacate *m.* (*Mex.*) grass

Zacatecas *the capital city of the state of Zacatecas*

zacateco Zacatecan, from Zacatecas

zafarse to escape

zafir *m.* sapphire, sky

zafirina sapphirelike

zaguán *m.* entrance way

zahurda pigsty

zaino chestnut

zapatilla (*dim. of* **zapata**) slipper

zapato shoe

zapatón (*aug. of* **zapato**) large shoe

zarco blue

¡zas! bang! zowie!

zopilote *m.* (*Mex.*) buzzard

zozobra worry, anxiety, fear; **sin —s** relieved

zumbar to buzz, hum

zurdo left

Why fight - Cervantes ?
Macías ?

Personajes - Macías, Cervantes, Margarito,
Pintada, Camila

Porque la Revolución Mexicana